D1397721

80
6—

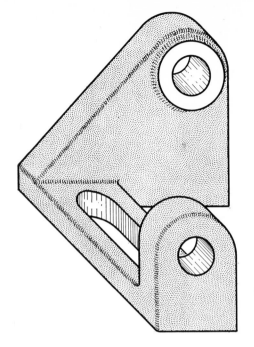

OBLIQUE

ISOMETRIC

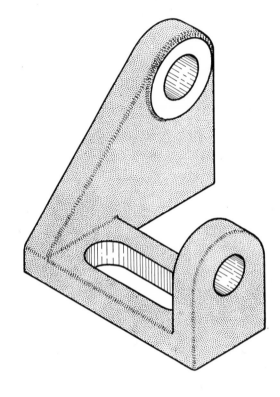

TOP VIEW

ORTHOGRAPHIC

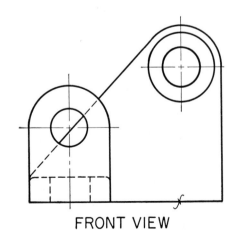

FRONT VIEW

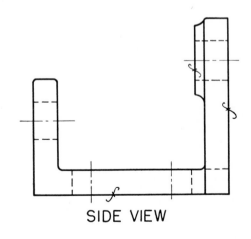

SIDE VIEW

ENGINEERING DRAWING

FRANK ZOZZORA

PROFESSOR AND HEAD, DEPARTMENT

OF ENGINEERING DRAWING

AND DESCRIPTIVE GEOMETRY

THE UNIVERSITY OF DELAWARE

McGRAW-HILL BOOK COMPANY, INC.

NEW YORK

TORONTO

LONDON

1953

ENGINEERING DRAWING

Copyright, 1953, by the McGraw-Hill Book Company, Inc. Printed in the United States of America. All rights reserved. This book, or parts thereof, may not be reproduced in any form without permission of the publishers.

Library of Congress Catalog Card Number: 51–12659

VI

THE MAPLE PRESS COMPANY, YORK, PA.

PREFACE

Engineering drawing is a required subject in all trade, vocational, technical, and engineering schools, and this book has been written for the teacher, student, or practicing engineer who is seeking a text that presents the fundamentals and essentials of the subject in a concise and easily understood fashion. For the teacher of the subject it may serve as a guide in arranging a satisfactory course that is adequate for his present-day crowded curriculum. Because there is so much to cover in the regular engineering curriculum, the time allotted to drawing has been more and more curtailed and a teacher must produce maximum results in a minimum given time. Therefore, he may, with some sense of relief, feel secure in assuming that when assigning the problems in this book, no previous knowledge of drawing, mechanics, or design is required other than that acquired in the text, and that the problems are not meaningless "time-killers" and wearying drill exercises. The illustrations for the text and for the problem sections have been carefully annotated so as to make them as nearly self-explanatory as possible. In addition, it is hoped that the numerous step-by-step illustrations and the hundreds of pictorials that aid in visualizing the problems and procedures under discussion will reduce the need for individual assistance and make the book practically a self-teaching text.

The chapters have been arranged in a logical sequence that permits the student to obtain a firm grasp of each topic before moving on to the next. Orthographic-projection theory and freehand detail drafting are discussed before instruments and geometrical constructions, since this allows the student to become acquainted with the fundamentals of engineering drawing and to apply them at an early stage. Since dimensioning principles and practices depend on the fabricating procedures required to produce mechanical parts, the chapter on Shop Processes covers all small shop operations, includes a glossary of shop terms, and immediately precedes the discussion of dimensioning.

The chapters on primary and secondary auxiliaries have been given more than the usual stress. Typical problems have been solved in a step-by-step fashion, and the perspective views that accompany the text should prove helpful in overcoming the difficulties that are usually encountered. In recent years industry has placed more and more emphasis on pictorial drawing. Thus the chapter on this subject covers, again in a complete step-by-step progression, the theory and fundamental constructions of oblique and isometric projection. The chapter on Intersections and Developments is carefully illustrated and contains an unusually large number of pictorial representations to assist the student in gaining a clear understanding of this subject.

The chapter on Fasteners includes the latest information on the unified and American Standard screw threads, on welding, on rivets and their use in structures, and on other standard and special fastening devices, for which additional informative material and tables have been placed in the Appendix.

Wherever applicable, the accepted practices indicated by the American Standards Association, the Society of Automotive Engineers, authoritative handbooks in engineering, and pamphlets and catalogues prepared by recognized reliable manufacturers have been referred to in the preparation of the text, illustrations, and the tables that appear in the Appendix. Drafting manuals, such as those prepared by General Motors, Ford, Allis-Chalmers, and Curtis-Wright for use by their own designers and engineers, were carefully scanned to make sure that all drawing techniques and procedures presented in the text were in accord with present-day industrial practice.

While no attempt has been made to cover the fields of architectural drawing, aircraft drawing, jigs and fixtures, charts, graphs, perspective, and illustration, extensive lists of texts and pamphlets dealing with these allied subjects have been placed in the bibliography. Included also is a list of visual aids in the form of motion pictures and filmstrips, the use of which the author strongly recommends in conjunction with lectures and informal classroom discussions.

The problems have been selected and arranged so that a minimum amount of searching, selecting, and repetitive learning of fundamentals is required in order for the student to practice and display the knowledge acquired as he moves from the work in one chapter to that of the next. The problems are of varying degrees of difficulty, permitting selective assignment based on individual ability and on the level reached by the entire class group. As an aid in visualizing the objects, most of the problems are presented as pictorials. To simplify assignments, the problems are designed to fit the two smaller standard drawing sizes, namely $8\frac{1}{2}$- by 11-in. and 11- by 17-in. sheets. The approximate time for solution has been indicated for most of the problems to assist the instructor in estimating how much time to allow an average student. The time for each problem was arrived at by averaging the results of assignments to a large number of beginning students. Obviously, however, one beginner may grasp certain fundamentals more readily than another and finish sooner than the naturally slow student or the extremely conscientious student interested in fine techniques.

A separate problem book keyed to the text is available.

This text was written in an area considered as one of the most highly industrialized in the world. It was inevitable, therefore, that the author sought the help, advice, and suggestions of practicing engineers and designers employed by the many industrial concerns in the vicinity. To them, to my associates on the staff of the Engineering School of the University of Delaware, and to the hundreds of students whose contributions make up more than a minor part in the development and approach of this text, the author wishes to express his sincerest thanks and to assure them that their anonymity is due only to the largeness of their number and the lack of space for naming them. Thanks and appreciation is also offered to the organizations that have been kind enough to supply original drawings and other material used throughout the text.

FRANK ZOZZORA

NEWARK, DEL.
March, 1953

CONTENTS

Chapter 1

INTRODUCTION

Drawing has often been called the universal language, and engineering drawing is the particular phase of this graphic language that the engineer uses to convey to others his idea of the size, shape, and construction of a part or mechanism. Although an engineer is not always required to make a carefully finished drawing, he must be able to produce an acceptable representation that can be followed accurately, speedily, and with an economy of time and effort by those who are to perform the operations or tasks required in making the object shown in the plan. The engineer must understand completely the fundamentals involved, for, in addition to making his own sketches and drawings, he must supervise and counsel others. The technical student should not require strong urging. When he is ready to embark on his career, regardless of the branch of engineering he has chosen to follow, the chances are that he will earn his first money at the drawing board.

This text has been prepared with the following main objectives in mind: (1) To give the practicing engineer the opportunity to quickly review and readily reassimilate the fundamentals of the subject. (2) To offer the teacher the assurance that in covering the essentials of the subject in the limited time allotted him in his curtailed curriculum he is giving his students the basic knowledge required of them for further development in specialized industry and the profession. (3) To provide the student with the essentials and tech-niques of engineering drawing without requiring him to learn specialized details that will prove of little value to him in his professional career.

It has been said that 90 per cent of all learning is acquired through seeing. Accordingly, visual aids in the form of three-dimensional drawings of all types have been employed freely in conjunction with the orthographics wherever it has been felt that pictorial treatment would further aid the student in the understanding of the points set forth. Careful study by the student of the simple but direct illustrations will relieve the teacher of the need for discussing much that is elementary but time-consuming.

Although brevity is the keynote throughout the text, it has not been gained at the expense of omitting essential material. Instead, whatever might have appeared as repetitive or superfluous has been excluded to avoid confusing the reader.

Long experience has suggested a chapter sequence that should lead to easy progress in the study of the subject. Following the chapter on lettering, the student is introduced directly to the basic theory of orthographic projection, which has been carefully pictured and explained. This is followed by a chapter on freehand detail drafting, which permits the student to apply the ortho-graphic-projection theory immediately without first having to master the use of instruments. It is hoped that this arrangement will help to establish clearly the aims and principles of engineering

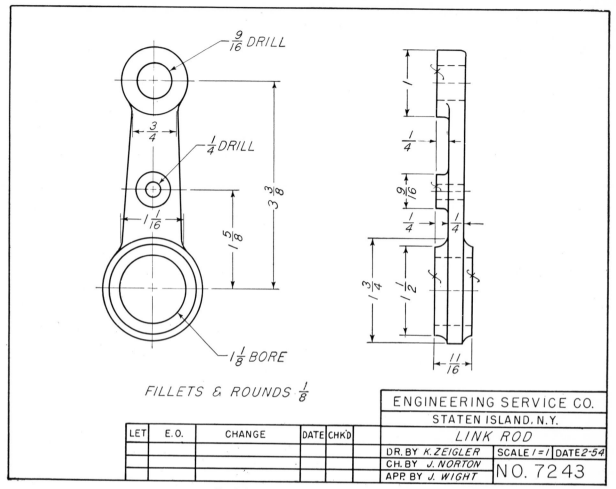

Fig. 1-1. A typical engineering drawing.

drawing at an early stage and to stimulate the student's interest in drafting techniques and instrument work, including the seemingly meaningless exercises in geometrical constructions. The chapter on freehand drafting should prove a delight to the practicing engineer or to the student who has a desire to improve upon his ability along that line. It should be noted here that most of the drawing the busy engineer will do in the future will be freehand sketching; the finished drawings will be executed by his assistants or by the draftsmen in the drafting room.

Whenever applicable, discussions and techniques outlined in this text have been made to conform to the recommendations of the American Standards Association (ASA). This organization is made up of representatives from the teaching profession and from industry. The Association is constantly working toward the standardization of various practices and procedures in the manufacturing in-

dustries and in the engineering profession. More than 100 of their publications, called "Standards" or "Tentative Standards," are very helpful not only to the designer but also to the draftsman. Of the many Standards published, perhaps the most helpful to the draftsman is "Drawings and Drafting Room Practices." Of almost equal importance, however, are the Standards that have been prepared on more specialized phases of engineering-drawing procedure, such as those on symbols, abbreviations, and layouts, and on piping, welding, electrical, and chemical diagrams. A complete list of the Standards may be obtained by communicating with the American Standards Association at their offices in New York.

The bibliography at the back of this book provides a list of many of the commonly used Standards. Also included in the bibliography is a list of books on subjects allied to engineering drawing which the beginning draftsman should find of assistance when more detail is required than it is possible to give in this text.

The draftsman can get much valuable information on design, drawing, and dimensioning by referring to the several types of engineers' handbooks and the many manufacturers' catalogues. A collection of catalogues should complement the equipment of every practicing draftsman, because many unstandardized but commonly used parts are illustrated in these special publications made up under the direction of the engineers associated with the manufacturing companies.

A glossary of the most commonly used shop terms will be found on page 104. The glossary explains the meanings of various specialized terms used in industry and also includes illustrations for ready comprehension.

The Appendix contains tables and design information on commonly used fastening devices, on the classification of fits, and on other detail matters which the student will find helpful in working the problems in this text. Also included are a conversion table and a table of trigonometric functions.

The pursuits in which a technically trained person may apply a knowledge of engineering drawing are many and diversified. Engineering-drawing ability is a requisite for any practicing engineer, for it will be found useful in all branches of the engineering profession. The brief descriptions in the following paragraphs, covering the four main branches of engineering, indicate a number of typical ways in which engineering drawing is useful to the practicing engineer.

Civil engineering. The education of the civil engineer is intended to equip him with a knowledge that will enable him to design and construct roads, bridges, railways, subways, tunnels, airports, harbor installations, etc. He is trained in the principles of planning and maintaining transportation facilities, water and power supply, and irrigation and drainage systems. In order to do his work well he must have a sound knowledge of engineering drawing so as to be able to prepare structural, erection, installation, and plant-layout drawings, as well as maps and route surveys.

Electrical engineering. Electrical engineers may find their interests in several special fields, such as communications, power, or electronics. In each of these fields, the practicing electrical engineer may expect to utilize his knowledge of engineering drawing in the preparation of plans and diagrams for the erection or installation of equipment and apparatus. He must be fully acquainted with the conventional electrical drawing procedures and symbols in order to make wiring and circuit diagrams speedily and efficiently.

Chemical engineering. The chemical engineer's training is intended to enable him to devise and construct equipment for chemical cracking and synthesis and to develop new products for general and industrial use. The chemical engineer should be prepared to make the sketches and finished drawings of flow and process diagrams and the details and assemblies of the mechanisms he designs for his work. He must also prepare diagrammatic, installation, and erection drawings for his workmen to follow.

Mechanical engineering. As a general rule, the mechanical engineer will be primarily interested in the design and development of machines and mechanisms, and he must be familiar with all phases of their operation and proper maintenance. He will apply a knowledge of engineering drawing in the preparation of original sketches and designs, in the construction of graphs and charts expressing engineering calculations and solutions, and in the drawing of detail and assembly plans for the machines and mechanisms that he creates. As a plant engineer he should also be able to construct erection and installation drawings and plant layouts.

A scientifically and technically minded person may also find his life work in one of the related engineering fields, such as industrial, aeronautical, agricultural, or sanitation engineering. These all require many of the basic courses necessary to the training of the civil, electrical, chemical, and mechanical engineer. And for all, a thorough understanding of the fundamental principles of engineering drawing is an indispensable part of their educational background and equipment.

Chapter 2

ENGINEERING LETTERING

In order to construct a part or structure, the workman must have a complete description of its shape and size. The various views on the drawing sheet show the part's contours, but figured dimensions and lettered notes are needed to explain the pictured forms. In keeping with the principle that a good engineering drawing enables the worker to do his job quickly, easily, and economically, the simplest of lettering forms, the single-stroke modern gothic, has been adopted almost universally for all letters and numerals. In addition to perfect legibility, the single-stroke gothic letters may be drawn rapidly, which is a significant advantage to the draftsman. The term *single-stroke* means that there is no variation in the width of the lines that make up the letter, and not that the letter is begun and completed in a single movement of the pencil.

To become adept at the art of lettering, the draftsman must:

1. Acquire a thorough knowledge of the proportion and design of each letter and the order and the direction of the strokes used to produce it.

2. Learn to compose letters in the formation of words and to space words properly in sentences.

3. Practice consistently and conscientiously. The beginning draftsman should form the habit of lettering the entire alphabet and a practice sentence each day.

Lettering is a form of freehand drawing, and its attractiveness and legibility enhance the entire graphic presentation on the drawing sheet. The lettering of notes, dimensions, specifications, finishes, and other required information should never be crowded, placed haphazardly, or appear to have been done hurriedly.

Two types of gothic letters are used on engineering drawing—the vertical and the inclined. Both styles are widely used in industry. The vertical letters are more difficult to produce because the slightest variation from verticality is easily detected by the eye. They are becoming increasingly popular in professional practice, however, because of their easy readability. The slant letters seem to flow more readily from the pencil. The beginning draftsman should learn to produce both types satisfactorily.

2-1. Uniformity. The lettering on the drawing sheet should be uniform in appearance. The inclination or verticality, the weight and strength of lines, the height and width of each letter, and the spacing of letters in words and words in sentences are the important considerations in assuring a good appearance (see Fig. 2-1).

2-2. Proportions of letters. Good lettering consists essentially of spacing and arranging the lines and masses of the individual letters so they will have a pleasing effect on the observer. A

LETTERING THAT IS VERTICAL, UNIFORM IN HEIGHT, AND MADE WITH THE PROPER WEIGHT OF STROKE LINE, IS BOTH PLEASING AND EFFECTIVE.

Fig. 2-1. Vertical single stroke modern gothic lettering.

DECREASE OR INCREASE THE WIDTH OF LETTERS IN WORDS IN ORDER TO FILL A PARTICULAR SPACE

ENGINEERING
Normal letters

ENGINEERING
Condensed letters

ENGINEERING
Extended letters

Fig. 2-2. Normal, condensed, and extended letters.

thorough study and knowledge of the particular and individual characteristics of each letter and the space it is to occupy in the word structure is of the utmost importance to good lettering.

At times space considerations may demand that the letters be made either narrower or wider than normal. Such letters are known as *condensed* and *extended* letters, respectively (see Fig. 2-2). In lettering a drawing, the condensed, extended, and normal types of lettering should never be inter-mixed in the forming of a word or sentence.

2-3. Boldface and lightface letters. Dominance or subordination may be achieved by varying the thickness of the pencil stroke without changing the style or the height of the letters (Fig. 2-3).

LIGHTFACE
BOLDFACE

Fig. 2-3. Lightface and boldface lettering.

2-4. Pencils for guide lines and lettering. Guide lines are indispensable for producing good lettering. The extremely light vertical and horizontal guide lines are drawn with a hard pencil such as a 4H or 5H. The letters themselves require a lead of medium soft grade but black enough and hard enough to produce a clean, dark line. An HB or 2H lead that is well pointed and kept so by frequent sharpening will bring satisfactory results.

2-5. Pens for lettering. A complete discussion of the various types of pens that may be used for lettering can be found in Chap. 17, Inking Practice.

2-6. Guide lines. Horizontal guide lines are used to regulate the height of the letters, and vertical or slope guide lines help to keep the angle of the letters uniform (see Fig. 2-4a). Horizontal guide lines should be drawn with a T square, and vertical guide lines with a T square and triangle (see Fig. 2-4b). The vertical guide lines are drawn at random spacing, since they are not intended to space the letters either in words or sentences.

Guide lines should be drawn so lightly that they will not require erasing. The horizontal guide lines,

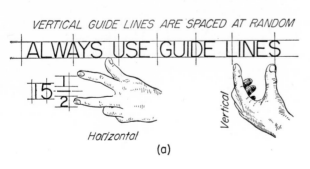

VERTICAL GUIDE LINES ARE SPACED AT RANDOM

ALWAYS USE GUIDE LINES

Horizontal

(a)

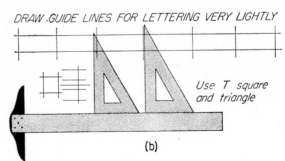

DRAW GUIDE LINES FOR LETTERING VERY LIGHTLY

Use T square and triangle

(b)

Fig. 2-4. Horizontal and vertical guide lines.

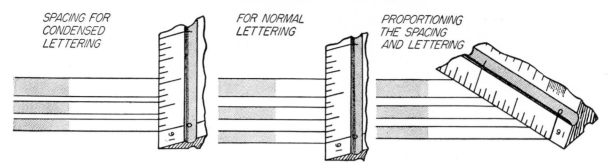

SPACING FOR CONDENSED LETTERING

FOR NORMAL LETTERING

PROPORTIONING THE SPACING AND LETTERING

Use 4H or 5H pencil for guide lines

Fig. 2-5. Laying out and spacing guide lines with the scale.

which regulate the height of the letters and the space between lines of lettering, may be located by using the scale as shown in Fig. 2-5, although practice will eventually enable the draftsman to space by eye. The space between guide lines and the height of the letters may be increased or reduced while still retaining the proper proportion between the height of the letters and the space between lines by holding the scale at an angle, as in the right-hand portion of Fig. 2-5.

The lettering for working drawings is commonly ³⁄₁₆ in. high for the titles and ⅛ in. high for the notes, etc., with a space of ⅛ in. between the lines of lettering. As illustrated in Fig. 2-5, if condensed lettering is used, the space between lines should be less than the height of the letters, say ¹⁄₁₆ in. if the letters are ⅛ in. high, or ranging anywhere between one-half to three-fourths the height of the letter. A safe procedure to follow would be to make the spaces between lines smaller than the height of the letters when compressed lettering is used, equal to the height of the letter when the letters are normal, and greater than the height of the letters when the letters are of the extended type (see Fig. 2-6).

Lettering devices, such as the Braddock-Rowe triangle and the Ames lettering instrument, are often used in drawing and spacing guide lines (see Fig. 2-7). The point of the pencil is inserted into the proper hole, and the guide lines are drawn by moving the instrument along the edge of the T square with the pencil. Various groups of holes on the instruments allow the drawing of a great variety of properly spaced guide lines.

2-7. Lettering strokes. The individual letters of the alphabet are comprised of various strokes. In one or two cases a single stroke will produce the letter; in all other instances the letters are made up of straight lines, curved lines, or straight and curved-line combinations. A knowledge of the direction in which these strokes move and a mastery of the method by which they are produced constitute the essence of the study of lettering.

The vertical stroke of a letter is produced by a finger movement from above downward (Fig. 2-8a). The horizontal stroke starts at the left and moves toward the right with a complete hand movement, as in b. The inclined, or slant, strokes start from above and move downward toward the right (c) or left (d), whichever is required. These

SPACES BETWEEN LINES
OF LETTERING

SHOULD BE NOT LESS THAN HALF NOR MORE THAN 1½ TIMES THE HEIGHT OF THE LETTERS

Fig. 2-6. Spaces between lines.

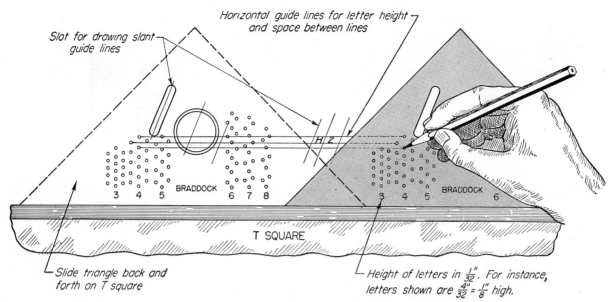

Slot for drawing slant
guide lines

Horizontal guide lines for letter height
and space between lines

Slide triangle back and
forth on T square

Height of letters in $\frac{1}{32}$". For instance,
letters shown are $\frac{4}{32}$" = $\frac{1}{8}$" high.

T SQUARE

Fig. 2-7a. Braddock lettering triangle.

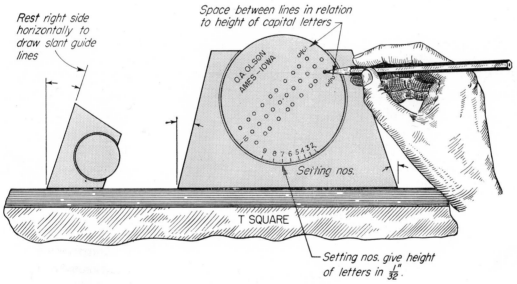

Rest right side
horizontally to
draw slant guide
lines

Space between lines in relation
to height of capital letters

Setting nos.

T SQUARE

Setting nos. give height
of letters in $\frac{1}{32}$".

Fig. 2-7b. Ames lettering instrument.

strokes are a combination of finger and hand movements. The curved strokes (Fig. 2-8e and f) always start from above and move in the desired direction by a combination finger and hand movement made possible by resting the hand on the ball of the palm. To form a proper foundation for good lettering, the student must make a serious effort to become familiar with, and master, the direction and order of each stroke for every letter in the alphabet and for every number.

2-8. Balance and stability. In order to overcome the effect of top heaviness, the upper portions of certain letters and numerals are made smaller than the lower parts. As Fig. 2-9 illustrates, in drawing the straight-line letters, the cross bars are located slightly above the mid-line. The mid-strokes of letters such as *B* and *E* are drawn shorter than the base strokes. For elliptical forms, the upper ellipse of the letter or figure is usually made a trifle smaller and narrower than the lower part. Rounded

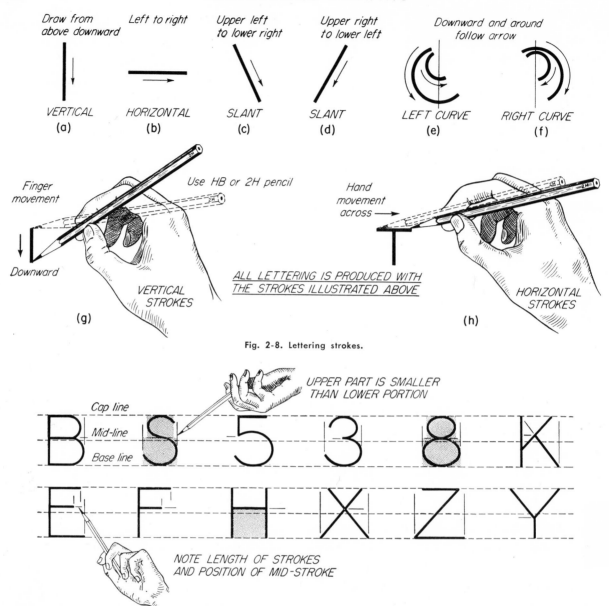

Fig. 2-8. Lettering strokes.

Fig. 2-9. Balance and stability in lettering.

Fig. 2-10. Treatment of rounded and pointed letters.

and pointed letters create the illusion that they are smaller than their neighbors unless their points or rounded extremities run well into the guide lines (Fig. 2-10). To overcome the stilted results inevitable when a standard design for each letter is employed, the clever draftsman will develop a pleasing pattern and style by learning to vary the horizontal, vertical, slanting, and elliptical lines to suit the special conditions confronting him. This flexibility in lettering style leads to the creation of a feeling of easy movement and stability throughout the complete word, phrase, and sentence.

2-9. The left-handed draftsman. Left-handers should expect no great difficulty learning good lettering. It is true that the material in the following sections is discussed with the right-handed draftsman in mind; however, the basic principles of letter formation are equally applicable for left-handed letterers. In general, the *order* of the letter strokes is the same for both left and right-handers. The *direction* of the strokes will be different for the left-hander, however, since it is obvious that he will draw horizontal lines from right to left rather than vice versa. After becoming thoroughly familiar with the forms of the letters, the left-hander should adopt the approach that feels most natural to him.

2-10. Vertical straight-line capitals. Figure 2-11 shows the capital letters produced by straight-line strokes. For the purpose of studying the proportions and design of the various letters, each letter has been placed in a square. The sides of the square are divided equally into six portions. These divisions enable the reader to note at a glance the relationship between the height and width, and the positions of the lines that make up each letter. Below each of the letters in the large squares is shown the same letter, but smaller in size, with arrows pointing in the direction in which each stroke is made. The numbers indicate the proper sequence of each stroke.

It is suggested that the beginner use cross-section paper, with its vertical and horizontal lines as the guide lines, to assist in regulating the height and stability of the letters. At first the letters should be drawn quite large. Not until the proportions and design of the letters have become familiar should lettering be practiced at the small regular sizes of ¼, ³⁄₁₆, and ⅛ in. by using the hand-ruled vertical and horizontal guide lines.

The *I* is made with a vertical downward stroke. The slant strokes of the *A* intersect slightly above the cap line, while its horizontal stroke is placed slightly less than one-third the distance up from the base line. The *T* and *L* consist of vertical and horizontal strokes. The length of the horizontal strokes of the *T* and *L* may be varied to suit the position of the letters in the word (for instance, when a *T* precedes the letter *A*, the horizontal stroke of the *T* should be slightly wider than usual; when an *L* precedes an *A*, the *L*'s horizontal stroke should be narrower than usual).

The middle horizontal stroke of the *H*, *F*, and *E* are placed just above the mid-height line. The length of this stroke in both the *E* and *F* should be about three-fifths the length of the cap-line stroke. The base-line stroke of the *E* is longer than either its mid-line or cap-line horizontal strokes. The slant strokes of the *V* intersect slightly below the base line.

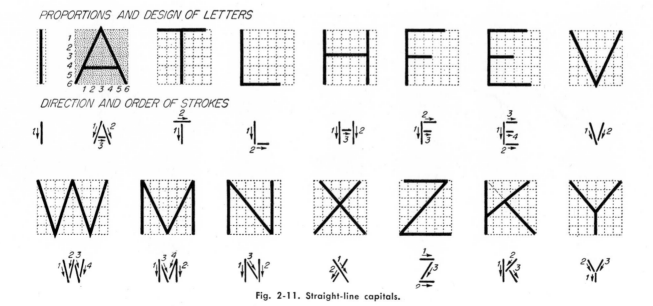

Fig. 2-11. Straight-line capitals.

The *W* is the widest letter of the alphabet, being 1⅓ times the width of a normal letter. Its base-line intersections extend below the guide line. The vertical strokes of the *M* and *N* should always be drawn before the slant strokes. The slant strokes of the *M* intersect at the base line. Strokes 2 and 3 of the *N* also intersect at the base line. Note the starting points of the slant strokes of the *X*. The slant strokes intersect just above the mid-line and finish at the outer corners of the square. The horizontal base line of the *Z* is longer than the cap horizontal line. The slant stroke 2 of the *K* intersects the vertical one-third up from the base line. Stroke 3 starts at stroke 2 and is drawn to the right lower corner on a diagonal that would intersect the top of the vertical if extended. The three strokes of the *Y* intersect at a point slightly below the center of the square.

2-11. The curved and straight-line combinations. Curved letters and letters that are made up of a combination of straight and curved lines are shown in Fig. 2-12. The *O* and *Q* are complete circles. The tail of the *Q* is a short slant line and is placed so that it appears to steady the letter. It makes an angle of about 45° with the horizontal base line. The *C* and *G* are also circular in design but they are not the full width of the square. The vertical and horizontal strokes of the *G* may be considered as additions to the letter *C*. The hori-zontal stroke lies on the mid-line and starts at the center of the circle. Note that the *O*, *Q*, *C*, and *G* extend very slightly above and below the outline of the square.

The *D* is made with one vertical, two horizontal, and a curved stroke. The curved stroke 4 is a portion of a circle. The *J* consists of a vertical stroke and an elliptical stroke. The half-ellipse stroke is one-third the height of the letter. The *U* is similar in construction to the *J* but is slightly wider.

The letter *P* is made with four strokes. Horizontal stroke 3 should be slightly below the mid-line and be the same length as stroke 2. Stroke 4 is circular. The *R* is similar to the *P*. Horizontal stroke 3 of the *R* rests in the mid-line. Note the direction of the slant stroke and the fact that it ends beyond the circular stroke 4. The letter *B* is made with six strokes. Strokes 2 and 3 are of the same length, while stroke 4 is slightly longer. Stroke 3 lies just above the mid-line. Strokes 5 and 6 are elliptical. The strokes of the *S* form ellipses, the upper one smaller than the lower, with the curves extending very slightly above and below the guide lines. The ellipses are tangent just to the left of the center line. Three varieties of the ampersand (&) are shown. The basic construction of each involves a small upper and a large lower ellipse. The ampersand on the right is the American Standard.

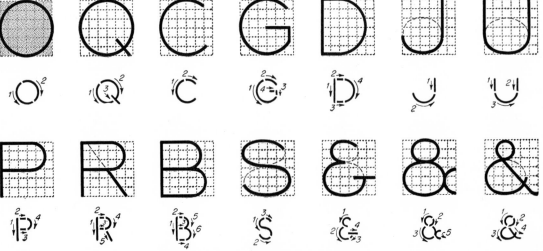

Fig. 2-12. Curved and straight-line combinations.

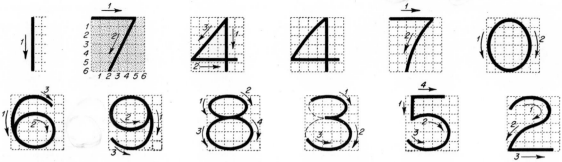

Fig. 2-13. Vertical numerals.

2-12. Vertical numerals. As in the case of letters, horizontal and vertical guide lines are drawn for numerals. Figure 2-13 shows the numerals in squares as an aid to the beginner for the study of the construction and proportions of the individual figures. Numerals should never be crowded or made too small for easy legibility. The need for careful study of the sequence and direction of the strokes required and the design and proportion of each figure cannot be overemphasized.

All the numerals, with the exception of the *1*, are five units wide. The *1* is made like the *I*, a downward vertical stroke. The *7* is made with a horizontal and a straight or slightly curved slant stroke ending directly below the middle of the horizontal stroke. The *4* is made up of three strokes, with the horizontal stroke about one-quarter up from the base line. Stroke 3 may curve slightly if desired. The zero (*0*) is elliptical, as distinguished from the letter *O*, which is circular. The *6* and *9* are of the same elliptical construction as the zero, with the loops being two-thirds the height of the figures. The *6* is a *9* upside down. The *8* is made up of a small ellipse on top of a larger one. The ellipses are tangent just above the mid-line. The *3* is constructed like the *8* but has the left portions of the ellipses lopped off. The ellipse of the *5* is two-thirds the height of the figure and is wider than the horizontal stroke. The *2* is made with three strokes. Stroke 1 is part of an ellipse, stroke 2 part of a circle, and stroke 3 a horizontal line lying in the base line. Notice that the elliptical and circular strokes are tangent at the mid-line.

2-13. Vertical fractions. The full height of a fraction is twice that of a whole number (see Fig. 2-14). The mid-line serves as the position for the crossbar, which is always drawn horizontally. The numerals in the fraction are three-fourths the height of a whole number and are centered about a common vertical. The fraction bar extends slightly beyond the numerals. Five horizontal guide lines are required for lettering fractions appearing alone; seven are necessary when whole numbers and fractions occur together.

2-14. Vertical lower-case letters. Lower-case letters are rarely used in machine drawing. They are used frequently, however, in map drawing and graphical computations. Like the capitals, the fundamentals of their design are based on the circle, the circle arc, and the straight line. The body of a lower-case letter is two-thirds the height of a capital (see Fig. 2-15). Four horizontal guide lines are used for the construction of the lower-case letters. The body lies between the middle two, the top line indicates the height of the ascenders, and the bottom line marks the extent of the drop

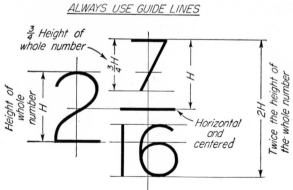

Fig. 2-14. Whole numbers and fractions.

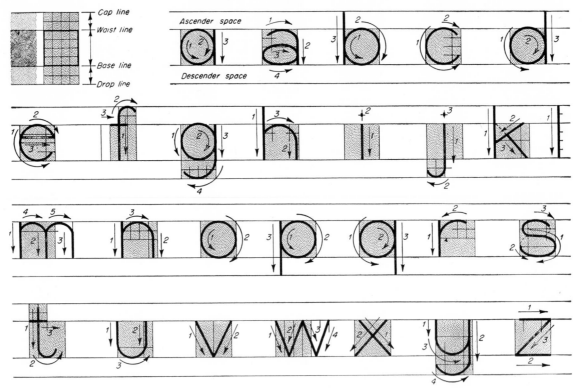

Fig. 2-15. Vertical lower-case letters.

of the descenders below the base line. As with capital letters, random vertical guide lines should be included.

As shown in Fig. 2-15, all descenders should meet the drop line, and with the exception of the *t*, all ascenders should reach the cap line. The dots for the *i* and the *j* are located just below the cap line. The horizontal crosses for the *f* and *t* lie on the waist line and extend the same distance on either side of the vertical stroke. Note that the vertical strokes of the *a*, *b*, *d*, *g*, *p*, and *q* join with the circular strokes and do not tend to widen the appearance of the letter at the tangent point. The descending curves of the *g*, *j*, and *y* touch the drop line. The ascending curve of the *f* touches the cap line. The horizontal stroke of the *e* is above the mid-line of the body. The curved strokes for the *h*, *m*, *n*, and *r* start about two-thirds of the way up between the base and waist lines. The single vertical stroke of the *l* touches the cap line; so does the vertical stroke of the *k*. Note that slant stroke 2 of the *k* starts at the waist line and intersects the vertical just below the mid-line of the body. Stroke 3

starts from stroke 2 and is drawn along a diagonal that would, if extended, meet the intersection of the vertical stroke and the waist line.

Strokes 3 of both the *p* and *q* are straight and vertical and terminate in the drop line. The curved strokes 2 of the *f*, *j*, and *t* are of the same height but not of the same breadth as the curved strokes of the other letters.

2-15. Capital and lower-case combinations. Figure 2-16 illustrates the use of capitals with lower-case letters. Four horizontal guide lines are drawn. The capital letter occupies the space between the cap line and the base line. The waist line, which indicates the height of the bodies of the lower-case letters, is located two-thirds the distance up from the base line to the cap line. The spaces for the ascenders and descenders are each one-third the height of the capitals. The space between the lines of lettering should be equal to or slightly greater than the height of the ascenders and descenders. (Referring to the illustration, the spacing between lines 4 and 1 is equal to or greater than the spacing between lines 1 and 2.)

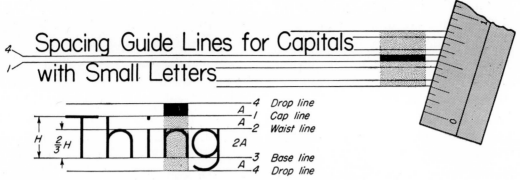

Fig. 2-16. Capital and lower-case combinations.

2-16. Capital and small capital combinations. If desired, large and small capitals may be used in combination to produce an attention-demanding effect. The small capitals are drawn two-thirds to three-fourths the height of the large capitals (Fig. 2-17).

2-17. Inclined letters. Inclined, or slant, letters are drawn at an angle of approximately $22\frac{1}{2}°$ from the vertical. Aside from this, the design, construction, and order of strokes of the slant letters are quite similar to the vertical type. Horizontal guide lines are drawn the same as for vertical letters. The inclined guide lines may be drawn by scaling five divisions vertically and two divisions

horizontally with an ordinary scale. The slope of the line produced will be approximately the desired $22\frac{1}{2}°$ (see Fig. 2-18a). The circles of the vertical letters become ellipses in the inclined letters, with their long axes making angles of 45° with the horizontal (Fig. 2-18b). In the drawing of such letters as the V, X, and Y, the inclined guide line should be drawn first and the letter balanced symmetrically about it (see Fig. 2-18c). The lower-case inclined letters (see Fig. 2-18d) are drawn with the same proportions and order of strokes as the vertical lower-case letters. They are formed on the same principles as the inclined capital letters.

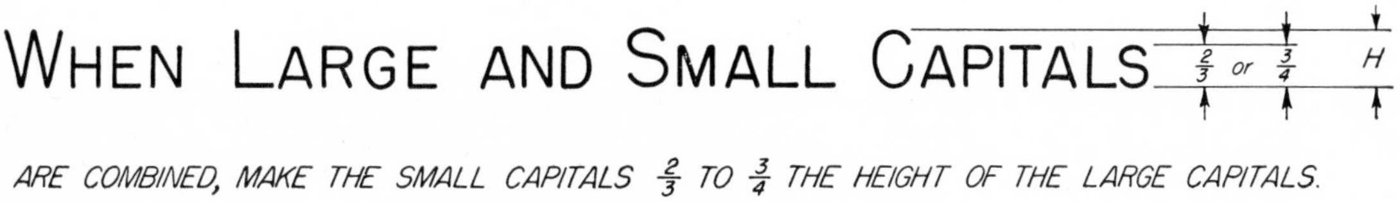

Fig. 2-17. Combining large and small capitals.

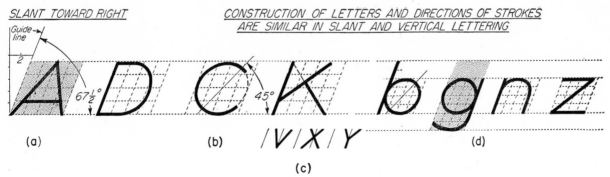

Fig. 2-18. Construction of slant capital and lower-case letters.

Inclined numerals and fractions are based on the vertical figures and are drawn in the same fashion as the inclined letters. Care should be used when lettering fractions to be sure that the figures are balanced symmetrically about the slope line and that they have the proper slant. The cross bar is always horizontal.

A complete alphabet of the inclined letters and numerals is shown in Fig. 2-19.

2-18. Spacing letters in words. When spacing letters in words, the areas between the letters rather than the clearances should appear approxi-

mately uniform (see Fig. 2-20a and b). A word appears as a unit when the areas between its component letters are equal or nearly so (as in Fig. 2-20b and d). Note in Fig. 2-20a how the L seems to pull away from the *IFE*, even though its actual clearance with the I is the same as the clearance between the I and the F and the F and the E. At b the in-between areas are better balanced and the whole word holds together as a unit. At c, note how the word *BITTER* seems to fall apart at a point between the T's. The letter B appears too close to the I. At d, with a proper balance of the

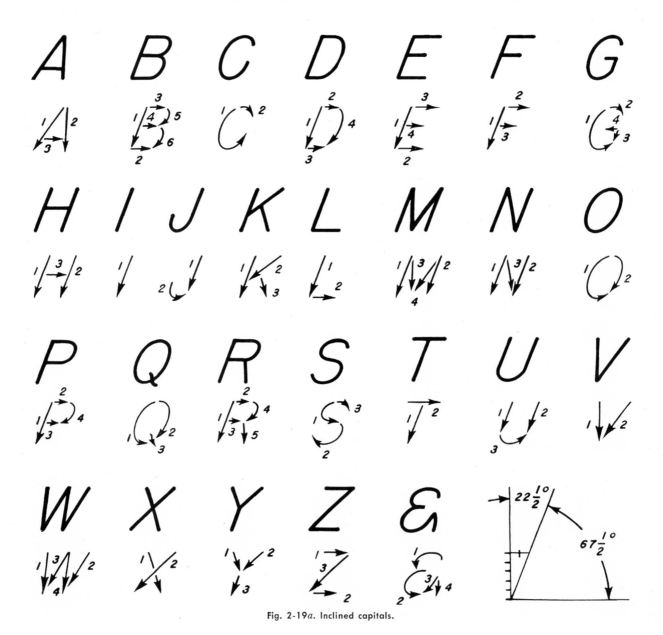

Fig. 2-19a. Inclined capitals.

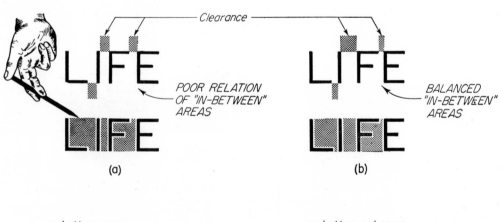

Fig. 2-19b. Inclined numerals and fractions.

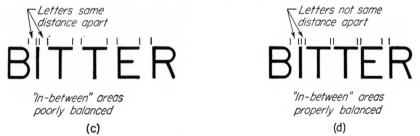

Fig. 2-20. Letter spacing and word construction.

Fig. 2-21. Word spacing.

in-between areas and a disregard of the clearances between the individual letters, the letters combine into a well-knit unit. A little practice is required to avoid the common fault of spacing the letters too far apart.

Although no definite rules can be set up for word spacing, the distance between words ordinarily should be approximately equal to the width of the letter *M* (Fig. 2-21a). This same distance should be used to separate the comma and the period from the first letter of the following word on the same line (Fig. 2-21b). (It should be men-

tioned here, however, that punctuation marks should be used very sparingly on engineering drawings.)

2-19. Arrangement of title blocks. A title form should appear on all drawings. The complete descriptive title block is usually placed in the lower right corner of the sheet as shown in Fig. 2-22b to d. (For complete information on size, arrangement, and spacing of the title block see Fig. 14-4.) The block is composed symmetrically about a center line as shown in Fig. 2-22. In many shops the title block is printed on the drawing

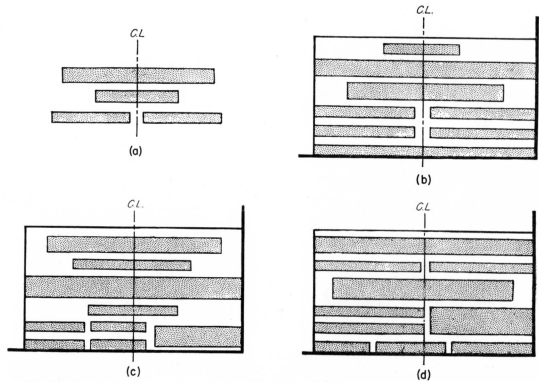

Fig. 2-22. Symmetrical title forms: (a) is simple detail title; (b), (c), and (d) are forms of block titles.

sheet. Obviously the title and important details should occupy the more prominent positions. Capital letters should be used for all lettering in the title block.

2-20. Lettering procedure. Since in industry practically all drawings are now produced on tracing paper or tracing cloth, the problem of arranging and spacing the lettering for titles, notes, specifications, etc., has lost much of its challenge. Because the drawing sheet can be seen through, trial lettering and spacing may be done on a piece of spare paper and then slipped under the drawing sheet and traced. A quick and easy method is illustrated in Fig. 2-23. Fix a scrap of tracing paper over the space the lettering will ultimately occupy. Draw the horizontal and vertical guide lines to ensure proper height and verticality. Next space the letters into the desired words, and the words into the required phrase or sentence. Once a pleasing arrangement has been made, slip the scrap with the trial lettering under the drawing sheet. If the phrase or sentence is to be centered, the mid-point should be marked on the scrap and then registered with the mid-point on the drawing sheet; otherwise the phrase may be placed in any position that appears suitable.

If the drawing sheet is opaque, the scrap sheet may still be utilized for arranging and spacing purposes by any number of ways that will come to the draftman's mind as he moves his scrap trial sheet over the drawing and perceives the relation of the available lettering spaces to his trial lettering.

2-21. American Standard lettering. Vertical and slant lettering, with its various sizes and uses and other special recommendations of the American Standards Association, are shown in Figs. 2-24 and 2-25. Note particularly the statement "It is not desirable to grade the size of lettering with the size of the drawing except when a reduced photographic reproduction of the drawing is to be made."

2-22. Special lettering devices. There are several lettering aids on the market that make it possible to produce lettering more speedily than by freehand. In using these devices the need for guide lines is dispensed with, although it is still necessary to understand the fundamentals of spacing. Whereas the result secured through mechanical lettering appears stiff and unartistic, it is always preferable to careless or unskilled freehand work.

Figure 2-26a shows the Wrico lettering device with two types of available pens, the template, and the guide. The template is a plastic stencil in which have been cut various partial and complete letters. The partial letters may be completed by other letter elements cut into the template. The letters are made by sliding the template back and forth along its grooved retaining guide. A sample line of lettering produced by this instrument is shown at the top of the illustration. Templates with various styles of letters and figures up to 1 in. in height are available.

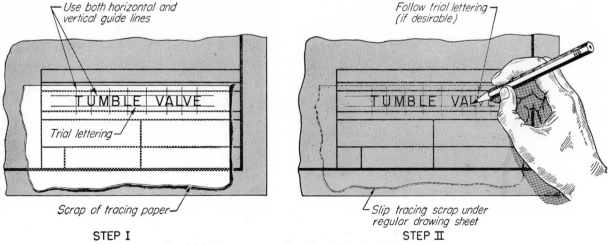

STEP I
STEP II

Fig. 2-23. Arrangement and spacing of lettering in title blocks.

SECTION 9—LETTERING

The most important requirement for lettering as used on working drawings is legibility. The second is ease and rapidity of execution. These two requirements are met in the single stroke commercial gothic letter, now in almost universal use throughout the technical world. Preference seems to be divided between the vertical and the inclined styles.

The following standard practice is recommended:

(a) That single stroke commercial gothic lettering either vertical or inclined at a slope of 2 in 5 be used on all working drawings for titles, notes, etc.

It is not desirable to grade the size of lettering with the size of the drawing

TYPE 1

ABCDEFGHIJKLMNOP
QRSTUVWXYZ&
1234567890 $\frac{1}{2}$ $\frac{3}{4}$ $\frac{5}{8}$
TITLES & DRAWING NUMBERS

TYPE 2

FOR SUB-TITLES OR MAIN TITLES
ON SMALL DRAWINGS

TYPE 3

ABCDEFGHIJKLMNOPQRSTUVWXYZ&
1234567890 $\frac{1}{2}$ $\frac{3}{4}$ $\frac{5}{8}$ $\frac{9}{32}$
FOR HEADINGS AND PROMINENT NOTES

TYPE 4

ABCDEFGHIJKLMNOPQRSTUVWXYZ&
1234567890 $\frac{1}{2}$ $\frac{3}{4}$ $\frac{5}{8}$ $\frac{23}{64}$
FOR BILLS OF MATERIAL, DIMENSIONS & GENERAL NOTES

TYPE 5

OPTIONAL TYPE SAME AS TYPE 4 BUT USING TYPE 3 FOR FIRST
LETTER OF PRINCIPAL WORDS. MAY BE USED FOR SUB-TITLES
AND NOTES ON THE BODY OF DRAWINGS.

TYPE 6

abcdefghijklmnopqrstuvwxyz

Fig. 2-24. American Standard lettering.

Figure 2-26*b* shows the LeRoy lettering instrument and the type of point used with it. This device consists of incised letters on a guide which can be moved along a straight edge (the T square). A pin on the instrument follows the grooved letters on the guide, and the letters are reproduced on the drawing by the scriber. This device can be obtained with a fixed scriber that will produce only vertical letters or an adjustable scriber that can be set to produce either the vertical or slant type. Various guides with letters and numerals from heights of 0.08 in. up to 2 in. and points making lines of varying thicknesses suitable to the heights of the letters, are available. A sample of lettering produced by this instrument is shown along the top of the illustration.

except when a reduced photographic reproduction of the drawing is to be made. In other words the size and weight of the lettering should be such as will produce legible prints from tracings either in pencil or in ink.

Lettering should not be underlined except for particular emphasis.

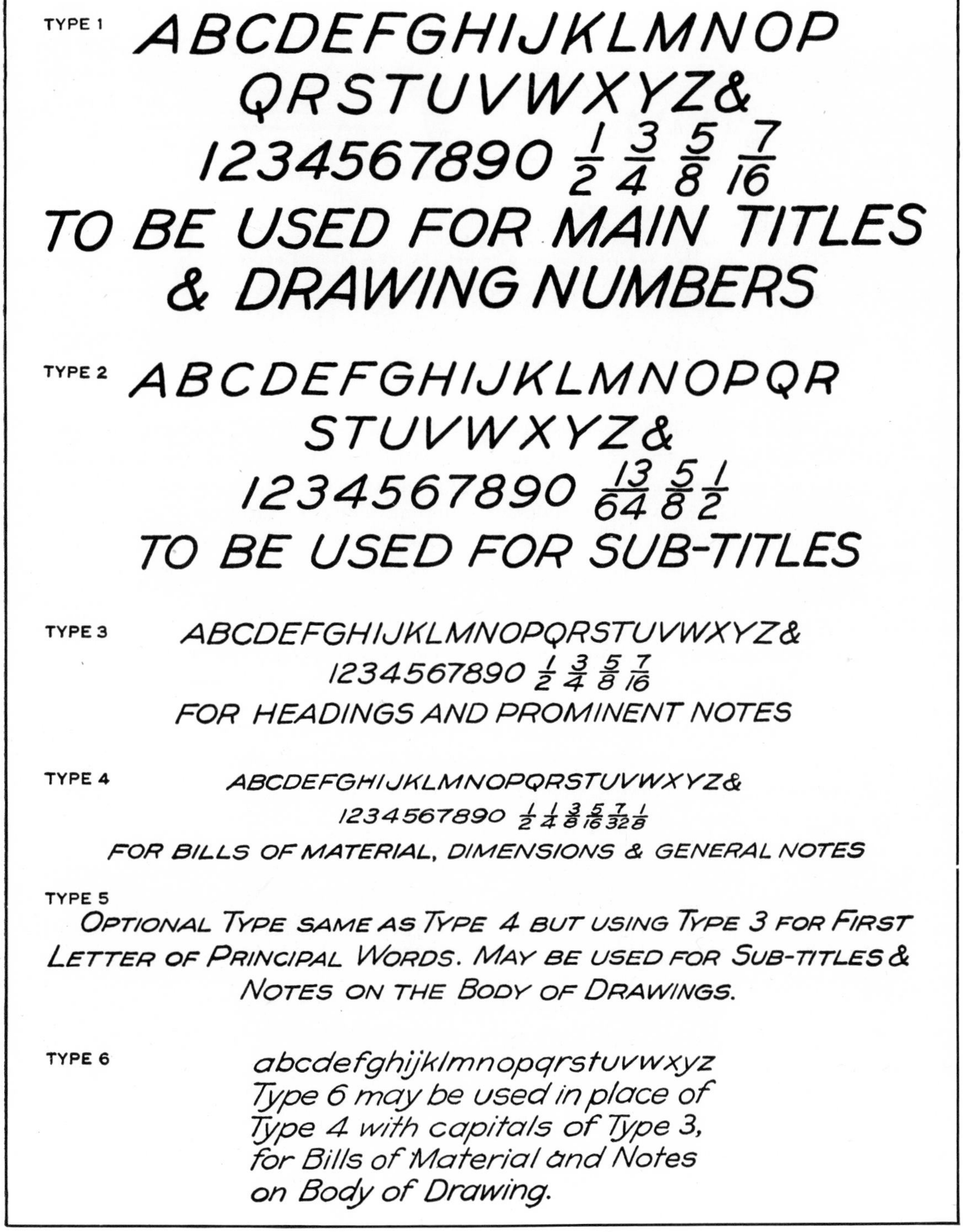

TYPE 1

$$ABCDEFGHIJKLMNOP$$
$$QRSTUVWXYZ\&$$
$$1234567890 \quad \frac{1}{2} \frac{3}{4} \frac{5}{8} \frac{7}{16}$$
$$TO\ BE\ USED\ FOR\ MAIN\ TITLES$$
$$\&\ DRAWING\ NUMBERS$$

TYPE 2

$$ABCDEFGHIJKLMNOPQR$$
$$STUVWXYZ\&$$
$$1234567890 \quad \frac{13}{64} \frac{5}{8} \frac{1}{2}$$
$$TO\ BE\ USED\ FOR\ SUB\text{-}TITLES$$

TYPE 3

$$ABCDEFGHIJKLMNOPQRSTUVWXYZ\&$$
$$1234567890 \quad \frac{1}{2} \frac{3}{4} \frac{5}{8} \frac{7}{16}$$
$$FOR\ HEADINGS\ AND\ PROMINENT\ NOTES$$

TYPE 4

$$ABCDEFGHIJKLMNOPQRSTUVWXYZ\&$$
$$1234567890 \quad \frac{1}{2} \frac{1}{4} \frac{3}{8} \frac{5}{16} \frac{7}{32} \frac{1}{8}$$
$$FOR\ BILLS\ OF\ MATERIAL,\ DIMENSIONS\ \&\ GENERAL\ NOTES$$

TYPE 5

OPTIONAL TYPE SAME AS TYPE 4 BUT USING TYPE 3 FOR FIRST LETTER OF PRINCIPAL WORDS. MAY BE USED FOR SUB-TITLES & NOTES ON THE BODY OF DRAWINGS.

TYPE 6

abcdefghijklmnopqrstuvwxyz
Type 6 may be used in place of
Type 4 with capitals of Type 3,
for Bills of Material and Notes
on Body of Drawing.

Fig. 2-25. American Standard lettering.

THIS LINE WAS LETTERED WITH THE WRICO
INSTRUMENT SHOWN BELOW. 123456789

THIS LINE WAS LETTERED WITH THE LEROY
INSTRUMENT SHOWN BELOW. 0123456789

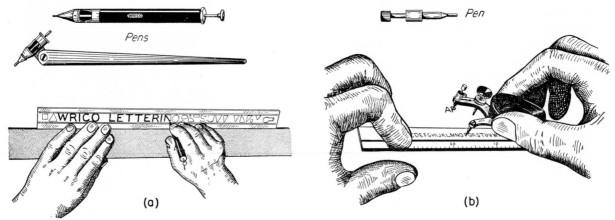

Pens

Pen

(a)   (b)

Fig. 2-26 (*a*) Wrico lettering device; (*b*) LeRoy lettering device.

PROBLEMS

It is recommended that the beginner use cross-section paper and make letters between ½ and 1 in. high while he is learning the construction and order of strokes for the letters, numerals, and fractions. After the individual letters have been practiced, the instructor should assign a short sentence exercise that can be lettered in from 10 to 15 min at the opening of every laboratory period throughout the whole term. This constant practice will lead to proficiency in the art of lettering. The following exercises are suggested as aids in making assignments.

2-1. Make a suitable layout on a 5½- by 8½-in. sheet with a ½-in. border, spacing the horizontal guide lines to accommodate capital letters ¼ in. high with $\frac{3}{16}$-in. spaces between lines. Letter the straight-line letters shown in Fig. 2-11. Fill the sheet.

2-2. Make a suitable layout on a 5½- by 8½-in. sheet with a ½-in. border for capital letters $\frac{3}{16}$ in. high with spaces between lines of ⅛ in. Letter the following sentence consisting of straight-line letters only: LET LAX MEN LIVE LAZILY IF THEY WILL. Repeat it, filling the entire sheet.

2-3. Using the layout suggested in Prob. 2-1, letter the curved-line letters shown in Fig. 2-12. Fill the sheet.

2-4. Using the layout suggested in Prob. 2-2, letter the following: JACK SAYS, "POOR LETTERING WILL MAR THE APPEARANCE OF AN OTHERWISE QUITE ACCEPTABLE DRAWING." Repeat. filling the sheet.

2-5. Make a suitable layout on a 5½- by 8½-in. sheet for figures ⅛ in. high with spaces between lines ⅛ in., and letter the numerals shown in Fig. 2-13. Repeat, filling the sheet.

2-6. Make a suitable layout on a 5½- by 8½-in. sheet, and letter the following numerals with their fractions. (Whole numbers ⅛ in. high, entire height of fraction ¼ in., numbers in fraction about $\frac{3}{32}$ in. high.) $2\frac{5}{64}$, $3\frac{3}{32}$, $4\frac{9}{16}$, $5\frac{1}{2}$, $8\frac{3}{4}$, $9\frac{7}{8}$, $1\frac{1}{8}$, $7\frac{1}{16}$, $10\frac{1}{4}$. Repeat, filling the sheet.

2-7. Letter the following statements: ENGINEERING DRAWING IS THE GRAPHIC LANGUAGE THE ENGINEER EMPLOYS TO CONVEY HIS THOUGHTS, IDEAS, AND DESIGNS TO OTHERS.

AT LEAST TWO COMPLETE PRINCIPAL VIEWS ARE USUALLY REQUIRED TO CONVEY THE TRUE SHAPE AND SIZE OF AN OBJECT IN ORTHOGRAPHIC PROJECTION DRAWING.

Sheet size, 5½ by 8½ in. Capital letters ⅛ in. high. Spaces between lines $\frac{3}{32}$ in.

Problems 2-8 to 2-13. Letter the following problems on 5½- by 8½-in. sheets with a ½-in. border. Draw horizontal and vertical guide lines, and show letters and whole numbers ⅛ in. high, fractions ¼ in. high, and space between lines $\frac{3}{32}$ in. If available, a lettering triangle or other guide-line device may be used. Repeat the legends to fill the entire sheet.

2-8. ½ DRILL AND REAM | ½ SPOTFACE × $\frac{1}{32}$ DEEP | $\frac{5}{16}$ DRILL—4 HOLES EQUALLY SPACED ON A 3″ B.C. | $\frac{1}{16}$ × 45° CHAMFER, BOTH ENDS.

2-9. $\frac{15}{32}$ DRILL, C'BORE $\frac{5}{8}$ DIA. × $\frac{19}{64}$ DEEP—5 HOLES | KEYWAY ¼ WIDE, 1½ LONG, ⅛ DEEP | NECK ⅛ WIDE × $\frac{1}{16}$ DEEP | ¼ DRILL, C'SINK 82° × ½ DIA.

2-10. No. 20 DRILL THROUGH | No. 4 STANDARD TAPER PIN | NO. 14 PRATT AND WHITNEY KEY | ¼ × 1¾ STANDARD SQUARE KEY.

2-11. STANDARD PLAIN WASHER | STANDARD LOCK WASHER | KEYWAY ⅛ WIDE × ⅛ DEEP × ⅝ LONG | SEAT FOR WOODRUFF KEY NO. 808.

2-12. GROOVE ⅛ WIDE TO 1¼ DIA. | ½-13 NC-2 | $\frac{7}{16}$-20 NF-3 LH | ⅝-ACME 8 THDS. PER INCH | ⅞-SQUARE 6 THDS. PER INCH LH.

2-13. FILLETS AND ROUNDS ⅛ | FILLETS AND RDS. ⅛ UNLESS OTHERWISE SPECIFIED | FAO | FINISH ALL OVER | GRIND FINISH.

2-14. Letter the following simple detail titles arranged as shown, making the name of the part $\frac{3}{16}$ in. high, the spaces between lines of lettering ⅛ in., and the height of all other letters in the title ⅛ in. high.

MOTOR BRACKET
SCALE = FULL SIZE
CAST IRON 1 R'QD

VISE JAW
SCALE = HALF SIZE
WROUGHT IRON 1 R'QD

TOOL GUIDE
SCALE ¼″ = 1″
CAST IRON 1 R'QD

HANGER BRACKET
SCALE 1 = 1
ALUMINUM 1 R'QD

2-15. Make a layout as suggested by the dimensions given in Figure 14-4 and letter the following title block:

NAME OF YOUR INSTITUTION OR COMPANY
CITY WHERE LOCATED
JIG ASSEMBLY

DATE   SCALE 1 = 1   DRAWING NO.
DR. BY   TR. BY
CH. BY   APP. BY

Chapter 3

ORTHOGRAPHIC PROJECTION

Practically speaking, all objects that the draftsman is called upon to draw are three-dimensional. In pictorial drawing it is customary to represent the three dimensions by shading and perspective. Such techniques are not satisfactory for working drawings, however, since they cannot convey accurately the constructional features of the object. The draftsman's problem, then, is to represent three-dimensional parts and forms on the flat plane of the drawing paper in such a way that all features are shown in their true dimensions and in their true relationship to other features on the part. To do this, the draftsman must draw a number of views of the part from different angles and employ what is known as *orthographic projection*.

Orthographic projection means right-angular, or perpendicular, projection, and its principles may be readily understood by referring to Fig. 3-1. If it is imagined that an object is being viewed by an observer standing an infinite distance from it, and a transparent plane is placed between him and the object, the projectors (or perpendiculars) from the points on the object would carry the image to the plane without distortion because the projectors are all parallel to each other and perpendicular to the image, or picture, plane. The diminishing effects of perspective are absent in orthographic projection.

In Fig. 3-1 it will be noted that point 1 on the object appears as point 1 on the image plane. Point 2 appears as shown, and all the other points on the object project as illustrated to form the complete image. Note that on the object, line 2-3 is on a slant with line 1-2, while on the image plane it is perpendicular. The complete image or view formed always shows the outline of the object and the intersections of its various surfaces as seen from one direction.

3-1. Hidden details. In drawing an orthographic view, it is customary to represent all edges and intersections of a part even though some features may not be visible from the direction in which the view was taken. The hidden features are shown by dotted lines called invisible, or hidden, lines (see Sec. 4-7). If a hidden line coincides with an external contour line, the hidden line is not shown (see Fig. 4-9).

3-2. The primary planes and views. There are six principal, or primary, views corresponding to the six principal planes of projection. These are the front, back, top, bottom, left-, and right-side views.

3-3. Choice of views and related views. As mentioned above, it is almost always necessary to show more than one view of an object in order to describe completely its features and dimensions.

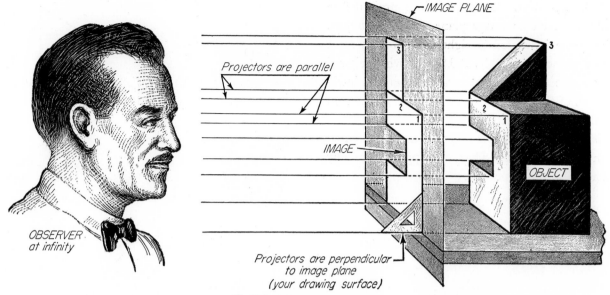

Fig. 3-1. Orthographic projection.

In selecting the views an orderly procedure and arrangement is always followed. After the first view has been chosen (usually the front view), each succeeding view is considered as being projected to and drawn on an image plane that is at right angles to the previously drawn view (see Fig. 3-5, for example). A view that is projected from another view is related, or adjacent, to that other view. Generally two related views are required to describe a simple object, and a more complicated piece may require three, perhaps four, and sometimes five or more views for complete and satisfactory description.

Of the six principal views, however, only three are usually employed in actual practice. These are the front, top, and right-side views. The three remaining principal views—the left-side, rear, and bottom—are used only when special need calls for any one or more of them.

3-4. Front view. The front view should show the most characteristic shape of the object or its natural appearance when observed in its permanent or fixed position. Because most parts used in mechanisms are small and may be viewed in any manner, it is permissible to use the view that shows the salient features of the part and the least number of hidden lines as the front view. The front view is always considered as lying in the plane of the paper, while all other views are rotated into this plane. To draw the front view, the image plane is placed parallel to the front face of the object (study Fig. 3-2), and the points of the object are projected perpendicularly to the image plane. The view as it appears on the drawing sheet is shown in the upper left portion of the illustration.

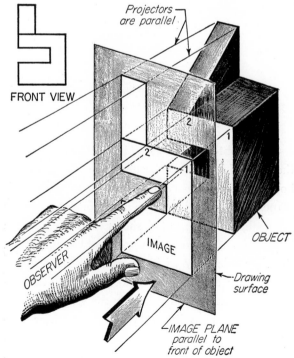

Fig. 3-2. Front view.

3-5. Top view. The top view is projected to and drawn on an image plane above the object. This plane is located at right angles to the front image plane (study Fig. 3-3), and when viewed in the direction of the arrow, the lines and intersections of the object will project the image shown on the image plane. Note that the intersections of invisible surfaces are also projected and represented with dotted lines. The view as it appears normally is shown at the upper left.

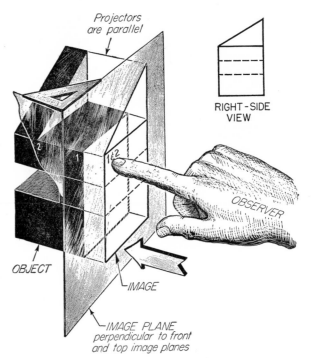

Fig. 3-4. Right-side view.

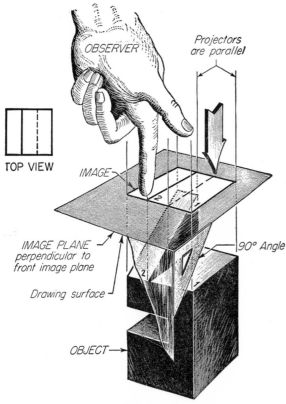

Fig. 3-3. Top view.

3-6. Right-side view. The image plane for the right-side view is located at right angles to both the front image plane and the top image plane, thus making all three image planes mutually perpendicular. Figure 3-4 shows the image on the image plane, and at the upper right is illustrated the right-side view as it appears on the drawing sheet. Here again, the invisible edges of the object are shown as dotted lines in the view.

3-7. Reference lines. When these three mutually perpendicular image planes are seen together, they may be imagined as forming a box-

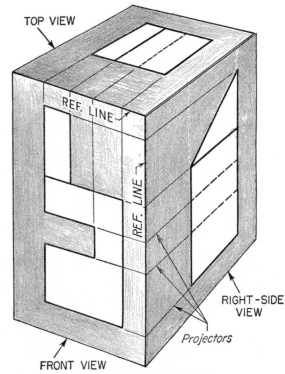

Fig. 3-5. Three views in projection.

like form of transparent material (see Fig. 3-5). The lines of intersection of the image planes are known as reference lines (sometimes called folding lines). The projectors between the views on the surfaces of the image planes extend from the front view to the top and side views. These projectors always cross, and are perpendicular to, the reference lines.

3-8. Revolving the planes. As noted previously the front view lies in the plane of the paper. In order to show the other two views on the surface of the drawing sheet, however, it is necessary to revolve the top and side image planes forward as though they were hinged to the front image plane (as shown in Fig. 3-6). Figure 3-7 shows the orthographic representation of the principal views after they have been revolved, with horizontal and vertical projectors included for clarity. In actual practice the projection lines are never drawn, but are only imagined as connecting the points on the various views.

Figures 3-6 and 3-7 show several significant points to keep in mind in regard to the arrangement of the various views on the drawing sheet. The top view is always located above the front view and projected from it. The right-side view is located at the right of the front view and is also in direct projection. This means that once the position of the front view has been fixed the positions of its related views are fixed and cannot be altered (except when the side views are drawn in the alternate position, as discussed in Sec. 3-13). Although the reference, or folding, lines are not always shown on a drawing, they too help fix the posi-

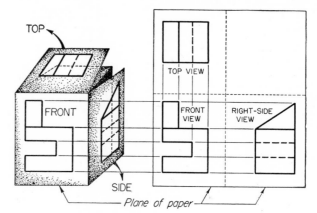

Fig. 3-7. The three views on the drawing sheet.

tions of the views in relation to each other, and on the drawing surface, as will be shown in later chapters.

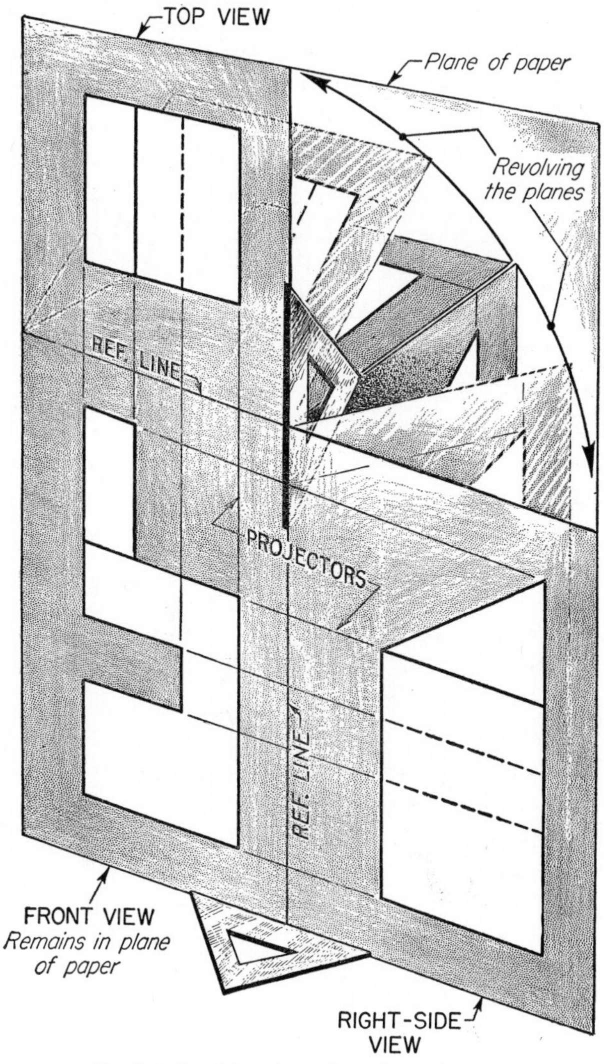

3-9. First- and third-angle projection. Extension of the horizontal and vertical planes of projection as shown in Fig. 3-8 will form four angles that may be numbered as in the illustration. In theory, an object could be placed in any one of these angles and its image drawn on the projection planes, which could then be rotated into the plane of the paper. In actual practice, however, projection in only the first and third angles is practical. *First-angle projection* is almost universally followed in Europe and was used in the United States until around 1890. In principle, projection in the first angle means that when the

Fig. 3-6. Revolving planes into plane of paper.

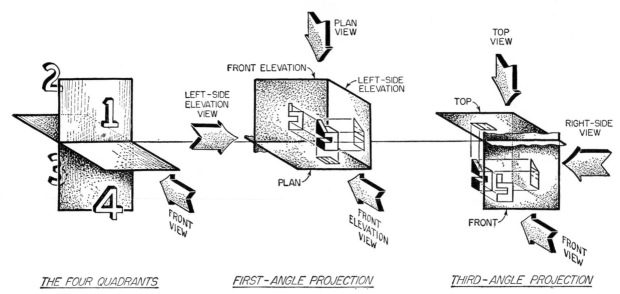

THE FOUR QUADRANTS FIRST-ANGLE PROJECTION THIRD-ANGLE PROJECTION

Fig. 3-8. First-angle and third-angle projection.

image planes are revolved into the plane of the paper the top view will appear *below* the front view and the left-side view will appear to the *right* of the front view. The present practice in this country, and the American Standard, is *third-angle projection*. It is the system of projection used in this chapter and throughout the text. In essence, third-angle projection means that the plane of projection is always placed between the observer and the object (that is, the object is viewed by looking *through* the projection plane).

3-10. The three dimensions. Any orthographic view standing alone, since it is represented on a flat surface, can show only two dimensions. The missing third dimension must be sought in a related view. When looking at the front view (see Fig. 3-9) we see the length and height dimensions of the object, but its depth is seen in the top and side views. The side view shows the height and depth, necessitating reference to the front or top for the length; while the top view shows length and depth dimensions, requiring the front or side to reveal the height.

3-11. Left-side, bottom, and rear views. The three additional principal views are the left-side, bottom, and rear. Their image planes are also

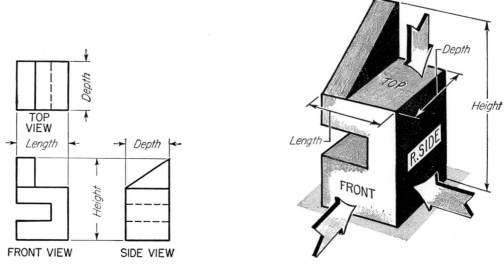

Fig. 3-9. Dimensions in views.

mutually perpendicular and, of course, perpendicular to the front, top, and right-side views. The observer moves to the left of the object to see the left side, he looks from below to see the bottom, and moves to the back to see the rear view. The points on the object project to the planes of projection in precisely the same way as they do for the other three principal views (see Fig. 3-10).

3-12. Positions of the principal views. When all six planes of projection with their respective images are seen together in space they form a transparent boxlike structure in which the object itself appears to be suspended in air. The technique that was employed to bring the front, top, and right-side views into the plane of the drawing surface is adopted for the rotation of the left-side, the rear, and the bottom views into the same plane of the paper. The left-side and bottom views are rotated toward the observer as though hinged to the front view, while the rear view is rotated toward the observer as if it were hinged to the left-side view (see the left-hand portion of Fig. 3-11). The front view always lies in the plane of the drawing surface and therefore does not require rotating.

The relative positions on the drawing sheet of the six principal views and their relationship to

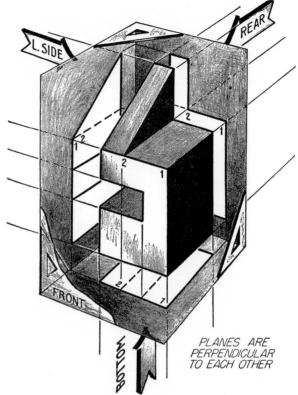

PLANES ARE PERPENDICULAR TO EACH OTHER

Fig. 3-10. Left-side, bottom, and rear views.

each other are shown at the right in Fig. 3-11. Notice that the front, right-side, left-side, and rear views line up in direct horizontal projection; the front, top, and bottom views line up in direct vertical projection. As noted in Sec. 3-3, any two adjacent

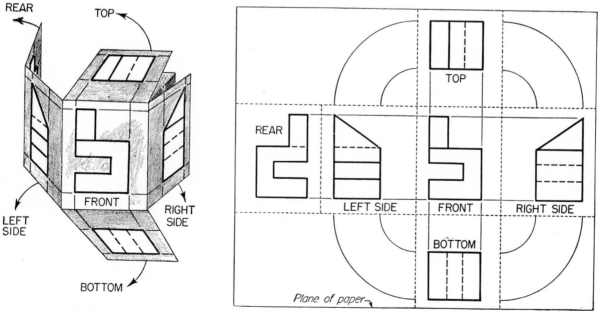

Fig. 3-11. Revolving left-side, rear, and bottom views. Positions of the six principal views on the paper.

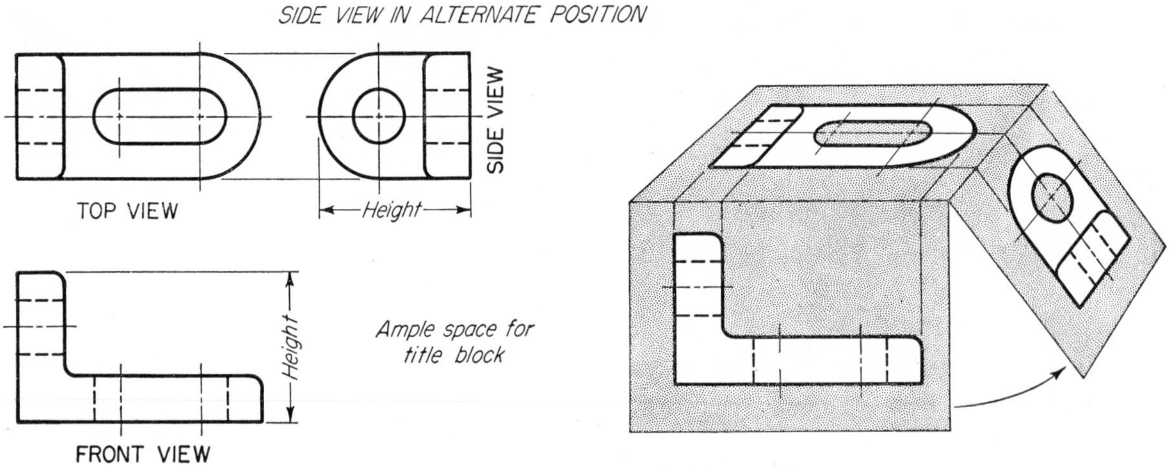

SIDE VIEW IN ALTERNATE POSITION

SIDE VIEW

TOP VIEW

Height

Ample space for title block

Height

FRONT VIEW

Fig. 3-12. Side view drawn in the alternate position.

views are related views. (Two views are related when one is directly projected from the other.) Each view has two of the three common space dimensions of height, length, and depth, while an adjacent view supplies the missing dimension.

3-13. Alternate position for the side and rear views. If a three-view drawing is necessary for complete description of a part, it may be desirable to draw the side view in an alternate position to allow room at the lower right for the title block and notes. To permit this alternate arrangement, it should be imagined that the plane of projection

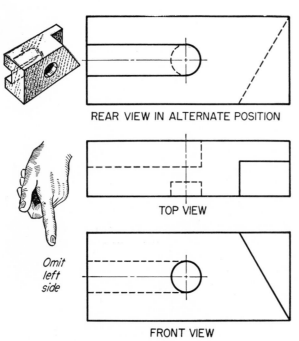

REAR VIEW IN ALTERNATE POSITION

TOP VIEW

Omit left side

FRONT VIEW

Fig. 3-13. Alternate position for rear view.

of the right-side view is hinged to the top view rather than the front (see Fig. 3-12). Note that this means that the side view is turned 90° from what its position would be in the normal three-view arrangement; in effect, the side view is shown on its side. The same principles may be applied to draw a left-side view in an alternate position.

A rear view may be drawn in an alternate position also, in which case it is considered to be hinged to the top rather than to the left-side view (see Fig. 3-13). On the drawing sheet the rear view would then appear above the top view and in direct projection from it. When the rear view is shown in this alternate position, the left-side view is not drawn on the same sheet.

3-14. Selection of views. The proper selection of views is of the utmost importance in orthographic drawing. In general, the draftsman should select the least number of views that will accurately describe the piece that is to be drawn and that will permit complete dimensioning. Unnecessary or poorly chosen views should be avoided, since they are confusing and waste valuable time in the shop. On the other hand, it is sometimes desirable to include a view that might technically be unnecessary in order to clarify a particularly intricate detail or to avoid a bewildering number of hidden lines in one of the other views. Proper selection of views is a skill that comes only with practice and with the development of the draftsman's ability to visualize the object on the drawing paper. Actual drawing experience and practice in reading drawings and blueprints will be of invaluable assistance to the beginning draftsman in developing skill and judgment.

Simple cylindrical pieces may be shown in a single view, the view that shows the axis as a center line (see the left portion of Fig. 3-14). This view is called a profile, or longitudinal, view. The diameters are dimensioned by an arrow-tipped leader that touches the part. The abbreviation "D" or "DIA" for diameter must always follow the dimension. When a cylindrical piece contains slots, holes, or other features that cannot be easily revealed in one view, additional views may be required (see the right side of Fig. 3-14).

A part that is symmetrical about either its main

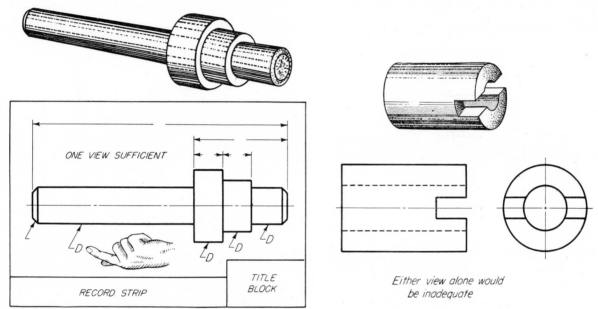

Fig. 3-14. Selection of views—cylindrical pieces.

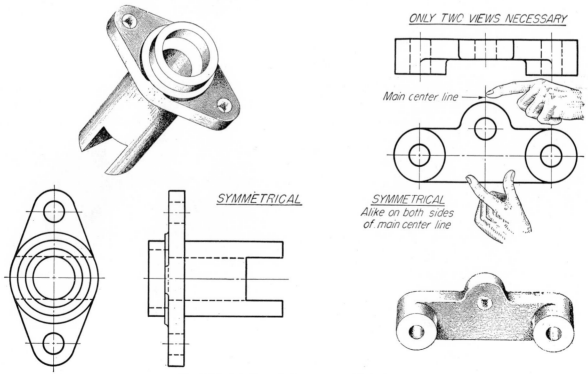

Fig. 3-15. Selection of views—symmetrical pieces.

vertical or main horizontal center line requires only two views. Careful analysis of the part will enable the draftsman to determine whether a side or a top view is called for after the front view has been selected (see Fig. 3-15).

Irregular objects generally require three principal views for complete shape description and dimensioning. Note that the part shown in Fig. 3-16 cannot be represented clearly by any two-view combination. Three views are absolutely necessary

to show the shape and features of the object. Some irregular or complicated objects may require more than the standard three views to describe them adequately. Sometimes what are known as primary auxiliary and secondary auxiliary views must be used to describe a piece properly. These views are discussed in detail in Chaps. 10 and 11.

Drawing views correctly and placing them in proper relation to each of the other views on the drawing sheet makes the entire drawing easy to

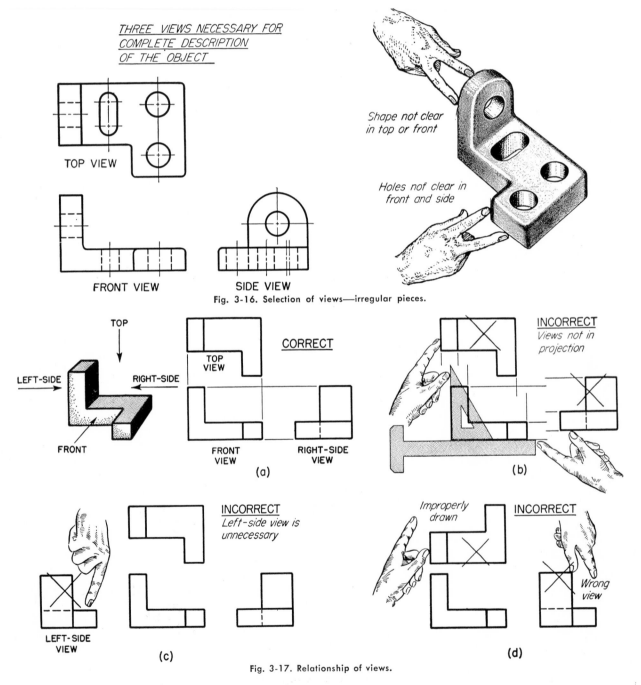

Fig. 3-16. Selection of views—irregular pieces.

Fig. 3-17. Relationship of views.

read and understand. As an illustration of this principle, see Fig. 3-17. At (*a*) the positions of the three principal views—front, top, and right-side—are shown in their proper projected relationship. The representation at (*b*) is not acceptable, however, since the top and side views, though correctly drawn, are not placed in direct projection from the front view. At (*c*) the left-side view adds nothing of importance to the description of the piece, and therefore it should be rejected as unnecessary. The top and side views shown at (*d*) are incorrectly drawn. The top view is a mixture of top and bottom views, and the right-side view is really a projection of the left-side view. The views are said to be "out of projection," and therefore the whole drawing is unacceptable.

Figure 3-18 illustrates an unwise choice of views. The front view could have been taken from the other side of the object to avoid extra dotted lines, thus changing the appearance of the top and side views. Better still, the present side view could have been taken as it is for the front view. Then the top view would be rotated 90° to the right and placed in direct projection above this newly selected front view. These two views alone would then adequately describe the piece.

3-15. Half views and partial views. Time, labor, and space may be saved by the use of half views and partial views. In addition, these views are often clearer because many of the dotted lines that would ordinarily be needed to show hidden features may be eliminated. A half view of uniform circular or elliptical pieces such as gears, pulleys, etc., may be drawn by showing only the portion of the object lying to one side of the center line (see Fig. 3-19). The half drawn should always be the nearest portion of the adjacent full view, unless the full view is a section view (see Chap. 9), in which case the half view should show the farthest portion.

Partial views can save the drawing of complete extra views of complicated or irregular parts. Lugs, ribs, bars, and portions containing special features can be shown quite satisfactorily in partial views. Partial views, like complete views, must

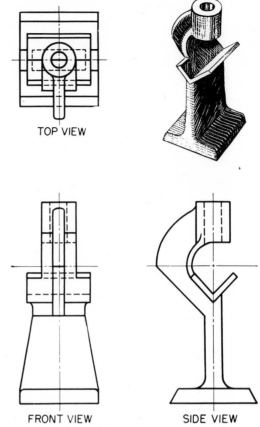

TOP VIEW

FRONT VIEW   SIDE VIEW
Fig. 3-18. Simplifying views.

always be placed on the sheet in accordance with the rules of projection, that is, in direct projection from the views to which they are related (see Fig. 3-19). Partial views may be portions of the top, side, front, etc., views, and may be drawn to an enlarged scale to facilitate visualization or dimensioning, in which case the scale is added as a note near the view. Note that break lines are used where necessary to indicate the incomplete nature of partial views. When a half or partial view is shown, at least one complete view of the object should always appear on the same sheet.

3-16. Analysis of lines. The draftsman should become thoroughly familiar with the appearance of the lines and planes of an object when projected to the image plane so that he can readily visualize which views will show the true lengths of the lines and the true shapes of the planes. A clear understanding of the principles of line and plane projection will help him to decide the probable num-

ber and types of views necessary to solve his immediate problem in representation and dimensioning
(see Fig. 3-20).

A line that is parallel to the top plane is a horizontal line and is seen in its true length in the top
view. Note from the figure that line 1-2 is parallel

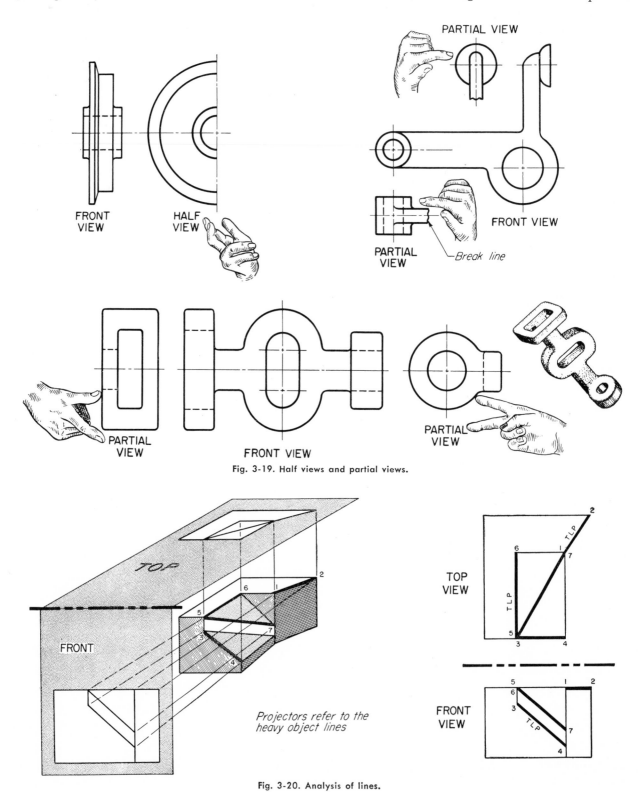

Fig. 3-19. Half views and partial views.

Projectors refer to the heavy object lines

Fig. 3-20. Analysis of lines.

to the reference line (folding line) in the front view and therefore appears in its true length in the top view.

A line that is parallel to the front plane is a frontal line and is seen in its true length in the front view. Line 3-4 is parallel to the reference line in the top view and therefore appears in its true length in the front view.

A line that is parallel to the side planes is a profile line and is seen in its true length in either side view. It lies parallel to the reference line for either view.

A line that shows as a point projection on one plane of projection always appears in its true length on any adjacent plane of projection. For example, line 5-6 shows as a point on the front plane and in its true length in the adjacent top plane. It would also appear in its true length in the side planes, which are also adjacent to the front view.

A line that is inclined to all three principal planes of projection (line 5-7, for example) cannot be seen in its true length in any of the prin-

cipal views. Such a line will be seen in its true length only in an auxiliary view, the principles of which are explained in the chapters on auxiliary views.

3-17. Analysis of planes. A plane appears in its true shape only when it lies parallel to the plane of projection. In Fig. 3-21, plane 1 is parallel to the front view and is seen in its true shape in that view, plane 2 is parallel to the top view and is seen in its true shape in that view, and plane 3 is parallel to the side view and will be seen in its true shape in either side view. Planes 4, 5, and 6, however, are each perpendicular to one of the principal planes and inclined to the other two. These are called *inclined planes*, and their true shapes can be seen only in primary auxiliary views. Plane 7 lies oblique to all three principal planes of projection and is called an *oblique plane*. The true shape of this plane can be shown only in a secondary auxiliary view. The manner in which the true shapes of inclined and oblique planes can be represented is explained in the chapters on primary and secondary auxiliaries.

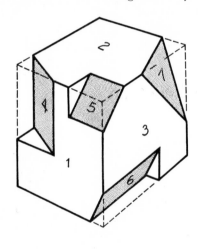

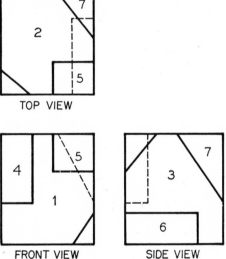

Fig. 3-21. Analysis of planes.

PROBLEMS

The problems for this chapter are intended to aid the student in visualizing and arranging the orthographic views of an object and to introduce him to the art of freehand sketching. It is suggested that

small preliminary layout sketches be made before attempting the final work on the drawing sheet. All pencil lines on the finished drawing should be done lightly at first and made heavy only after the student

feels they have been accurately interpreted. The drawings are not to be dimensioned, although they should
be reasonably proportionate to the views shown in
the text. They may be enlarged as suggested for each
group of problems. It is recommended that the
drawing sheet be a standard size, such as $8\frac{1}{2} \times 11$
or 11×17. If cross-section paper is available it
should be used, for it will aid the student in developing his sense of proportion and dimensioning and
in aligning the views in relation to each other.

Group 1. *Problems* 3-1 *to* 3-5. Use an $8\frac{1}{2}$- by 11-
in. drawing sheet for each problem. Place a $\frac{1}{2}$-in.
border all around. Sketch the pictorial in the upper
right corner of the sheet. Place the front view in the
area it should occupy on the sheet. Then select
among the other given views the top, left-side, right-
side, bottom, and rear views and place them in their
proper positions in relation to the front view. The
views should be drawn approximately twice the size
shown.

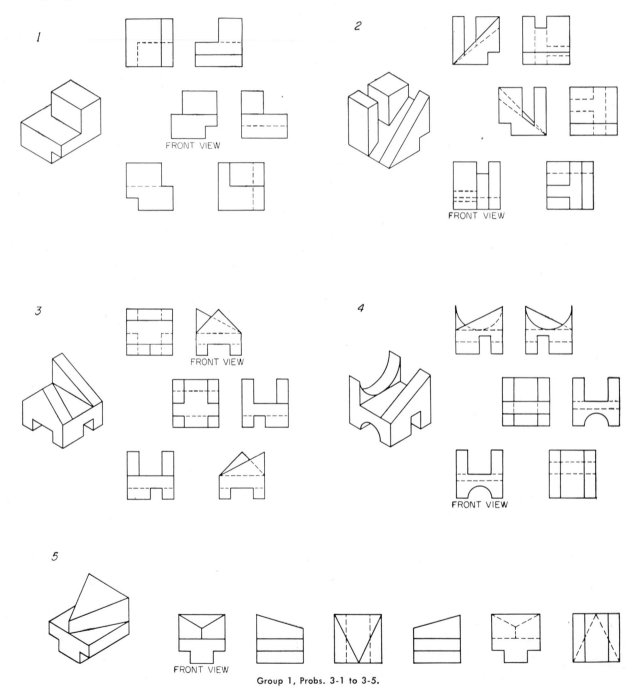

Group 1, Probs. 3-1 to 3-5.

Group 2. *Problems* 3-6 *to* 3-13. These problems should be drawn approximately three times as large as they appear in the text. Sketch the pictorial in the upper right corner of the sheet. Place the completed front view in the space it would normally occupy on the sheet. Complete the top and right-side views and add a left-side view.

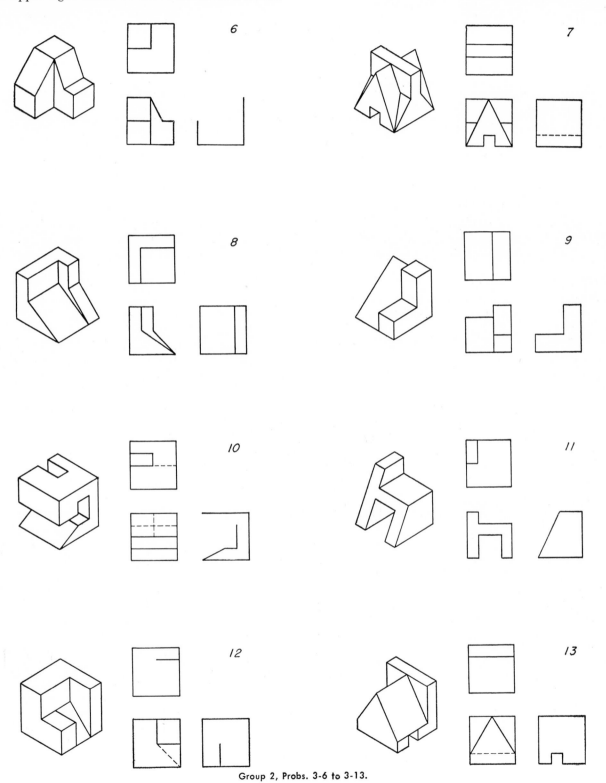

Group 2, Probs. 3-6 to 3-13.

Group 3. *Problems* 3-14 *to* 3-25. The views are to be shown about three times the size they appear in the text. Sketch the pictorial at the upper right of the sheet, omitting the dotted lines. Draw the given front and top views and add left- and right-side views. Check all four of the orthographics to see if they satisfy the structural requirements of your interpretation of the pictorial.

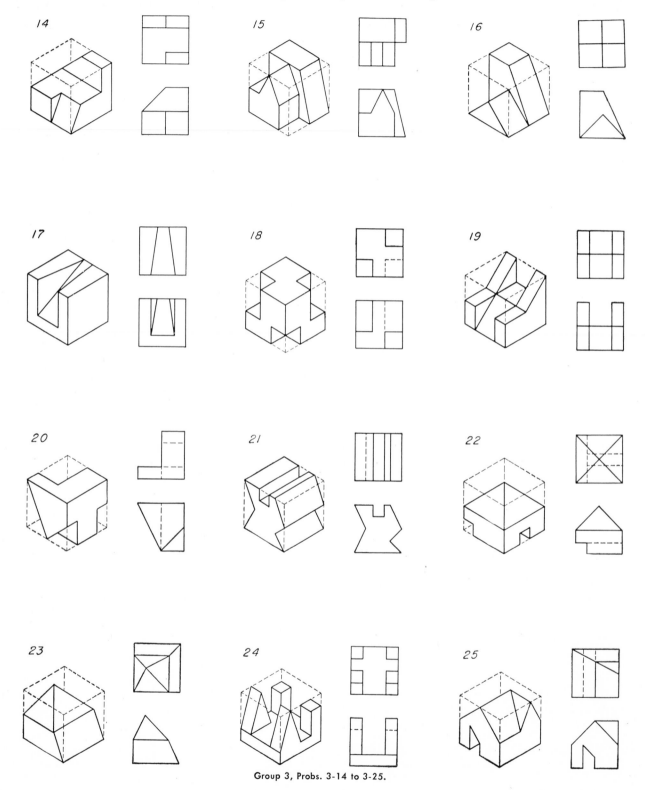

Group 3, Probs. 3-14 to 3-25.

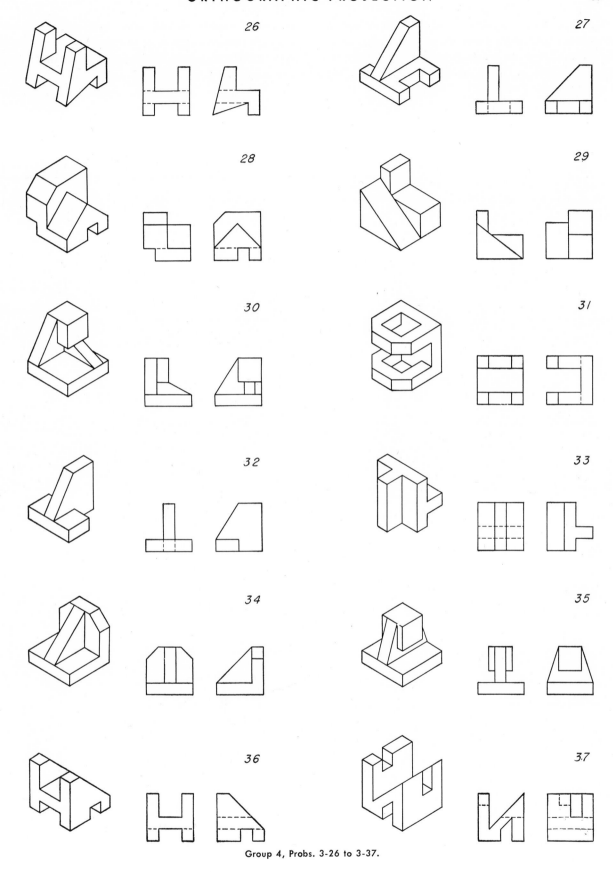

26 27 28 29 30 31 32 33 34 35 36 3.7

Group 4, Probs. 3-26 to 3-37.

Group 4. Problems 3-26 *to* 3-37. The views should be shown about three times the size they appear in the text. Sketch the pictorial at the upper right of the sheet. Add top and left-side views. Check the accuracy of the orthographics to see if they satisfy the structural requirements of your interpretation of the pictorial.

Group 5. Interpretation of lines. Problems 3-38 *to* 3-40. Redraw the three given views about twice the size shown in the text, and number the lines as shown on the pictorial. Leave enough room at the right above the side view to reproduce the chart illustrated. In the first column, list each numbered line. In the next columns, specify whether the line is a true-length projection, a point projection, or is inclined or oblique to the view shown at the top of the column.

Line	In front view	In top view	In side view
1-4	Point proj.	True length	True length
3-4	Inclined	Inclined	True length

(The two lines above appear in Prob. 3-38.)

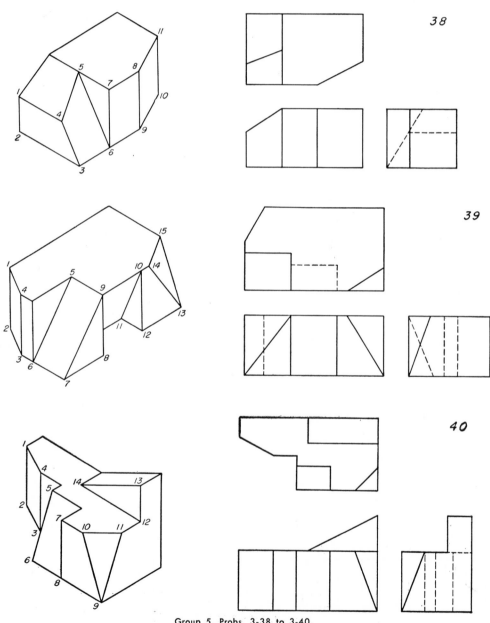

Group 5, Probs. 3-38 to 3-40.

Group 6. *Interpretation of planes.* Problems 3-41 to 3-43. Sketch the given orthographics about twice the size shown. Number the planes as they appear in the pictorial. At the right and above the side view reproduce the chart illustrated. List each plane in the left-hand column, and at the right indicate whether it appears in its true shape, or as an edge, or is inclined or oblique to the front, top, and right-side views.

Plane	In front view	In top view	In side view
1-2-3-4	Inclined	Edge	Inclined
5-6-7	Oblique	Oblique	Oblique

(The two planes analyzed above appear in Prob. 3-41.)

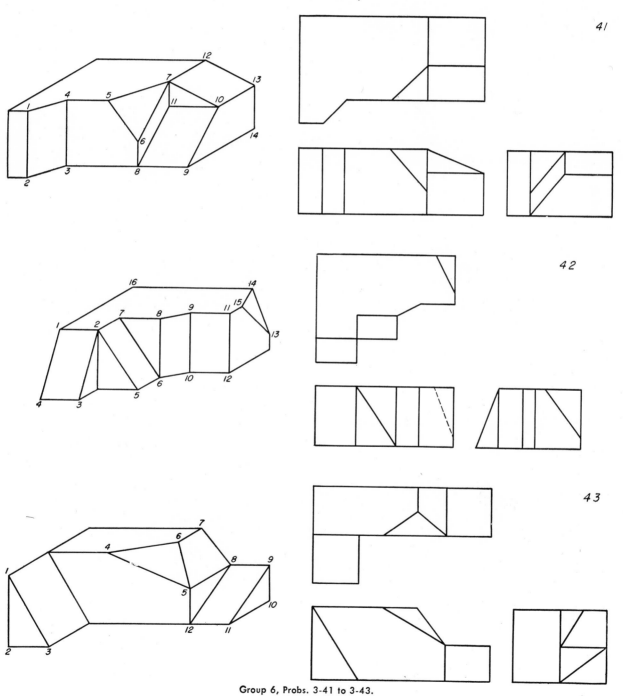

Group 6, Probs. 3-41 to 3-43.

Group 7. *Problems* 3-44 *to* 3-63. The problems in this group are presented as full-tone pictorials to give the student training in pictorial visualization. Analyze the object carefully, then sketch the min- imum number of orthographic views, in proper relation to each other, to describe the object ade- quately. Drawings should be made at a scale suit- able for an 8½- by 11-in. sheet.

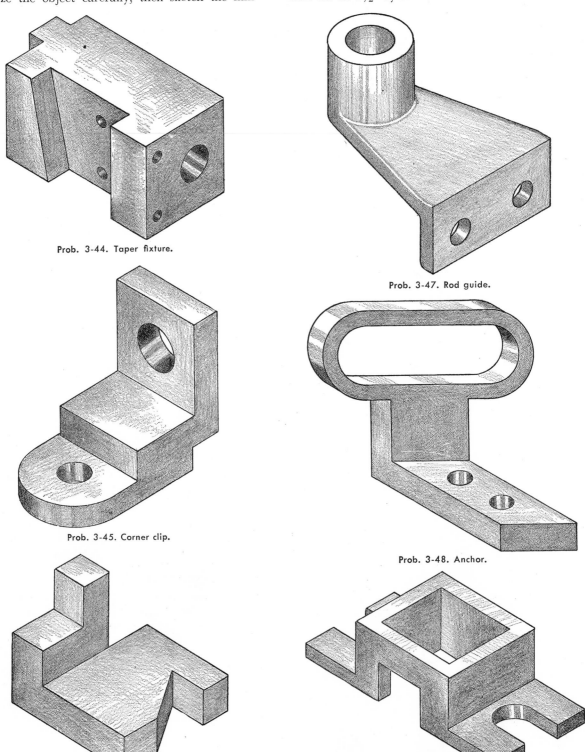

Prob. 3-44. Taper fixture.

Prob. 3-47. Rod guide.

Prob. 3-45. Corner clip.

Prob. 3-48. Anchor.

Prob. 3-46. Bench stop.

Prob. 3-49. Lock catch.

Group 7, Probs. 3-44 to 3-63.

Prob. 3-50. Bracket.

Prob. 3-54. Sliding block.

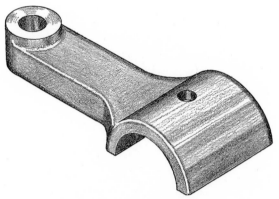

Prob. 3-51. Bearing clamp.

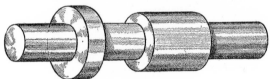

Prob. 3-52. Pulley shaft.

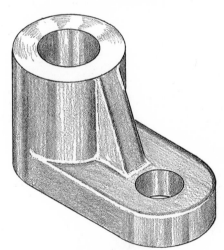

Prob. 3-55. Shaft guide.

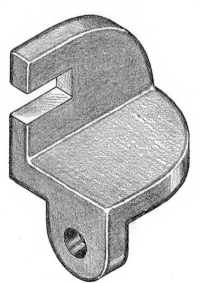

Prob. 3-53. Belt guide.

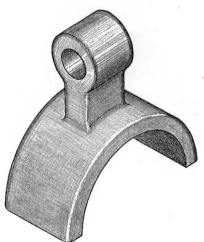

Prob. 3-56. Cable anchor.

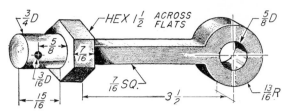

Prob. 3-57. Cable anchor.

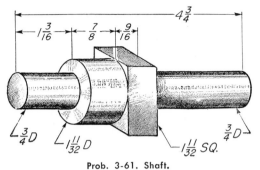

Prob. 3-61. Shaft.

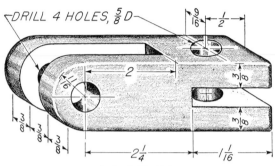

Prob. 3-58. Link.

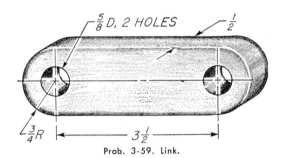

Prob. 3-59. Link.

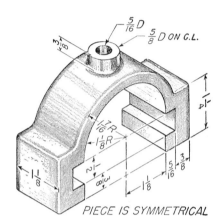

PIECE IS SYMMETRICAL

Prob. 3-62. Fixture clamp.

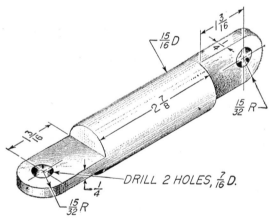

Prob. 3-60. Link.

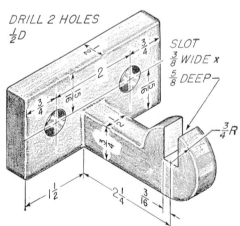

Prob. 3-63. Rod support.

Chapter 4

FREEHAND DETAIL DRAFTING

The practicing engineer seldom has his instruments available when the necessity arises for producing a working sketch or drawing for an idea that may come suddenly to his mind. Also, he may occasionally come upon some piece of equipment that needs repair and will have to make a sketch while lacking his complete complement of drawing tools. However, every engineer can find a sheet of paper, a pencil, and an eraser available no matter what the working conditions may be. With these, if he has been properly trained in the fundamentals of sketching, he can produce a drawing from which the draftsman or designer can prepare a complete instrumental representation.

Many teachers with industrial experience realize the value of freehand drawing ability. They have discovered also that a student can more easily grasp the basic concepts of orthographic projection and drawing procedure when started by freehand methods. Once the beginner is able to produce an acceptable freehand drawing, the transition to instrument work is easily accomplished, since the student has become acquainted with the fundamental procedures and techniques. Even more important is the fact that the student will have a feeling for his work and a true understanding of what he is trying to accomplish.

4-1. The detail drawing. A detail drawing is an orthographic representation of a single part which shows all the necessary views, dimensions, and notes, and which includes the title-block and record-strip information required for the manufacture or fabrication of the part.

In a large manufacturing plant with many departments or divisions, separate detail drawings that show only the specific operations required in each division are usually prepared. For example, a pattern detail is prepared for the pattern shop, a foundry detail is prepared for the foundry shop, a machining detail is prepared for the machine shop, etc. All these detail drawings are worked up from the designer's detail drawing by the designers and draftsmen in the drawing department. Small plants with limited facilities, on the other hand, encourage their draftsmen to prepare general-purpose detail drawings that will permit any worker to perform his required task. All the necessary notes and dimensions are shown on the one drawing, thus enabling any type of worker—the patternmaker, the foundry man, the machinist, etc.—to work from a single sheet. A large part is shown alone on the sheet. If a number of small parts can be represented clearly and completely, grouped in good composition at a suitable scale, several of them may be shown on a single sheet provided that they bear some relationship to each other in assembly.

In order to develop all-around ability, the stu-

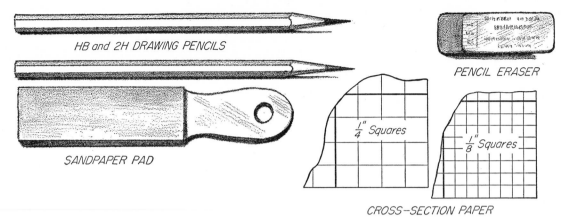

HB and 2H DRAWING PENCILS

PENCIL ERASER

SANDPAPER PAD

$\frac{1}{4}"$ Squares

$\frac{1}{8}"$ Squares

CROSS–SECTION PAPER

Fig. 4-1. Freehand drafting tools.

dent should concentrate on the preparation of general-purpose drawings. He should also become familiar with the particular requirements of drawings that go into individual departments or divisions, however, for he may be confronted at one time or another with the task of producing specialized drawings for the various shops.

4-2. Freehand drafting tools. The tools required for freehand drawing are illustrated in Fig. 4-1. Two pencils are desirable—a 2H for preliminary sketching and HB for darkening the lines. In addition, the draftsman will need a sandpaper pad to keep the pencils sharpened, a soft pencil eraser to remove undesirable lines and clean up the paper from time to time, and a pad of 8½-by 11-in. cross-section or rectangular-coordinate paper. The cross-section paper is divided up into ⅛- or ¼-in. squares with the inch line accented. These divisions enable the beginner to draw at a reasonably accurate scale and aid in producing straight lines.

4-3. Sharpening the pencil. To sharpen the pencil first remove the wood from around the lead by use of a mechanical sharpener or a penknife.

START OF STROKE

ROTATE

Sandpaper or file

FINISH OF STROKE

$\frac{3}{8}"$ to $\frac{1}{2}"$

Fine point

HB & 2H pencils

Fig. 4-2. Sharpening the pencil.

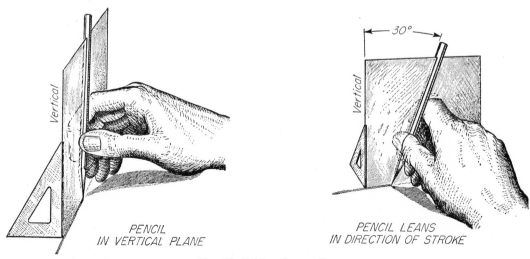

Vertical

PENCIL
IN VERTICAL PLANE

30°

Vertical

PENCIL LEANS
IN DIRECTION OF STROKE

Fig. 4-3. Holding the pencil.

The exposed lead should then be sharpened to a conical point by rotating the pencil in contact with a sandpaper pad or fine file (see Fig. 4-2). The undesirable needle point can be dulled by sliding it across a piece of scrap paper several times.

4-4. Holding the pencil. The pencil should be held gently in a fairly vertical plane and should be inclined approximately 30° in the direction of the stroke that is to be drawn (see Fig. 4-3). The thumb and forefinger should grip the pencil far

enough away from the point to permit the draftsman to follow the extreme point in all the various positions the hand may take while drawing.

4-5. Sketching straight lines. The easiest way to sketch a straight line is to swing the stroke in a horizontal direction from left to right. First mark the extremities of the desired line with light but distinct dots (if the line is long, intermediary dots should be used). Then hold the pencil about ¼ in. above the paper and swing the hand through the

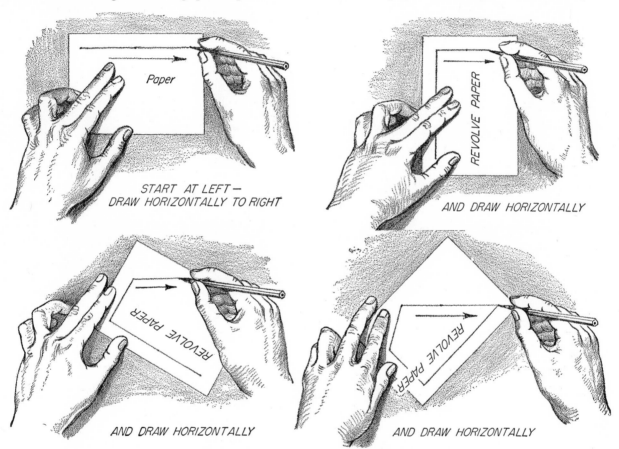

Fig. 4-4. All straight lines are drawn horizontally.

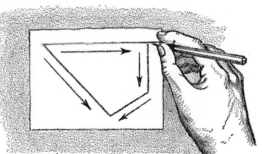

Fig. 4-5. Drawing straight lines.

path of the desired line from one dot to the other. After practicing this movement several times, touch the pencil lightly to the paper and swing in the desired line. Short scraggly dashed lines should be avoided. If the first line drawn is not satisfactory, erase it and try again. When this light practice line approaches perfection it may be darkened to the desired uniformity, intensity, and straightness.

Figure 4-4 illustrates how all straight lines, whether vertical, horizontal, or inclined, may be drawn with horizontal strokes by simply turning the drawing sheet. The experienced draftsman may draw short vertical and inclined lines in the direction of the arrows shown in Fig. 4-5, but a beginner is likely to have difficulty producing the inclined lines without considerable practice.

4-6. Classification of lines. In most engineering drawings, three *widths* of line are called for: thick, medium, and thin. Thick lines are used for the visible outline of the object being drawn. Me-

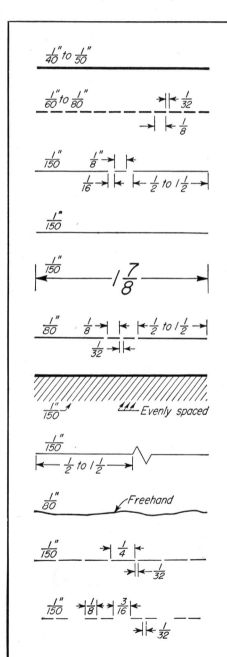

OBJECT LINES—Thick lines. Used to show the visible outline of parts. The thickness may be selected to suit the size of the drawing and the size of the sheet.

HIDDEN LINES—Medium lines. A dotted line consisting of equally spaced dashes. Used to indicate the hidden intersections of planes and other hidden features of the object.

CENTER LINES—Thin lines. Made with alternate long and short dashes. Used to indicate the centers of entire objects and locations of circular features.

EXTENSION LINES—Thin lines. Unbroken in their required length. Used as witnesses to the points on the object to be dimensioned.

DIMENSION LINES—Thin lines. Unbroken except to permit insertion of dimension figure. Terminate in arrowheads that touch extension lines.

CUTTING-PLANE LINES—Medium lines. Consist of alternating long and short dashes. Used in sectioning to show the path of the imaginary cutting plane.

SECTION LINING—Thin lines. Evenly spaced slant lines which are placed on the cut surfaces in section views.

LONG BREAKS—Thin lines. Drawn with a straightedge and a freehand zigzag. These lines indicate that structure has been broken to permit convenient location on the drawing sheet.

SHORT BREAKS—Medium lines. Drawn freehand and indicate short breaks in the structure shown on the sheet.

ADJACENT PARTS—Thin lines. Consist of long dashes used to show adjacent parts or alternate positions for the parts.

DITTO LINES—Thin lines. Consist of alternate small-spaced double dashes with a larger space between them. They are used to indicate repeated forms, details, or features.

Fig. 4-6. Classification of lines. Dimensions are approximate.

dium lines are used for the dotted lines representing hidden features and for cutting-plane, short-break, adjacent-part, and alternate-position lines. Center lines, dimension lines, long-break lines, ditto lines, extension lines, and section lining are represented by thin lines. A complete classification of these lines and their relative weights is shown in Fig. 4-6. Although these distinctions embody the ASA-preferred style, the Association does add that for "rapid practice" this may be simplified to two weights: "*medium* for outline, hidden, cutting-plane, short-break, adjacent-part, and alternate-position lines, and *thin* for section, center, extension, dimension, long-break, and ditto lines."

4-7. Hidden lines. Features or intersections of the planes of an object that are not visible in the direction from which a view is taken are shown in the drawing by the use of dotted lines. These lines are called hidden lines or invisible lines and as a general rule they should be shown unless coincident with solid object lines. In exceptional cases hidden lines may be omitted if they are overabundant and tend to confuse rather than to clarify the representation.

A dotted line is formed by a series of dashes about ⅛ in. long separated by spaces of about 1/32 in. (The terminology is a little confusing here; in practice hidden lines are called dotted lines even though they are made up of dashes rather than dots.) If dotted lines appear close together on the drawing, the dashes should be staggered as shown at 1 in Fig. 4-7. When one hidden line runs into another, the last dash of one line should touch a dash of the other, as shown at 2. Hidden lines forming a corner should touch as indicated at 3. A dotted line ending at a solid boundary line touches it as seen at 4. When a dotted line crosses a solid line, clearances should be left as illustrated at 5. A dotted line that is the continuance of a solid line begins with a space, or break, as shown at 6. Where several dotted lines show a hidden corner they are treated as seen at 7. If the radius of a hidden arc is ⅛ in. or less, the proper treatment is shown at 8; while 9 shows the method of representing hidden arcs with radii over ⅛ in. The rules applying to straight lines are followed in the treatment of hidden circles, circle arcs, and irregular curves, one example being shown at 10.

4-8. Center lines. Generally speaking, center lines are drawn to indicate the axes of cylindrical forms and the main vertical and horizontal axes of an entire part. In drawing cylindrical forms or ob-

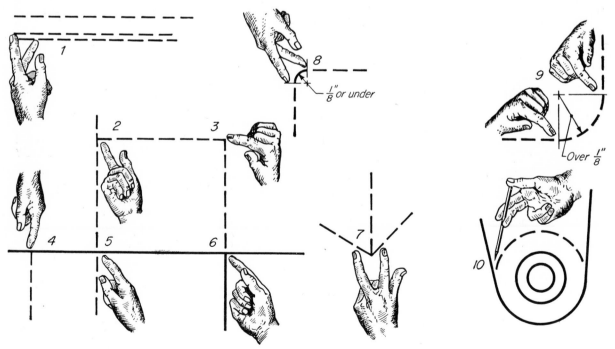

Fig. 4-7. Treatment of dotted lines.

jects containing cylindrical features (such as shafts or holes), center lines are the first lines placed on the drawing sheet, since they establish the common axes of symmetry for such features in all views. In this way center lines are of great assistance to the draftsman in laying out his drawing. Figure 4-8 illustrates typical uses of center lines. Although main center lines may be omitted if they are not required for clarity or dimensioning, the center lines for cylindrical features must always be shown. In the circular view of a cylindrical object, the center lines are vertical and horizontal with their intersection at the center of the circle (see Fig. 4-8). In the profile view, the center line coincides

with the horizontal axis of the cylindrical form. Center lines should always extend slightly beyond the view, or feature of the view, to which they apply. Ordinarily, however, they should not be extended to connect views unless it is necessary to do so for dimensioning purposes.

Center lines are thin, fine lines made up of alternate long and short dashes. The long dashes are approximately $\frac{3}{4}$ to $1\frac{1}{2}$ in. and the short dashes are $\frac{1}{8}$ in., with spaces of about $\frac{1}{16}$ in. between them (see Fig. 4-6). Although center lines are usually straight, they may also be circular, as in the case of a center line for a bolt circle (see Fig. 8-19, for example).

4-9. Precedence of lines. It is practically impossible to make a complete drawing without having some of the lines coincide. For example, a solid line may fall in the position of a dotted or center line, a dotted line may occur at the same spot as a center line, or a cutting-plane line may coincide with a center line (see Fig. 4-9).

The outer boundaries of a part are always solid

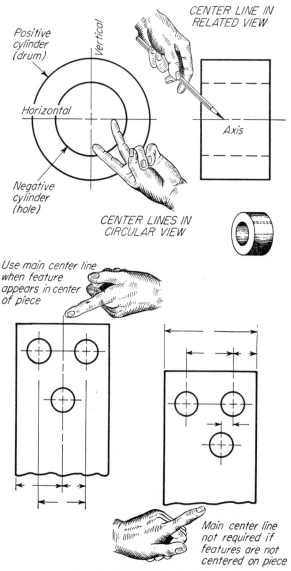

Fig. 4-8. Use of the center line.

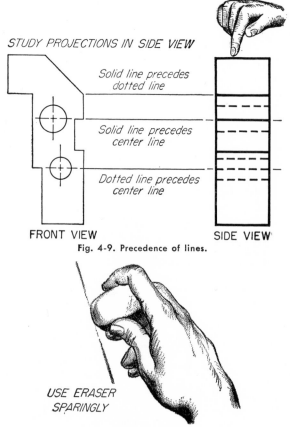

Fig. 4-9. Precedence of lines.

Fig. 4-10. The eraser.

lines. Since external features are of the utmost importance, at least for an intelligent reading of the drawing, solid lines always take precedence over any other coinciding lines. Hidden lines take precedence over center lines, although the center line may be extended as shown in the figure. If a cutting-plane line (see Sec. 9-2) and a center line coincide, the center line is shown instead of the line representing the imaginary cutting plane. Dimension lines and extension lines should never be placed to coincide with other lines in the drawing.

4-10. Line quality. In all freehand sketching it is important that the first strokes of the pencil be light enough so that they may be corrected without disturbing too many other lines already drawn. If the beginner follows this practice he will rarely need the eraser, for the light lines will apparently disappear or be absorbed during the finishing process when their weight and uniformity are being attended to.

In general, pencil lines should be reasonably straight, and black enough to produce an acceptable print if necessary. The size of the pencil point and the application of pressure on it will determine both the width and the intensity of the lines. In the finishing-up process great care should be taken to make sure that there is sufficient contrast between each type of line—solid, dotted, or center (see Fig. 4-6). Any fuzziness or raggedness should be eliminated. Always pay particular attention to the arcs of circles, ellipses, and irregular curves to make sure that they are of the proper weight.

4-11. Circles and circle arcs. Circles may be easily sketched by first drawing horizontal and vertical lines through a point marking the center of the desired circle and then laying off the radius on these lines by eye or by the use of a scrap of paper on which the proper radial length has been marked (see Fig. 4-11). If the circle is small (less than approximately 3/8 in.) it may then be drawn by sketching the arcs to connect the points. If large circles are to be produced, additional radii will facilitate the drawing of smooth arcs. In drawing the circle, the draftsman should sketch the first arc in the quadrant that seems most natural to him and then rotate the drawing paper so that the adjoining arc will appear and be drawn in the same quadrant.

4-12. The ellipse. When drawing a large ellipse, it is best to locate the long and short diameters within a rectangle and add inclined lines stemming from the center point as shown in the first panel of Fig. 4-12. The points indicating the paths of the curves that form the ellipse are located on these lines by eye. A little practice will enable the beginner to swing in the needed curves smoothly and neatly. To draw a smaller ellipse, locate the long and short diameters within a rectangle and lightly sketch straight lines joining the points where the diameters intersect the rectangle. Then mark points by eye at the center of the triangular areas thus formed and draw the four required curves to complete the ellipse. In drawing either the large or small ellipse, the paper should be rotated for convenience in the same manner used for drawing the arcs of the circle.

4-13. The irregular curve. A satisfactory irregular curve can be produced by locating points at

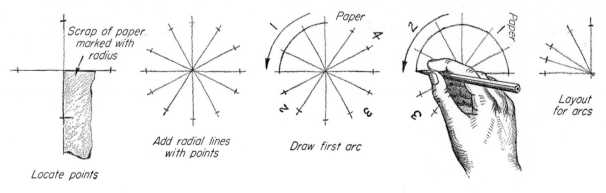

REVOLVE PAPER AND DRAW CONSECUTIVE ARCS IN SAME QUADRANT
Fig. 4-11. Drawing circles and circle arcs.

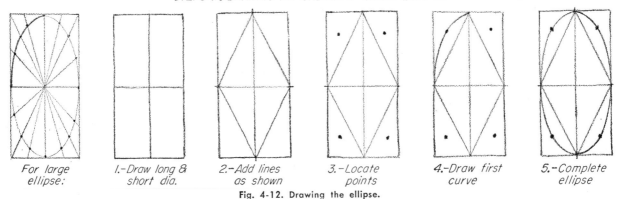

For large ellipse: | 1.—Draw long & short dia. | 2.—Add lines as shown | 3.—Locate points | 4.—Draw first curve | 5.—Complete ellipse

Fig. 4-12. Drawing the ellipse.

¼- to ½-in. intervals along its intended path, and then drawing a series of arcs through them (see Fig. 4-13).

4-14. Fillets and rounds. Inspection of a casting immediately after its removal from a mold will reveal that the intersections of surfaces are slightly rounded. Such rounded intersections are usually formed naturally when the metal cools, although

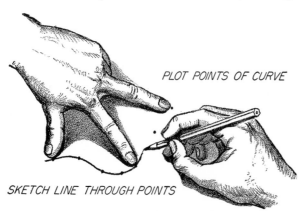

PLOT POINTS OF CURVE

SKETCH LINE THROUGH POINTS

Fig. 4-13. Sketching an irregular curve.

they may be made to a specified size by the patternmaker when he prepares the mold. Rounded inside intersections are called *fillets;* rounded external intersections are known as *rounds* (see Fig. 4-14). Fillets and rounds ordinarily are desirable features in a casting, since fillets provide greater strength and rounds improve the appearance and permit ease of handling. The size (the radius of the cross section) of a given round or fillet depends on the metal being used. Cast iron usually forms fillets and rounds of approximately ⅛ in. in radius; aluminum, zinc, and other white metals leave a round or fillet of about 1/16 in.

When making a drawing, fillets and rounds should always be shown at the intersections of unfinished surfaces. When an arc representing a fillet or round is small (⅛ in. or less), it should always be drawn freehand, even in an instrument-produced drawing. If an arc is larger than ⅛ in. use the method for drawing arcs illustrated in Fig.

AT THE INTERSECTION OF UNFINISHED SURFACES

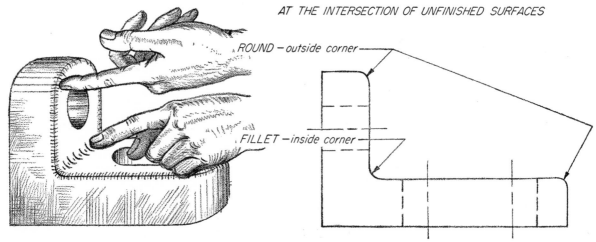

ROUND—outside corner

FILLET—inside corner

Fig. 4-14. Fillets and rounds.

4-11. A note on the drawing sheet such as "Fillets and rounds ⅛" will suffice for the dimensioning of the ordinary fillets and rounds of a cast-iron piece. When a fillet or round is large and approaches significance as a contour, its exact radius must be given on the view in which it appears in its true radius. If one or both of two intersecting surfaces are to be machined, the corner should appear sharp.

4-15. Treatment of rounded forms and edges. The question of whether a round that appears in one view will produce a line in the related view is often puzzling to the beginning draftsman. It may be taken as a rule that an intersection of two surfaces that has rounded by a natural cooling of the metal will show as a line in the related view. If the round is the result of a design specification then the matter in some measure rests with the draftsman. The two adjacent views in Fig. 4-15 have been prepared to help the draftsman with this problem. The profile view shows many of the rounded forms that will arise from time to time, while the adjacent view shows their suggested treatment.

4-16. Producing a freehand orthographic detail drawing. Suppose that you are required to make an orthographic sketch of the object shown in the upper left-hand corner of Fig. 4-16. As a first step, the drawing sheet should be attached firmly to the drawing board, preferably by taping down the corners. Make certain that the edges of the paper are parallel to the sides of the drawing board (this is of the utmost importance in instrument representations) and that the drawing sheet lies flat without wrinkles. The paper should be of the cross-section type so that the squares may be used for dimensioning. Lay out the borders on the drawing sheet as indicated in the upper right corner of the illustration, making the lines about as dark as the solid lines of the object will be.

Study the object carefully and select a front view that will show its most characteristic shape, or the one that will require the least number of hidden lines. Next determine the least number of views required to describe the object adequately, again selecting those views that will mean the fewest hidden lines. At this point it is helpful to form a mental picture of the general dimensions of each view so as to ensure good composition within the borders of the sheet. After the space between views and their arrangement on the sheet have been determined, locate the main center lines as shown in step 1. Once the center lines have been placed, block in the significant features of each view as shown in step 2, using the dimensions of the pictorial view. All views should be in direct projection with one another—the top above the front and the side at the right of the front—and should progress together. Next sketch in the circles and circle arcs (including fillets and rounds) as shown in step 3. In step 4, complete the circular forms and show the dotted lines located in their proper positions.

The preliminary work on the drawing has been

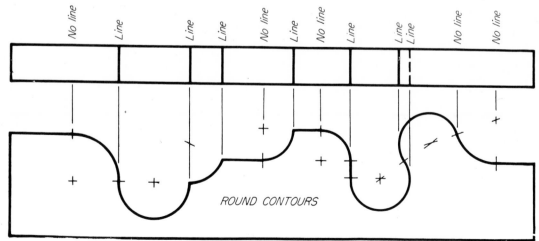

Fig. 4-15. Treatment of rounded edges.

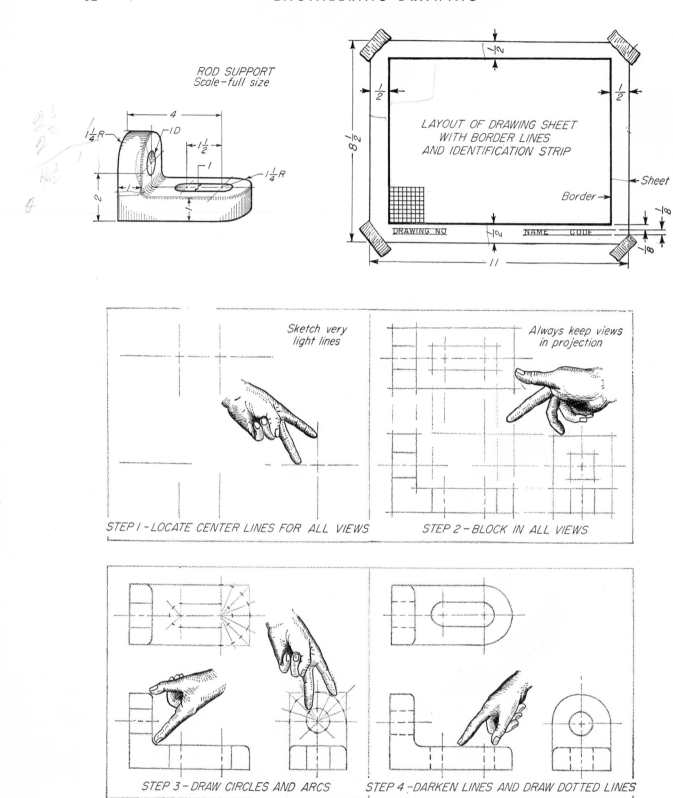

ROD SUPPORT
Scale—full size

LAYOUT OF DRAWING SHEET
WITH BORDER LINES
AND IDENTIFICATION STRIP

Sheet

Border

DRAWING NO   NAME   CODE

Sketch very
light lines

Always keep views
in projection

STEP I — LOCATE CENTER LINES FOR ALL VIEWS   STEP 2 — BLOCK IN ALL VIEWS

STEP 3 — DRAW CIRCLES AND ARCS   STEP 4 — DARKEN LINES AND DRAW DOTTED LINES

Fig. 4-16. Steps in making an orthographic detail drawing.

carried on with the harder pencil (2H). The softer pencil (HB) should now be employed to darken the object lines to the desired blackness and crispness and to bring about a proper contrast between the medium-toned dotted lines, the blacker object lines, and the light-toned center lines. It should be kept in mind that the width of a line and its blackness or intensity are determined by the point on the pencil and the pressure applied. If reasonable care has been used in the preparatory work, there will be only a few lines that will have to be erased.

4-17. Spacing the views on the drawing sheet. If the drawing is to be dimensioned (the beginner should not attempt to dimension his drawing until he is fully acquainted with the dimensioning rules outlined in Chap. 8) the locations of notes and dimensions will in some measure influence the position of the views in relation to each other and as a group within the borders of the sheet (see Fig. 4-17). As a general rule, however, considering *A*

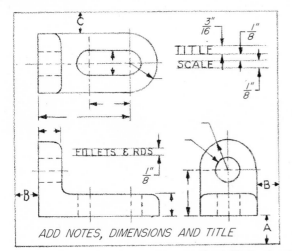
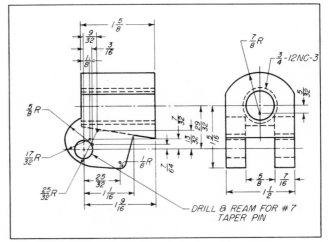

Fig. 4-17. Spacing the views on the drawing sheet.

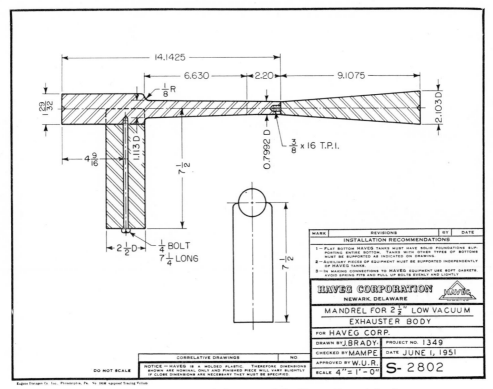

Fig. 4-18. The title block. (*Courtesy of the Haveg Corporation.*)

as the unit dimension, *B* should be approximately equal to ¾*A*, and *C* approximately equal to ¾*B*. Sufficient space must be left between views to allow for dimensioning, since one of the fundamental rules of drafting states that dimensions should be placed between views wherever possible. The drawing at the right in Fig. 4-17 shows an acceptable arrangement of a two-view drawing with complete dimensions and notes.

4-18. The title block. In general, the title block appears just inside the border lines at the lower right corner of the sheet. It is sometimes accompanied by a record strip that lies to the left of the block along the top of the lower border. The drafting and design divisions of many of the larger manufacturing companies use drawing sheets with printed title blocks that seem best suited to their particular manufacturing procedures (see Fig. 4-18). Smaller concerns often purchase ready-cut paper or cloth sheets with a blank title block already imprinted upon them.

The information listed in a title block may vary slightly depending on the object being drawn and the standards of the company for which the drawing is being prepared. However, in general the title block should list:

1. Name and address of the company
2. Name of the machine or unit (if assembly) or name of the part (if a single piece)
3. Drawing number
4. Number of parts required (if assembly) or the number of the part (if a detail drawing)
5. Scale
6. Date
7. Name of draftsman
8. Name of tracer
9. Name of checker
10. Name of man who approved the final drawing

When necessary, the title block or record strip should also include information concerning material, stock sizes, heat-treatment, finishes, corrections and revisions, etc.

All lettering in the title block should be in capitals. See Fig. 14-4 for additional information on the preparation of a title block.

PROBLEMS

The problems in this group should be drawn freehand (without kit instruments) on 8½- by 11-in. cross-section paper with a ½-in. border. The student is not expected to dimension any of the problems until he has familiarized himself with correct dimensioning procedures as explained in Chap. 8.

These problems have been selected to illustrate the proper application of the principles of orthographic projection, the technique of pencil sketching, and the proper use of the chart showing the classification of lines. Since the selection and arrangement of the views necessary to describe a piece accurately is of primary importance to a successful presentation, it is suggested that the student make a small thumbnail sketch on scratch paper for each layout before proceeding with the drawing on the final sheet.

The dimensions of the objects shown in Probs. 4-1 to 4-12 may be determined by the ¼-in. markings. Problems 4-13 to 4-22 have figured dimensions so that the instructor may also assign them as dimensioning problems following the study of Chap. 8.

Show a simple title block for each problem, indicating the name of the part, scale, the material from which the part is made, and the number required.

4-1. Sliding rest, steel. Draw three views.
4-2. Frame support, cast iron. Draw three views.
4-3. Gage block, steel. Draw three views.
4-4. Corner support, cast iron. Draw three views.
4-5. Gage block, steel. Draw three views.
4-6. Bracket, cast iron. Draw three views.
4-7. Motor support, steel. Draw three views.
4-8. Fixture, cast iron. Draw three views.
4-9. Rod guide, cast iron. Draw two views.
4-10. Bracket, cast iron. Draw three views.
4-11. Clamp, steel. Draw two views.

4-12. Rod support, cast iron. Draw two views.
4-13. Rod guide, steel. Draw three views.
4-14. Block, cast iron. Draw three views.
4-15. Guide block, cast iron. Draw three views.
4-16. Gage block, steel. Draw three views.
4-17. Column base, cast steel. Draw three views.
4-18. Stop block, cast iron. Draw three views.
4-19. Tool rest, steel. Draw three views.
4-20. Base connector, steel. Draw three views.
4-21. Cover plate, cast iron. Draw two views.
4-22. Rod support, cast iron. Draw two views.

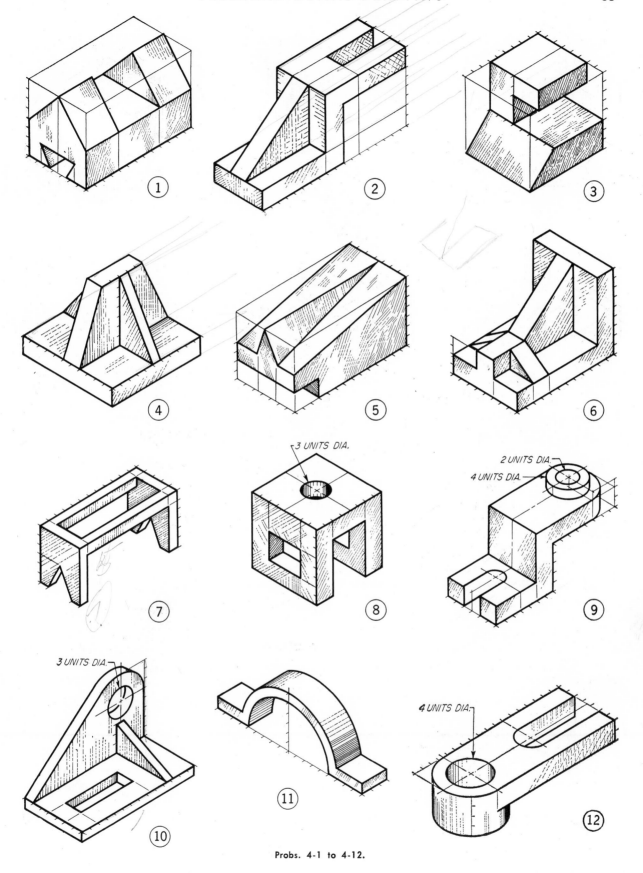

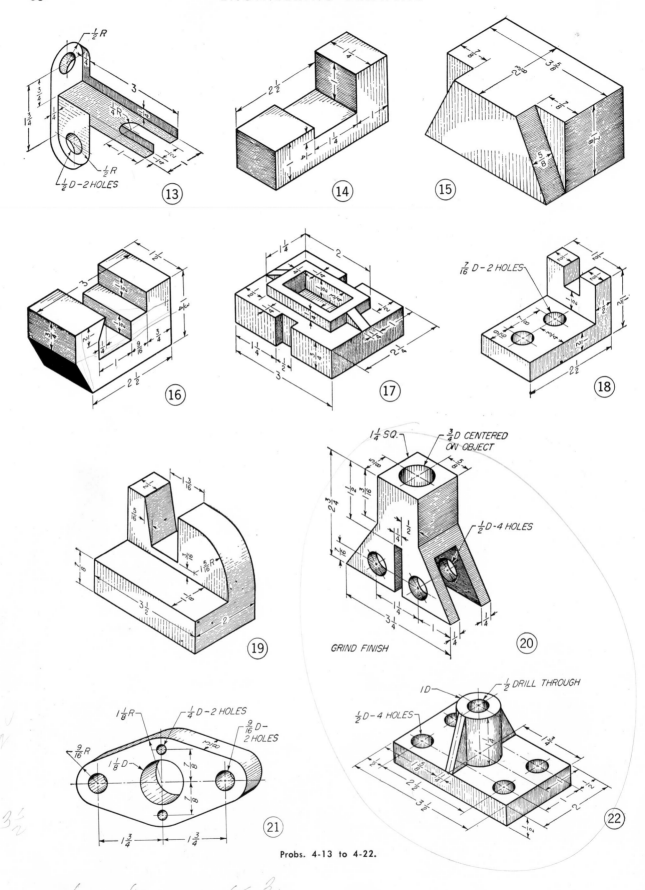

Probs. 4-13 to 4-22.

Chapter 5

INSTRUMENTS AND THEIR USE

The tools ordinarily used in the preparation of engineering drawings are shown in Fig. 5-1. It is advisable to secure simple but well-made instruments placed on the market by recognized manufacturers of these items. It is better to have a few good pieces than a large stock of unserviceable and shoddy equipment.

5-1. Drawing paper. The drawing papers come in white, buff, or light green. Rag-content papers, although expensive, afford excellent erasing

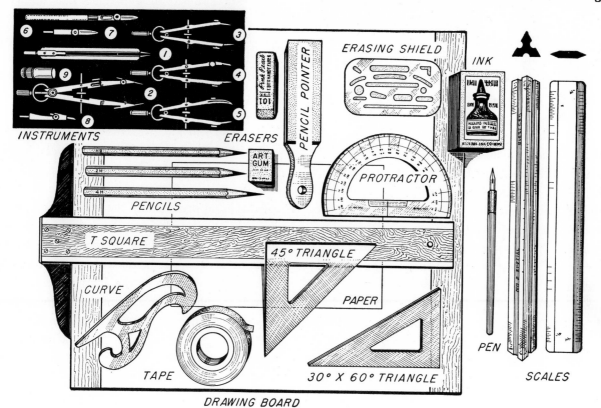

Fig. 5-1. The draftsman's working equipment.

qualities and can withstand frequent handling. The colored papers also permit frequent handling without soiling, and in addition minimize eyestrain. A paper with sufficient grain to produce sharp, clean lines is desirable for pencil drawings or for color work. A smoother surface is better for fine ink ruling and all complicated drawing. Drawing paper may be purchased in rolls or sheets. The rolled paper comes in lengths of 10 to 20 yards and in widths between 30 and 58 in. The more common sheet sizes are proportioned to the ordinary letter sheet, that is, $8\frac{1}{2} \times 11$, 11×17, etc. The American Standards Association (ASA) lists the following recommended sheet sizes for drawing paper and cloth:

A $8\frac{1}{2} \times 11$
B 11×17
C 17×22
D 22×34
E 34×44

5-2. Tracing paper. Tracing paper comes in white or blue tint. The better type has an unglazed and fairly smooth surface. It should be oil- and wax-free, and sufficiently transparent to allow the preparation of clear blueprints and ozalid reproductions from both pencil and ink drawings. The erasable quality of the tracing paper is an important factor. Tracing paper is available in standard-sized sheets and in rolls of 10 to 20 yards.

5-3. Tracing cloth. Cloth used for tracing is also commonly available in white or blue tint. The better cloths are manufactured without the use of oil, wax, or grease to gain transparency. They are strong and tough and will not discolor with age, nor will they leave ghost marks when erased repeatedly. For these reasons, cloth is more satisfactory than tracing paper for most types of work, but it is more expensive. Most tracing cloths are prepared with a glazed and an unglazed surface. The drawing work is done on the unglazed surface, on which either pencil or ink may be used. The better cloths, with excellent transparency, permit the making of all types of reproductions.

5-4. Use of paper, cloth, and tracing paper. The draftsman should be able to produce accept-able drawings on all types of drawing surfaces. In working the problems in this book, the student will first become familiar with drawing on cross-section paper in the chapter on freehand drawing. In the chapters calling for instrument work, the first five or six drawings should be done on paper (white, buff, or light-green opaque); thereafter the drawings should be produced on tracing paper. A few drawings should also be done on tracing cloth so that the student will become familiar with this material. The general practice in industry today is to use tracing paper or cloth for all working drawings. Tracing paper is used for most work, while tracing cloth is used for drawings that are likely to be heavily corrected or for those that are to be preserved.

All drawings should be done in pencil. Ink is used only for permanent work, and even then the work is done first in pencil and then traced in ink.

5-5. The drawing board. In order to prevent warping, the drawing board is made of narrow strips of well-seasoned soft wood. The two end cleats are fastened in a manner that allows for expansion and contraction. The board has two drawing surfaces. Both ends are true, and either may be used as a working edge for the head of the T square (see Fig. 5-2). A standard-sized board measures 20 by 26 in. The manner in which the drawing sheet is affixed to the drawing board is also shown in Fig. 5-2.

5-6. The T square. There are several types of T squares available for drawing purposes. They may be made of steel or wood. The T square should be approximately the same length as the drawing board and should be well made of wood that will not warp. One of the most serviceable types of T square is made with transparent edges that permit viewing of the lines underneath the edge of the blade. The edge of the T square should be straight and free from scratches or nicks.

The straight horizontal lines on a drawing are produced with the T square (see Fig. 5-3). The T square slides up and down along the left edge of the drawing board. The points that are to locate the lines are placed as close as possible to the left

Fig. 5-2. The drawing board and its use.

side of the drawing surface. With the pencil point resting very close to the bottom of the top edge of the T square and the head of the T square firm against the left edge of the board, the lines are drawn from the locating points toward the right. A proper weight of line may be secured by holding the pencil firmly and touching the paper gently enough to enable the lead to "lie" on the surface, instead of being "dug" into it. Ordinarily, the horizontal lines at the top of a drawing are produced before those below. A T square should never be used to draw vertical lines by placing the head of the instrument along the top or bottom of the drawing board.

5-7. The triangles. The triangles most desired by professional draftsmen are made of clear plastic and retain their shape and stability indefinitely. They do not mar and scratch easily or discolor with age. They should be flexible with no evidence of warpage and be large enough to permit the drawing of a vertical line of at least 8 in. in length without lifting the pencil. The 30°-60° and the 45° triangles are primarily used for the drawing of straight vertical and inclined lines. Besides the 30°-60° and the 45° triangles, there are others that have many and varied uses, among them being the lettering angles. These are generally designed to give a quick and easy method of making ac-

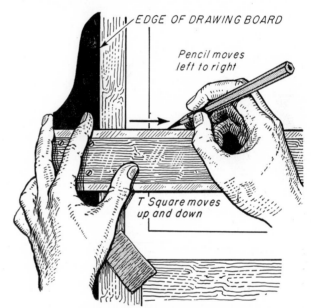

Fig. 5-3. Drawing horizontal lines.

curately spaced guide lines for the lettering and figure work appearing on drawings.

Vertical lines are drawn with the T square and 30°-60° or 45° triangles. As shown in Fig. 5-4, the head of the T square is brought firmly against the left edge of the drawing board and the triangle is placed in position against the top edge of the T-square blade. The vertical line is drawn upward along the edge of the triangle. The lines at the left side of the sheet are drawn first. By sliding the triangle toward the right and always keeping it in

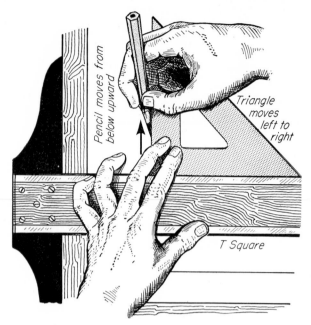

Fig. 5-4. Drawing vertical lines.

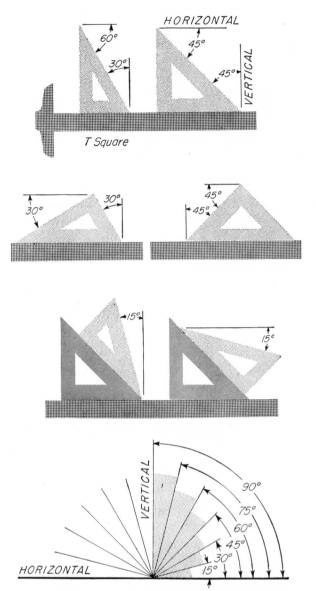

Fig. 5-5. Using the T square and triangles in combination.

contact with the T square, additional parallel vertical lines may be produced. The pencil and the triangle must make a close contact to produce an even, true line.

As illustrated in Fig. 5-5, with the T square and 30°-60° triangle combination, lines making angles of 30° and 60° with the vertical and horizontal may be drawn. When the T square is combined with the 45° triangle, lines making angles of 45° with the horizontal are produced. If the two triangles are used in combination, lines making 15° angles with the vertical and horizontal are obtainable; therefore any line that is at an angle which is a multiple of 15° can be drawn with the two triangles and T square. It is also obvious that the 45° triangle will divide a circle into 4 or 8 parts. The 30°-60° triangle will divide a circle into 6 or 12 parts, and the two triangles in combination will produce 24 equal portions of a circle (see the bottom part of Fig. 5-5).

5-8. Testing the T square, triangles, and drawing board. It is obvious that the draftsman can do accurate work only as long as his instruments remain "true" and in proper working order. Therefore the student, as well as the practicing draftsman, should form the habit of frequently checking the tools with which he works.

The screws that attach the blade of the T square to the head should be tight, otherwise there may be horizontal play in the T-square blade. The working edge of the T-square blade may be checked for straightness by very carefully drawing a sharp line through two widely separated points and then turning the T square over and drawing another line through the points along the same edge of the blade (see Fig. 5-6). If the lines do not coincide, or if there are marks and scratches in the blade, the error may be corrected by scraping and sandpapering the defective edge.

The edges of triangles may be checked for

CHECKING THE T SQUARE FOR LOOSENESS OR WARPING

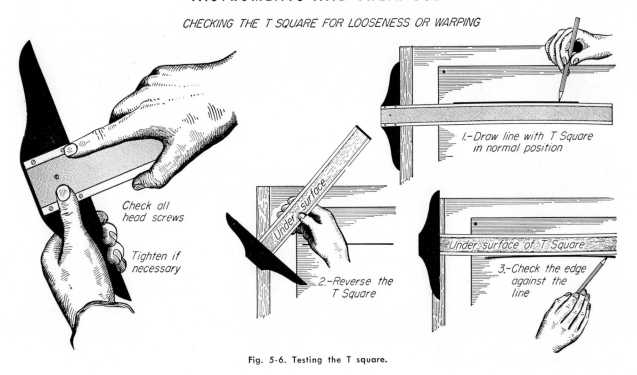

Check all
head screws

Tighten if
necessary

Under surface

2.—Reverse the
T Square

1.—Draw line with T Square
in normal position

Under surface of T Square

3.—Check the edge
against the
line

Fig. 5-6. Testing the T square.

straightness in the manner illustrated in Fig. 5-7. They may be tested for breaks and roughness by running a fingernail along the edges. As was the case with the T square, defects in the edges of the triangles should be removed by scraping and sandpapering.

The drawing board should always be wiped or dusted before it is used in order to assure a clean working surface and to remove any particles that might cause the pencil to break through the drawing sheet. The working edge of the board may be tested by laying the blade of a T square that is known to be true along the edge of the drawing board as illustrated in Fig. 5-8. The T square

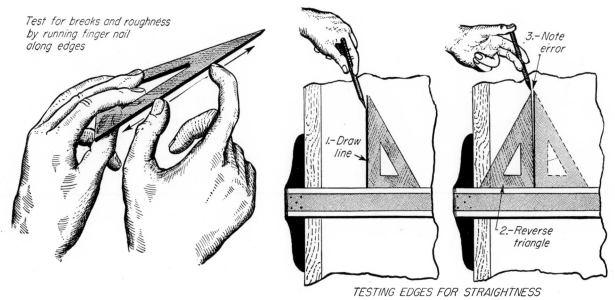

Test for breaks and roughness
by running finger nail
along edges

3.—Note
error

1.—Draw
line

2.—Reverse
triangle

TESTING EDGES FOR STRAIGHTNESS

Fig. 5-7. Testing the triangle.

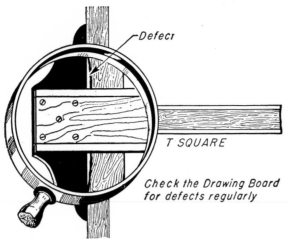

Check the Drawing Board
for defects regularly

Fig. 5-8. Testing the edge of the drawing board.

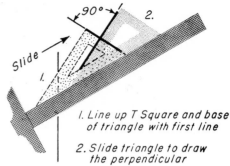

1. Line up T Square and base
of triangle with first line

2. Slide triangle to draw
the perpendicular

Fig. 5-10. Drawing perpendicular lines.

should touch the drawing board along its entire length and no light should be visible between the edges.

5-9. Parallel lines. To draw a line parallel to another line (Fig. 5-9), place the T square and triangle in combination so that the edge of the triangle coincides with the given line, and then slide the triangle to the required position to draw the other line.

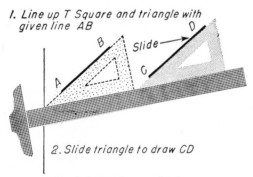

1. Line up T Square and triangle with given line AB

2. Slide triangle to draw CD

Fig. 5-9. Drawing parallel lines.

5-10. Perpendicular lines. To draw a line perpendicular to another line, place the T square and triangle in combination so that one edge of the triangle coincides with the given line. Then slide the triangle to the required position and draw the desired perpendicular line along the other leg (see Fig. 5-10). If the use of the T square in these

steps is awkward, another triangle may be substituted for it as a straightedge.

5-11. Inclined lines and angles. Inclined lines making 15° increments with other lines may be drawn by manipulating the triangles and using the T square as a straightedge. Figure 5-11 illustrates the procedure of drawing lines at various angles. Note that in some instances the 45° triangle or the 30°-60° triangle is used alone to get the resulting angle; in other cases the two triangles are used in combination.

5-12. Joining two points. Figure 5-12 shows an easy method of joining the two points that mark a measurement. With the pencil point firmly placed on point A, slide the triangle up to meet it; then pendulumlike swing the lower portion of the triangle until the leg lines up point B on a straight line with A. Check point B for alignment by putting the pencil point on it; then draw the line joining the two points.

5-13. The scale. The scale is actually a measuring stick. Scales are either flat or triangular, and the material used in their construction may be wood, celluloid, or metal. Although there is a great variety of scales available for special purposes and for different uses in the various engineering professions, scales that the draftsman will use are of two basic types. The scale most commonly used is called the architect's scale. It is divided into the familiar units of inches and fractions of an inch. This scale is usually *open-divided,* which means that only the units of the full-size scale and the

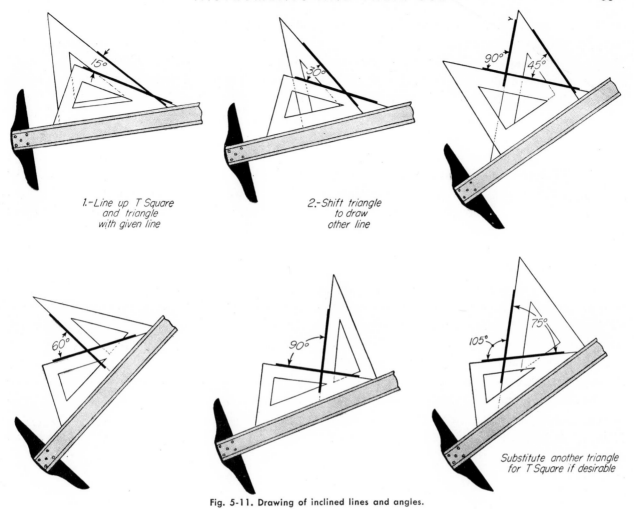

1.–Line up T Square and triangle with given line

2.–Shift triangle to draw other line

Substitute another triangle for T Square if desirable

Fig. 5-11. Drawing of inclined lines and angles.

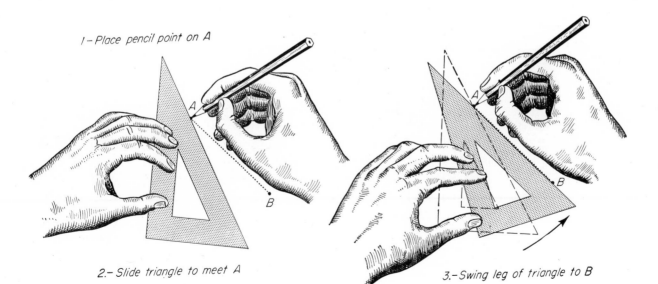

1–Place pencil point on A

2.–Slide triangle to meet A

3.–Swing leg of triangle to B

Fig. 5-12. Drawing a straight line between two points.

end unit of the other scales are subdivided into small fractions of an inch.

The second basic type of scale is the engineer's scale. It is usually divided into decimal parts of an inch, starting with 10 divisions to the inch along one edge and ranging to 50 or more decimal divisions to the inch along the other edges. The engineer's scale is usually *full-divided*, since the equal divisions and subdivisions are carried along the entire edge of the various scales; there being but one kind of division along each edge.

The divisions on the scales enable the draftsman to prepare drawings to actual size, enlarged, or reduced, as required. The architect's scale is used to represent a scale in inches or fractions of inches to the foot (*e.g.*, $6'' = 1'\text{-}0''$ or $1\frac{1}{2}'' = 1'0''$); the engineer's scale, with its decimal divisions, is used to represent feet to the inch (*e.g.*, $10' = 1''$). The latter type is therefore used for decimal dimensioning and for map drawing and plotting.

5-14. Use of the scale. The scale should never be used as a straightedge. The purpose of the scale is to transfer to the drawing the true relative dimensions of an object. Although the drawing itself may appear enlarged or reduced in scale depending on the size of the object and on the size of the sheet used, the actual true-length dimensions must always be shown on the drawing sheet.

Figure 5-13 shows the architect's scale. The main divisions, or units, of the scale represent inches, and these are divided into 16 subunits representing sixteenths of an inch. In order to mark off $\frac{1}{32}$ or $\frac{1}{64}$ in., the sixteenth is halved or quartered by eye. To lay off a measurement, place the initial mark 0 at the extremity of a line and scale toward the desired dimension. Be sure that the eye is directly over the scale. The desired dimension is indicated by an extremely light dot or a short dash drawn in a vertical direction from the edge of the scale. Greater accuracy can be obtained by taking the distance between the open points of a pair of dividers and transferring it to the sheet by lightly pinpricking its location. When a series of dimensions are to be marked off on one line, the measurements should be indicated without lifting the scale in order to avoid cumulative errors that are bound to result in moving the scale about.

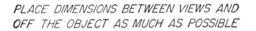

PLACE DIMENSIONS BETWEEN VIEWS AND OFF THE OBJECT AS MUCH AS POSSIBLE

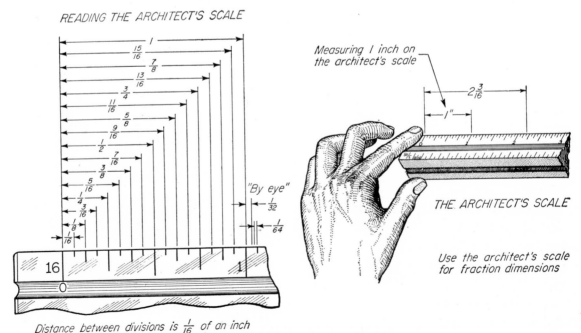

Fig. 5-13. The architect's scale and its use.

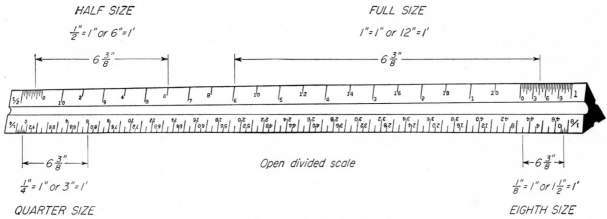

Fig. 5-14. Architect's (fractional) scale.

It is often necessary to show an object in an enlarged or reduced size. Large objects must of course be reduced in scale so that they may be represented on the drawing sheet. Small pieces are usually drawn to an enlarged scale for appearance's sake or so that constructional features may be adequately represented. For an enlarged representation, double size is common; for reduction, the scales most frequently employed are half size, quarter size, and eighth size. Figure 5-14 shows an open-divided architect's scale with the various reduced scales and their relationship to the full scale. When producing a drawing at a reduced size, the desired dimensions may be read directly by referring to the proper reduced scale on the measuring stick. Suppose the dimension 6⅜ in. is desired on a drawing prepared at half scale. Referring to the left edge of the stick where the figure ½ appears, start at 0 and read toward the right along the whole-unit divisions until the figure 6 has been reached. The distance from 0 to 6 represents 6 in. at half scale. The fraction ⅜ is obtained by reading from 0 toward the left on the subdivided unit extending toward the outer extremity of the scale. The other scales are used in a like manner.

5-15. The decimal scale. The decimal scale is full-divided; thus making it possible to read measurements from either end of the stick. The inch units are usually divided into 10, 20, 30, 40, 50, and 60 decimal parts of an inch. The 20-part division lends itself readily to drawings prepared at half size. Figure 5-15 shows the reading of various decimal dimensions. Note especially that on this particular scale the dimensions are shown in terms of tenths and fiftieths. The hundredths are obtained by splitting the fiftieths by eye.

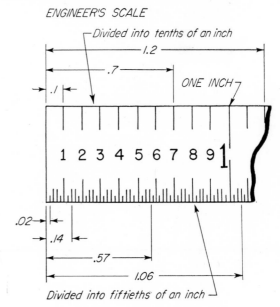

Use a decimal scale for decimal dimensions
The above scale is fully divided

Fig. 5-15. A decimal scale.

5-16. Indicating the scale on a drawing. If the drawing is twice the size of the object, the wording for the scale may read: Double Size, 2″ = 1″ (or 2′ = 1′). When the drawing is the same size as the object, the scale note should be: Full Size, 1″ = 1″ (or 12″ = 1′). For reduced scales, use: Half Size, ½″ = 1″ (or 6″ = 1′), etc., as was shown in Fig. 5-14.

5-17. The instrument kit. At the upper left corner of Fig. 5-1 is shown the instrument kit containing a typical group of tools. These are:

1. Large dividers
2. Large compass with knee joint
3. Small bow dividers
4. Small bow compass
5. Bow pen
6. Ruling pen
7. Interchangeable ruling pen used in compass leg
8. Box with spare parts and needles
9. Lengthening bar used with compass

When procuring a set of instruments, they should be carefully scrutinized for accuracy, balance, structural features, and finish. Checking on these details will assure the acquisition of tools that will give a lifetime of service. Good instruments cost more, but they are worth the extra investment.

5-18. The compass. The *large compass* is used to draw large circles and arcs. Some instruments have no knees, others may have one, and those most adaptable have knees on both legs (see Fig. 5-16). Auxiliary parts include adjustable, reversible, and replaceable needle points, a lengthening bar, and separate pen and pencil legs.

The *bow compass* is used for the drawing of the smaller arcs and circles. It may come equipped with either a center or side wheel adjustment. This instrument, with its even tension and positive adjusting mechanism, is very useful in securing the accurate results essential to fine drafting.

For very small accurate circles, a specially designed instrument is used which permits the center pin to remain stationary as the pen or pencil portion rotates around the center shaft. This convenient instrument is called a *drop compass* (see Fig. 5-17).

The *beam compass* consists of a long bar, on the ends of which the needle point and the pencil or pen attachment may be placed. Its simple design and ease of adjustment and operation are helpful in the drawing of the very large circles for which they are intended (Fig. 5-17).

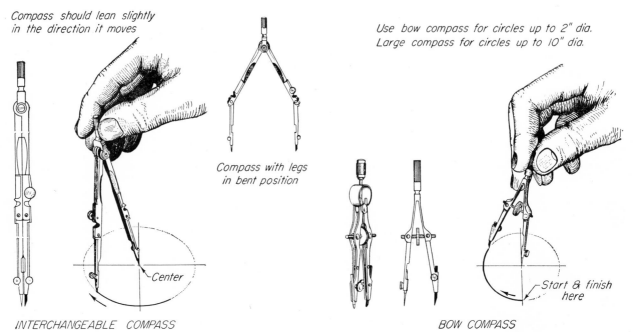

Compass should lean slightly in the direction it moves

Compass with legs in bent position

Center

INTERCHANGEABLE COMPASS

Use bow compass for circles up to 2″ dia.
Large compass for circles up to 10″ dia.

Start & finish here

BOW COMPASS

Fig. 5-16. The compass and its use.

5-19. Use of the compass. The use of the compass is illustrated in Fig. 5-16. Locate the center for the arc or circle by two very lightly drawn short intersecting lines. Adjust the opening of the legs of the compass to the desired radius. Hold the compass with the thumb and first and second fingers of the right hand and guide the steel point with the little finger of the left hand to the center, being careful to locate the compass point exactly. Now bring the pencil point down to the paper and, with the hand leading slightly beyond the pencil end, swing the compass with a twist of the thumb and two fingers in a clockwise direction until the arc or circle has been completed. When drawing concentric circles, draw the smallest one first.

5-20. The compass lead and needle point. For most drafting work, the lead for the compass should be softer than that of the drafting pencil. For example, if 2H and 4H pencils are used for the straight lines on a drawing, an HB or F lead should be used in the compass. In graphical solutions and design work, however, fine lines are often required and a harder lead may be necessary.

In sharpening the compass lead, draw it evenly across the file or sandpaper in the manner shown in Fig. 5-18 until a bevel point has been achieved. The cut surface should be about ¼ in. or slightly more. Place the lead in the leg so that ⅜ in. of it is exposed, and adjust the needle point so that it is a trifle longer than the lead. Readjust the lead after each sharpening since a dull lead may cause the steel point to slip from its center when the compass is next used. The accuracy of a compass may be

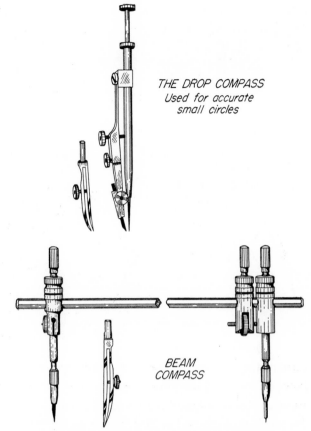

THE DROP COMPASS
Used for accurate small circles

BEAM COMPASS

Fig. 5-17. Drop compass and beam compass.

tested by bending both legs at the joints and checking to see whether the points meet. If they do not, the instrument should be adjusted or a new one obtained.

5-21. The dividers. The dividers are made in three basic styles (see Fig. 5-19). The plain type has two solid legs. More useful is the hairspring dividers which has a spring attached to one of the legs that permits the regulation of minute variations in the distances between points by a slight

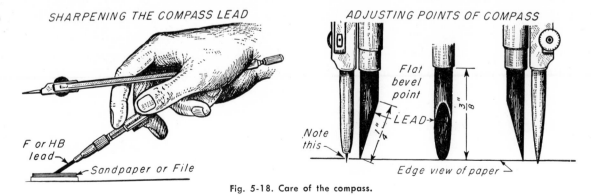

SHARPENING THE COMPASS LEAD

F or HB lead — Sandpaper or File

ADJUSTING POINTS OF COMPASS

Note this

Flat bevel point

LEAD

Edge view of paper

Fig. 5-18. Care of the compass.

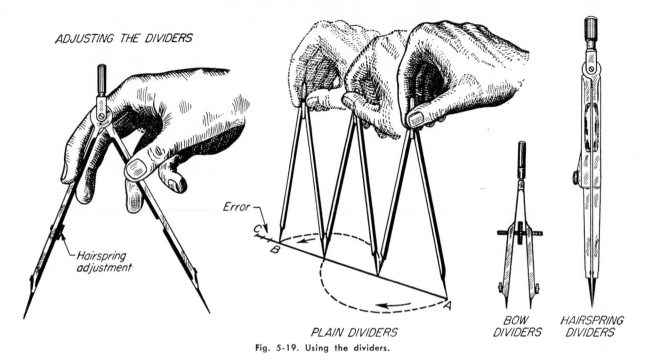

ADJUSTING THE DIVIDERS

Hairspring adjustment

Error

PLAIN DIVIDERS

BOW DIVIDERS

HAIRSPRING DIVIDERS

Fig. 5-19. Using the dividers.

turn of the adjusting screw. The third type is the bow dividers, which, like the bow compass, is equipped with either a center or side wheel that permits fine adjustments. The bow type is particularly useful in very exacting work because the wheel adjustment effectively holds the setting and therefore there is little danger of error through inadvertent spreading or contracting of the points. Some dividers have fixed needles; others are designed with adjustable, reversible, and replaceable needle points.

5-22. Use of the dividers. Dividers are used to measure or set off given distances, to divide curved or straight lines, and to transfer measurements. Before using the dividers see that all attachments are secure, and adjust the screw in the yoke at the top of the instrument to give enough friction—not too loose or too tight—to permit easy one-hand manipulation. By holding one leg in the grip of the thumb and third finger and the other

PROPORTIONAL DIVIDERS

Used for copying to an enlarged or reduced scale

Fig. 5-20. Proportional dividers.

leg by the first and second fingers (Fig. 5-19), the draftsman can easily manipulate the setting of the instrument. In closing the dividers, the second and third fingers are slipped from between the legs, while the first finger and thumb bring the legs together. Facility in handling comes through practice.

Suppose it is desired to divide a line *AB* into three equal parts (see Fig. 5-19). Open the legs to a distance estimated by eye to be one-third the length of the line. Start at one extremity (point *A*) and swing the compass legs in half circles, alternately, until the other extremity has been approached. If the compass point does not fall on the end point *B*, do not lift the dividers until the error in distance (length of *BC*) has been corrected by increasing or decreasing the setting, whichever is necessary, by one-third the length of the error. Repeat the operation, beginning at point *A,* until the required setting is found. The bow dividers, with its sturdier adjustments, is recommended for work on small circles and short lines, and also where many short divisions are required.

5-23. Proportional dividers. Proportional dividers (Fig. 5-20) consist of two legs on a sliding and adjustable pivot. The instrument is provided with a scale that makes it possible to lay off measurements at a given proportion, since the distance between the points of the legs at one end bears a definite proportion to the distance between the points at the other end. When adjusted by means of the sliding pivot, a line may be divided into any number of parts or lengthened to any given proportions, the circumference of a circle divided into any number of parts, or the diameter or radius of a circle enlarged or reduced.

5-24. The protractor. Protractors are semicircular in shape and are made of paper, wood, plastic, or metal. Draftsmen prefer the transparent types with beveled edges, graduated to $\frac{1}{2}°$ or $1°$, numbered at $10°$ intervals, and permitting readings from both ends (Fig. 5-21). If great accuracy is desired, the tangent method of laying out an angle should be employed (see Sec. 6-17). For most drafting procedures, however, the use of the protractor is acceptable.

5-25. Use of the protractor. The protractor is used for measuring or setting off angles that can-

not be obtained by manipulating the triangles. Suppose it is desired to draw a line making an angle of $24°$ with a given line. Place the vertex indicator at the spot on the line where the vertex of the required angle is to be located (follow second finger in the illustration). Place the zero indicator aligned with the given line (first finger in illustration), and read the figure $24°$ along the beveled rim of the instrument (at pencil point). Mark this point very lightly, then draw a line through this point and the vertex. The angle thus formed equals $24°$. To measure an angle with the protractor, place the vertex indicator on the vertex of the angle, align one of the lines of the angle with the zero mark on the rim, and read the angle where the other line appears to cross the rim.

5-26. Irregular curves. Curved lines other than circles and circle arcs may be drawn uniformly and accurately with the help of irregular curves like the french curves (Fig. 5-22), or adjustable curves and splines (Fig. 5-23). Irregular

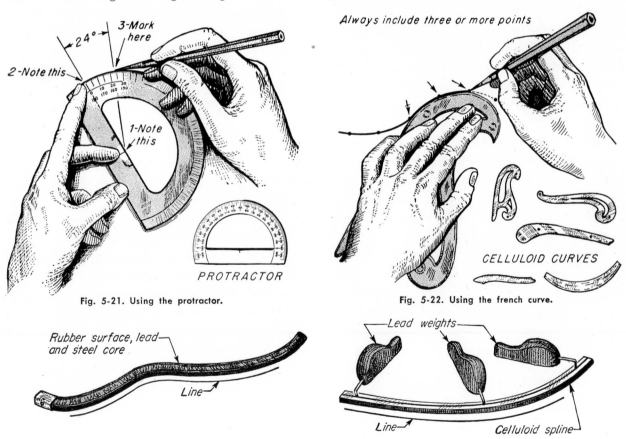

Fig. 5-21. Using the protractor.

Fig. 5-22. Using the french curve.

Fig. 5-23. Adjustable curve and spline.

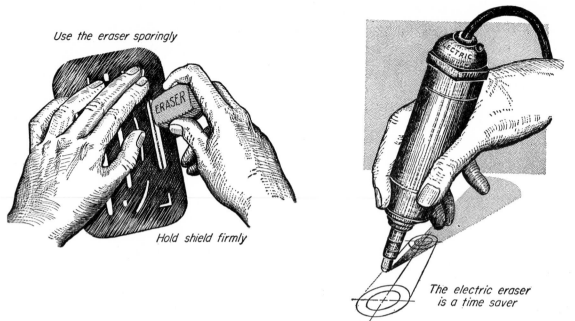

Use the eraser sparingly

Hold shield firmly

The electric eraser is a time saver

Fig. 5-24. The erasing shield and the electric erasing machine.

curves are generally made of a transparent material with a highly polished surface. The edges are portions of the ellipse, parabola, hyperbola, and other geometric curves. Some irregular curves are developed as radii of different sizes of circular arcs. An acceptable "fair" curve can be secured with these tools when three or more points have been plotted for the drawing of each segment of the entire line.

5-27. Erasing procedures. Care must be used in selecting erasers that will remove the pencil or ink lines without damaging the surface of the drawing sheet. A soft rubber or Artgum eraser will accomplish practically all required erasing work.

USE OF PANTOGRAPH

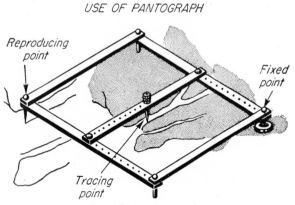

Reproducing point

Fixed point

Tracing point

Fig. 5-25. A pantograph.

The author has found the kneaded eraser superior to all others. This is a type of eraser used by artists. It is made of dough rubber, is kneadable in the hand, and has the advantage of leaving little refuse on the paper to be brushed off following erasures. The use of gritty ink erasers and the removal of lines with a knife blade are never to be recommended because both devices tend to destroy the smooth surface of the drawing paper, tracing paper, or tracing cloth. Light pencil lines are removable from tracing cloth and the better grade of tracing papers by gentle rubbing with a soft cloth dipped in benzine or carbon tetrachloride.

The erasing shield is a very handy device for erasing unwanted lines while protecting others (see Fig. 5-24). It also prevents wrinkling the paper and the possibility of undue damage to the surface. Although the thin spring-steel types of erasing shields remain flat over a longer period, the hard-rolled nickel-alloy shields have the advantage of being practically rustproof.

The electric eraser (Fig. 5-24) is a common tool in many commercial drafting rooms. One hand only is necessary for starting the motor, the erasing procedure, and stopping the motor. With a little practice, accuracy and satisfactory control of the instrument can be developed. The machines come equipped with interchangeable pencil and ink eraser points.

5-28. Special drafting aids. The pantograph is a useful instrument that aids in the quick and easy copying of maps and other drawings to an enlarged or reduced scale, according to a ratio selected by the operator (see Fig. 5-25). Pantographs are designed in several styles and either wood or metal is employed in their manufacture. The tracing and pencil points are interchangeable.

Among the many special drafting aids available in the modern drafting room, the drafting machine is probably the most useful (see Fig. 5-26). The use of separate T square, triangles, scale, and protractor is dispensed with, since the instruments are all combined in the drafting machine. One hand manipulates the central control to secure the proper settings while the other draws the required line. The use of fewer instruments means a considerable saving of time and effort.

In addition to these two representative devices, there is an almost unlimited number of special drafting tools and aids to speedier, more efficient work that the student will find in use in commercial drafting rooms.

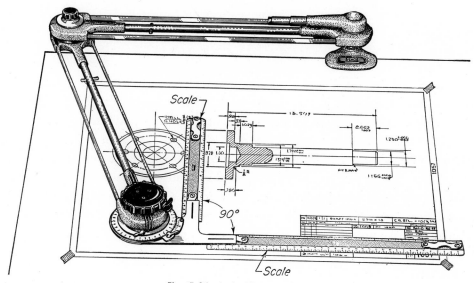

Fig. 5-26. A drafting machine.

Chapter 6

GEOMETRICAL CONSTRUCTIONS

Every draftsman should be familiar with the geometrical constructions that appear in this chapter. Many of them will be encountered in the working of ordinary problems, and others often come up in the solution of problems in engineering design.

6-1. To bisect an arc or a straight line (Fig. 6-1). Given arc AB and line AB. From the extreme points A and B, strike arcs that intersect at C and D. A line drawn through points C and D bisects the arc and the line at F and E.

6-2. To bisect an angle (Fig. 6-2). With the vertex A as a center strike any arc BC. With B and C as centers, strike arcs intersecting at D. A line drawn through points A and D bisects the angle.

6-3. To draw a perpendicular through a point to a line (Fig. 6-3). *a.* With the given point O as

a center, strike arc AB. With centers A and B, strike arcs intersecting at C. The line through O and C is perpendicular to AB.

b. With the given point O as a center, strike arcs intersecting the line at A and B. With A and B as centers, strike arcs intersecting at C. The line through C and O is perpendicular to AB.

6-4. To divide a line into a given number of equal parts (Fig. 6-4). *a.* Line AB is to be divided into five equal parts. Through point A draw any line AC and scale off five equal divisions on this line. From point 5 draw line $5B$. Through the other points draw lines 4-4, 3-3, 2-2, and 1-1 parallel to $5B$. The line AB is divided into five equal divisions by the parallel lines thus drawn.

b. Line AB is to be divided into five equal parts. At point B erect the perpendicular BC. Take any

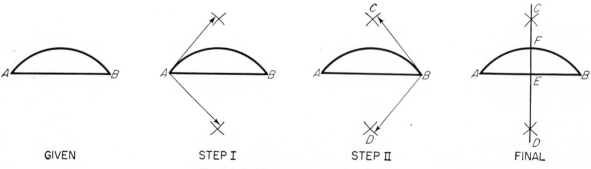

GIVEN STEP I STEP II FINAL

Fig. 6-1. To bisect an arc or straight line.

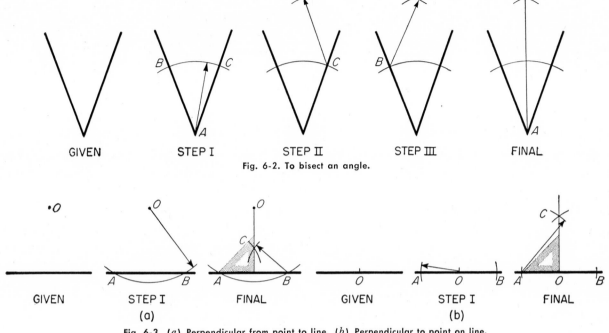

Fig. 6-2. To bisect an angle.

Fig. 6-3. (*a*) Perpendicular from point to line. (*b*) Perpendicular to point on line.

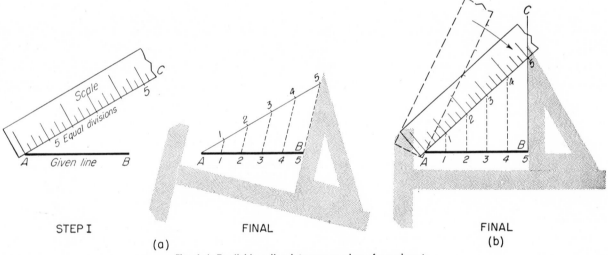

Fig. 6-4. To divide a line into any number of equal parts.

evenly divided line (a scale for instance) and place one point at *A* and the fifth division marker on *BC*. Draw the lines from points 4, 3, 2, and 1 on this line perpendicularly to *AB*. These lines divide *AB* into five equal parts.

6-5. To construct a square (Fig. 6-5a). Erect a perpendicular *AC* to *AB* at point *A*. With the length of the given side *AB* as a radius, strike the arc *BC*. With a radius equal to *AB* and with points

B and *C* as centers, strike arcs intersecting at *D*. The points *A*, *B*, *C*, and *D* form the square.

6-6. To draw a triangle when its three sides are given (Fig. 6-5b). The sides *A*, *B*, and *C* of the triangle are given. Lay out one side equal to *A*. From its extremities strike arcs with radii equal to *B* and *C*. The intersection of these arcs at *O* locates the required point that fixes the shape of the triangle.

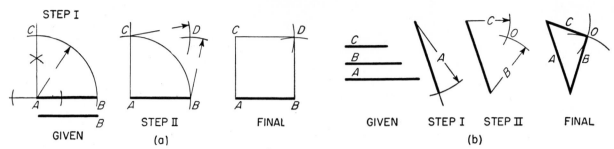

Fig. 6-5. (*a*) To draw a square. (*b*) To draw a triangle when its three sides are given.

6-7. To construct a regular pentagon (Fig. 6-6). The circumscribing circle is given. Bisect the radius *OA* of the circle. With *B* as a center and a radius equal to *BC*, strike arc *CD*. With *C* as a center, strike the arc *EF* passing through the point

D. Distance *CE* or *CF* is equal to the length of **one** side of the pentagon. The other sides are stepped off with the dividers.

6-8. To draw a regular hexagon (Fig. 6-7). *a.* The circumscribed circle is given (marking **the**

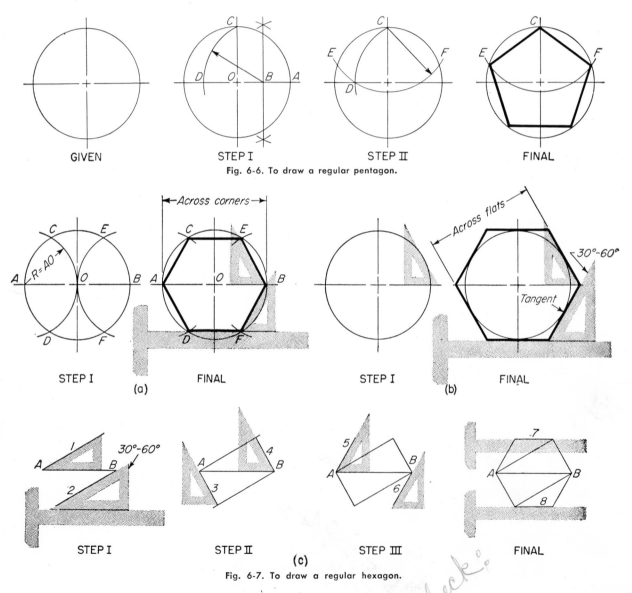

Fig. 6-6. To draw a regular pentagon.

Fig. 6-7. To draw a regular hexagon.

distance across corners of the hexagon). The radius of the circle and the length of each side of the hexagon are equal. With *A* as a center and a radius equal to *AO*, strike arc *CD*. With *B* as a center and radius *BO*, strike arc *EF*. The points *A*, *D*, *F*, *B*, *E*, and *C* indicate the lengths of the sides. Use instruments as shown in the illustration to complete the figure.

b. If the circle is inscribed (distance across flats), the hexagon may be drawn with instruments, as shown in the figure.

c. If *AB*, the distance across corners, is given, use instruments and draw the lines in the numbered sequence shown in the illustration to form the hexagon.

6-9. To draw a regular octagon (Fig. 6-8). *a.* Given the square, draw the diagonals *AD* and *BC*. With *C* and *D* as centers, and radii equal to one-half the diagonals, strike arcs to mark points *E* and *F*. *EF* equals the length of one of the sides. Continue the procedure and join the points.

b. The inscribed circle is given. Using the **T** square and 45° triangle, draw the sides of the octagon tangent to the inscribed circle.

6-10. To draw a regular polygon when one side is given (Fig. 6-9). A regular seven-sided figure is required, and side *AB* is given. Draw the semicircle *BC* with *AB* as a radius. Divide the semicircle into seven equal divisions. Draw the radial lines through point *A* and the numbered points on the arc. With point 2 as a center and a radius equal to *AB*, strike the arc intersecting line *A*3 at *D*. With *D* as a center and a radius equal to *AB*, find point *E* on *A*4. Find *F* in the same manner. Point *G* can also be found in this manner or, better, by striking the arc from point *B* across *A*6.

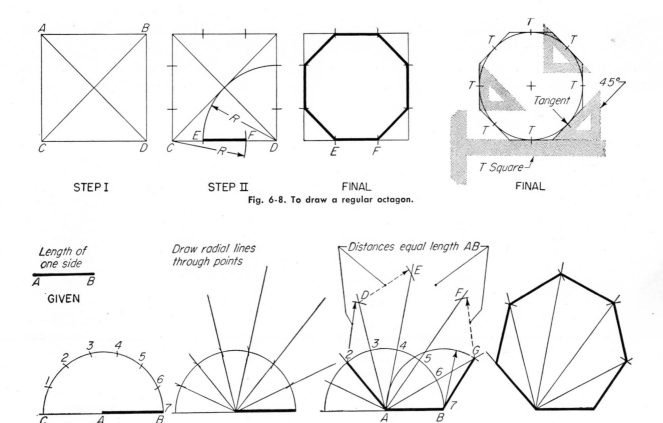

Fig. 6-8. To draw a regular octagon.

Fig. 6-9. To draw a regular polygon when one side is given.

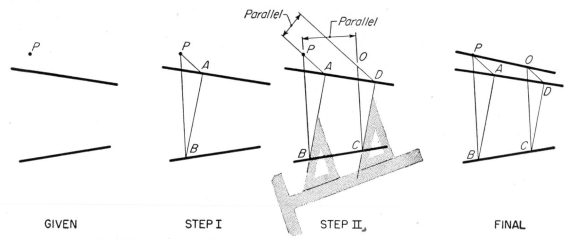

Fig. 6-10. To draw a line through a point and the inaccessible intersection of two lines.

6-11. To draw a line through the inaccessible intersection of two lines and a given point (Fig. 6-10).   The given lines and the point P are shown. Draw any triangle ABP with one vertex through the point P and one on each line. Draw another triangle CDO at any convenient position parallel to ABP with vertexes C and D on the given lines. The line through P and O is the required line.

6-12. To divide the area of any triangle (or trapezoid) into a given number of equal parts (Fig. 6-11).   The triangle ABC is to be divided into five equal parts. Divide any side AC into five equal parts. Draw a semicircle as shown, with AC as a diameter. Draw perpendiculars from the points on AC to the arc. With C as a center, draw arcs from the points on the semicircle to intersect side AC. Lines drawn through the points on AC parallel to AB divide the triangle into five equal parts.

6-13. To draw a circle or an arc through three points not in a straight line (Fig. 6-12).   Join the given points A, B, and C as shown. Bisect lines AB and BC. The bisectors of AB and BC intersect at O, which is the center for the required circle or arc. Note that AB and BC are chords of the circle.

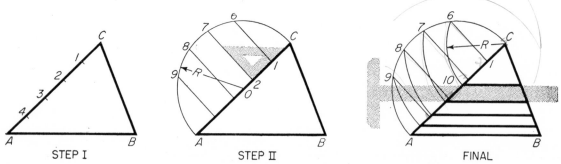

Fig. 6-11. To divide the area of a triangle into any number of equal parts.

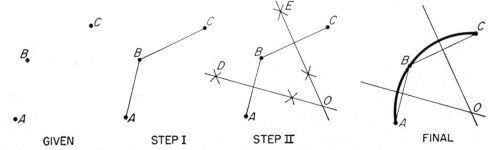

Fig. 6-12. To draw a circle through three points not in a straight line.

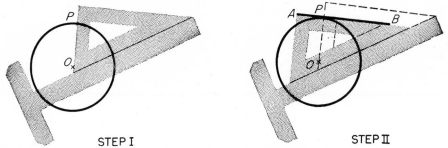

P
O
A
P
B
O
STEP I
STEP II

Fig. 6-13. To draw a tangent through a point on a circle.

6-14. To draw a tangent through a point on a circle (Fig. 6-13). The circle with center at O and the point P are given. Manipulate the T square and the triangle until one side passes through P and O. Then slide the triangle until the other side appears tangent to the circle at P. Draw the required tangent line AB.

6-15. To draw a tangent through a point not on a circle (Fig. 6-14). *a.* Join the center O and the point P. Bisect OP. Using mid-point C as a center and distance CO as a radius, strike an arc intersecting the circle at points D and E. These two points indicate where the lines DP and EP are tangent to the circle.

b. Manipulate two triangles until one goes through point P and appears tangent (at T) to the circle. Then slide the top triangle to check that the center of the circle and the apparent tangent point T lie in the line of the other leg. Slide the top triangle to its original position to draw the tangent line TP.

6-16. To draw a line tangent to two circles or arcs (Fig. 6-15). Two arcs with centers at D and O are given. A and B are the radii. With O as a center, draw arc C equal to radius B minus radius A. Draw a tangent to this arc from center point D. Extend a line from point O through the tangent point E to H. Draw the required tangent line FH parallel to DE.

6-17. To construct an angle by the tangent method (Fig. 6-16). Along one side AB of the required angle measure off 10 equal units, either half inches or inches, extending the line if necessary. At point 10 erect a perpendicular to the line AB. Suppose it is desired to show an angle of 33°. Look up the trigonometric function in the tangent

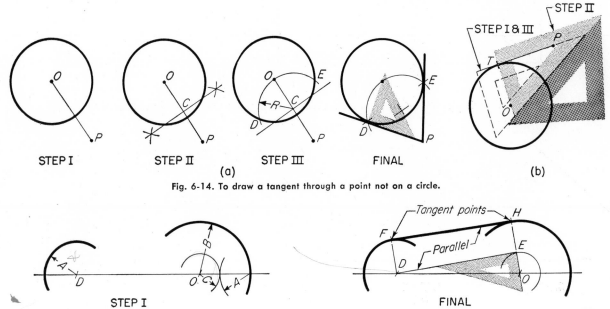

O
P
STEP I
O
C
P
STEP II
O
E
R
C
D
P
STEP III
E
D
P
FINAL
(a)
STEP II
STEP I & III
P
T
O
(b)

Fig. 6-14. To draw a tangent through a point not on a circle.

A
D
B
O
C
A
STEP I
Tangent points
H
F
Parallel
E
D
O
FINAL

Fig. 6-15. To draw a line tangent to two circles or arcs.

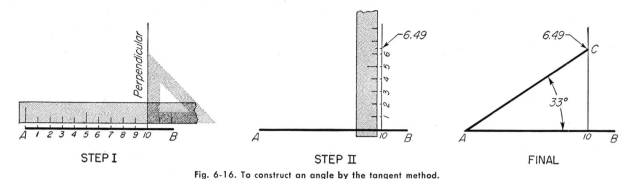

Fig. 6-16. To construct an angle by the tangent method.

table and find the figure .649. Multiply this figure by 10 (units) and locate this distance on the perpendicular at C using the decimal scale. Join points A and C. Angle CAB equals 33°.

6-18. To draw an arc of a given radius R tangent to two lines that form a right angle (Fig. 6-17). With O as a center and with the given radius R, strike the arc AB. With A and B as centers and with the same radius, strike the arcs intersecting at C. C is the center of the required arc tangent to the lines. The tangent points A and B may be checked by drawing perpendiculars to the lines through point C.

6-19. To draw an arc of a given radius R tangent to two lines (Fig. 6-18). *a. Lines that form an acute angle.* The lines forming the angle are given. Draw lines parallel to the given lines at a distance equal to the given radius R. These lines will intersect at the point C, which is the center for the required tangent arc. The tangent points A and B are found by drawing perpendiculars through C to the given lines.

b. Lines that form an obtuse angle. The lines that form an obtuse angle are given. Follow the identical procedure used to find the arc tangent to two lines that form an acute angle.

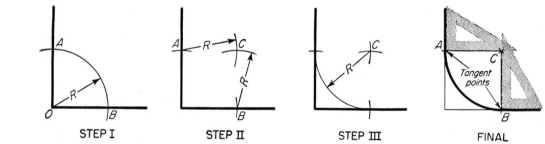

Fig. 6-17. To draw a circular arc of a given radius tangent to two lines (forming a right angle).

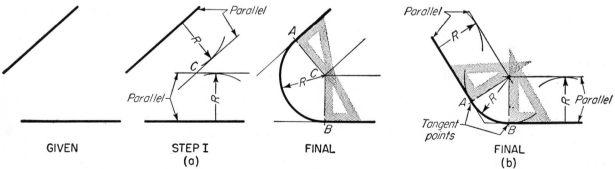

Fig. 6-18. To draw a circular arc tangent to two lines: (*a*) forming an acute angle, (*b*) forming an obtuse angle.

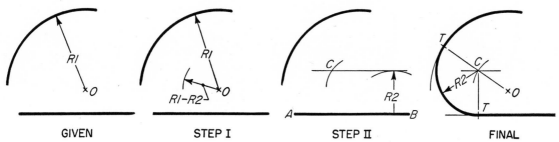

Fig. 6-19. To draw an arc of a given radius $R2$ tangent to an arc and a straight line.

6-20. To draw an arc of a given radius $R2$ tangent to an arc and a straight line (Figs. 6-19 and 6-20). *a.* Given the arc with center O and radius $R1$, the line AB, and the radius $R2$ of the required arc, as shown in Fig. 6-19. With a radius equal to the arc $R1$ minus the arc $R2$ and with O as a center, strike an arc. Draw a line parallel to the given line at a distance equal to $R2$ intersecting this arc. The point C, the intersection of the line and the arc, is the center for the required arc. The line OC extended to T marks the tangent point of the arcs. The perpendicular through C to the line AB marks the tangent point on the line.

b. Given the arc with center O and radius $R1$, the line AB, and the radius $R2$ of the required arc, as shown in Fig. 6-20. With a radius equal to $R1$ plus the radius of the required arc $R2$ and with O as a center, strike an arc. Draw a line parallel to the given line AB at a distance equal to $R2$ from it. The point C, the intersection of the arc and the line, is the center for the required arc. A perpendicular through C to the line determines the tangent point on the line. Joining centers C and O determines the tangent point T of the arcs.

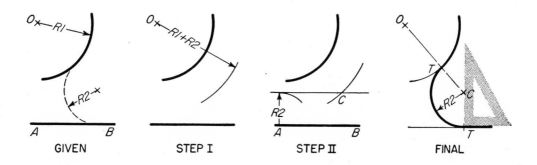

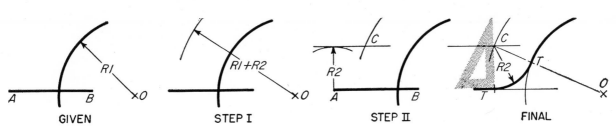

Fig. 6-20. To draw an arc of a given radius $R2$ tangent to an arc and a straight line.

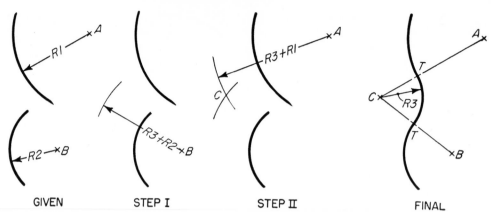

Fig. 6-21. To draw an arc of a given radius $R3$ tangent to two arcs.

6-21. To draw an arc of a given radius $R3$ tangent to two arcs (Figs. 6-21, 6-22, and 6-23).
a. The arcs with radii $R1$ and $R2$ and the radius of the required arc $R3$ are given, as shown in Fig. 6-21. With B as a center and a radius equal to $R2$ plus $R3$, strike an arc. With A as a center and a radius equal to $R1$ plus $R3$, strike another arc intersecting the first arc at C. Point C is the center

for the required arc. To find T, the tangent points, join A with C and B with C.

b. As shown in Fig. 6-22, with B as a center and a radius equal to $R2$ plus $R3$, strike an arc. With A as a center and a radius equal to $R1$ minus $R3$, strike another arc intersecting the other at point C. Point C is the center for the required arc. Draw the line CB and extend the line AC to find the tangent points T.

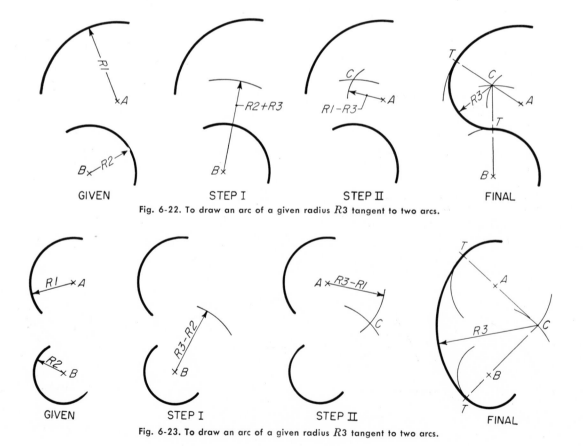

Fig. 6-22. To draw an arc of a given radius $R3$ tangent to two arcs.

Fig. 6-23. To draw an arc of a given radius $R3$ tangent to two arcs.

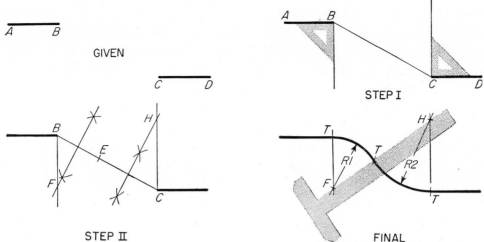

Fig. 6-24. To draw a reverse curve (ogee) connecting two parallel lines.

c. In Fig. 6-23, with *B* as a center and a radius equal to the *R3* minus *R2*, strike an arc. With *A* as a center and a radius equal to *R3* minus *R1*, strike another arc intersecting the first arc at point *C*. Point *C* is the center for the required arc. Lines joining points *A* and *B* with *C* when extended will locate the tangent points *T*.

6-22. To draw a reverse curve (ogee) connecting two parallel lines (Fig. 6-24). The parallel lines *AB* and *CD* are given. At *B* and *C*, the extreme ends of the reverse curve, erect perpendiculars to the given lines. Join points *B* and *C*. Select point *E* anywhere on *BC* as the point where the two curves are to meet. Draw the perpendicular bisectors of *BE* and *CE*. The points *F* and *H*, which are the intersections of the perpendiculars and the bisectors, will serve as the centers of the arcs that form the required reverse curve.

6-23. To lay off the approximate length of a circular arc on its tangent (Fig. 6-25). *a.* The arc of the circle is given. Draw the tangent *AC* through *A*. Extend the chord *AB*. Bisect the chord *AB*. Locate point *D* by making distance *AD* equal to *AE*. With *D* as a center, strike the arc intersecting the tangent *AC* at *H*. *AH* is the approximate length of arc *AB*, being shorter than the arc by about 6 ft. to the mile when the angle between the chord and the tangent is less than 60°, down to about 5 in. to the mile when the angle reaches 30°.

b. Draw the tangent to the arc. With the dividers step off equal distances on the arc starting at point 5 and moving toward *T*. Step off these same distances on the tangent. The distance on the tangent will be slightly shorter than the length of the arc, a margin of error that can be disregarded in graphic representation.

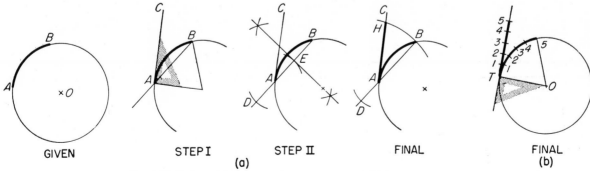

Fig. 6-25. To lay off the approximate length of a circular arc on its tangent.

6-24. The ellipse. Very frequently inclined and oblique cylinders and holes must be represented in engineering drawings. The outline of the elliptical shapes encountered may be projected by locating points in one view and projecting them to their proper positions in the related view. This tedious procedure is not required in many practical instances, however, especially when the major and minor axes of an ellipse are shown. The several methods shown in the following paragraphs are acceptable in drawing practice.

The ellipse is a conic section, the result of passing a plane through the lateral surface of a cone inclined to the base (see Fig. 15-5b).

6-25. To draw an ellipse—four-center method (Fig. 6-26). Join points C and A of the given long diameter CD and the short diameter AB. Lay off the distance AE equal to the difference between CO and AO. Bisect CE. The points at the intersections of the bisector with the two given diameters locate the centers H, K, L, and M for the

large and the small arcs forming the ellipse. (The short diameter may be extended if necessary to find the points H and L.) Note the tangent points T for the large and small arcs.

6-26. To draw an ellipse—foci method (Fig. 6-27). The major and minor axes of the ellipse are given. With one end A of the short axis as a center and a radius equal to OC (one-half the length of the major diameter), strike arcs intersecting at E and F. These are the foci of the ellipse. Divide EO into any number of parts (the larger the ellipse the greater the number). With point E as a center and a radius equal to distance C1, strike an arc in the upper left quadrant. With F as a center and a radius equal to D1, strike an arc to intersect the first arc. This intersection forms one point on the required ellipse. Like points are placed in the other quadrants by reversing the centers. To find point 2, take E as a center and a radius equal to C2 and strike an arc in the upper left quadrant to intersect an arc equal to D2 struck

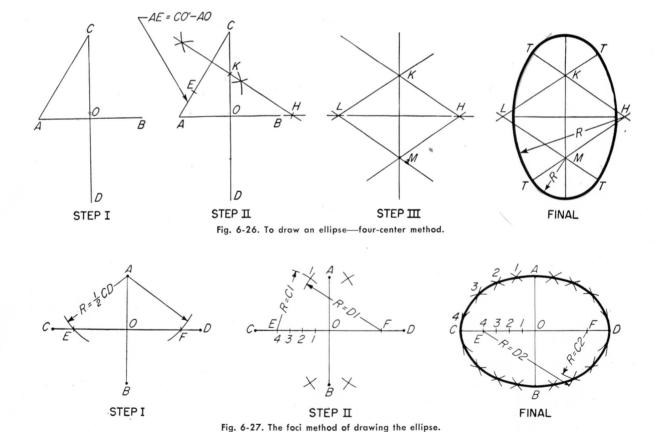

STEP I   STEP II   STEP III   FINAL

Fig. 6-26. To draw an ellipse—four-center method.

STEP I   STEP II   FINAL

Fig. 6-27. The foci method of drawing the ellipse.

from the center F. Interchange centers to find point 2 in the other quadrant. Proceed in a like manner to find the remaining points. Then complete the drawing of the ellipse with an irregular curve.

6-27. To draw an ellipse—the Slantz method (Fig. 6-28). The long diameter AB and the short diameter CD are given. With A as a center and a radius equal to CD, strike an arc intersecting AB at E. Take a distance EF equal to two-thirds EB and mark it off on AB on both sides of its intersection with CD. These distances locate points O and P. Through points O and P draw 60° lines intersecting CD (extended if necessary) at X and Y. Points X and Y serve as centers for the large arcs, and O and P as centers for the small arcs of

the ellipse. Note that the tangent points T are found on the 60° lines.

6-28. To construct an ellipse—parallelogram method (Fig. 6-29). The major (CD) and minor (AB) axes are shown in the rectangle and the parallelogram. Divide CO and CE into the same number of equal divisions starting at C. From A draw a line to point 3 on CE. From B draw a line through point 3 on CO intersecting the previous line. The point of intersection of the two lines is one point on the desired ellipse. The other points in that quadrant are found by following the same procedure. The points in the other three quadrants are similarly located. A smooth line may be drawn through the points by the use of a french curve.

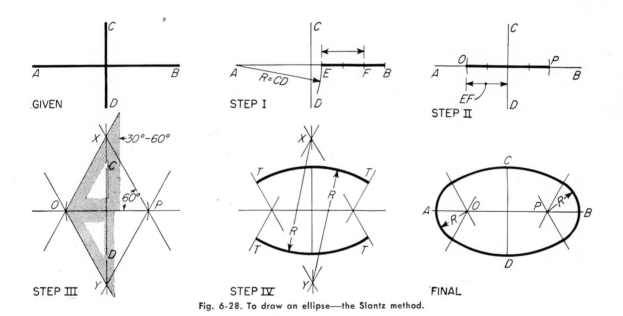

Fig. 6-28. To draw an ellipse—the Slantz method.

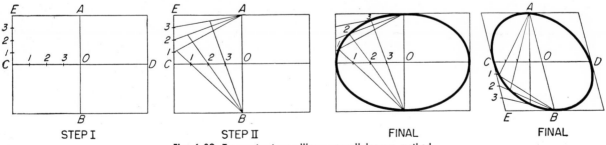

Fig. 6-29. To construct an ellipse—parallelogram method.

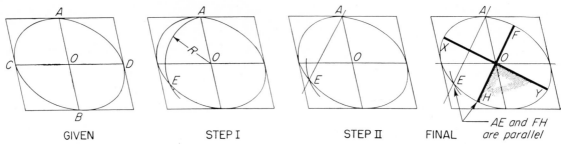

GIVEN　　　　　　STEP I　　　　　　STEP II　　　FINAL　　AE and FH
are parallel

Fig. 6-30. Given the conjugate diameters, to find the major and minor diameters of an ellipse.

6-29. Given the conjugate diameters, to find the major and minor diameters of an ellipse (Fig. 6-30). The conjugate diameters AB and CD intersecting at O are given. (The diameters of an ellipse are said to be conjugate when each diameter is parallel to the tangents drawn at the extremities of the other.) With O as a center and a radius equal to AO, strike an arc intersecting the ellipse at point E. Join points A and E. Through O draw the line FH parallel to AE. FH is the minor diameter of the ellipse. The line XY drawn through the point O, perpendicular to FH, is the major diameter.

6-30. To draw a tangent to an ellipse (Fig. 6-31). The ellipse with its two foci, $F1$ and $F2$, and the point P on the ellipse are given. Join $F1$ with P and extend the line to any convenient point A. Join $F2$ with P and extend the line to point B anywhere outside the ellipse. Bisect the exterior angle $F2PA$. The bisector of the exterior angle is tangent to the ellipse at the point P.

6-31. The parabola. The parabola is a curve generated by a point that moves along a path

equidistant from the focus (a fixed point) and the directrix (a fixed line). In geometry, it is the curved line formed by the intersection of a plane passed through a cone parallel to one of its elements. Thus the parabola is a conic section (see Fig. 15-5c).

6-32. To construct a parabola (Fig. 6-32). The directrix AB, the axis OE, and the focus F are given. Draw a line parallel to AB intersecting the axis at any point C. With F as a center and a radius equal to OC, strike an arc intersecting this line at points G and H. These points are two points on the curve of the parabola. Repeat the process until a sufficient number of points are located to permit the drawing of the required curve. The vertex V is midway between the focus F and the point O.

6-33. To construct a parabola—tangent method (Fig. 6-33). Given the limiting points A, B, and C, which are joined as shown. The lines AB and BC are divided into an equal number of parts. Number the division points as shown. Draw lines connecting like numbered points 1 and 1, 2 and 2, etc. These lines are tangents to the required para-

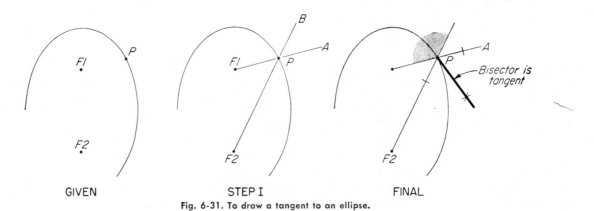

GIVEN　　　　　　　STEP I　　　　　　FINAL

Fig. 6-31. To draw a tangent to an ellipse.

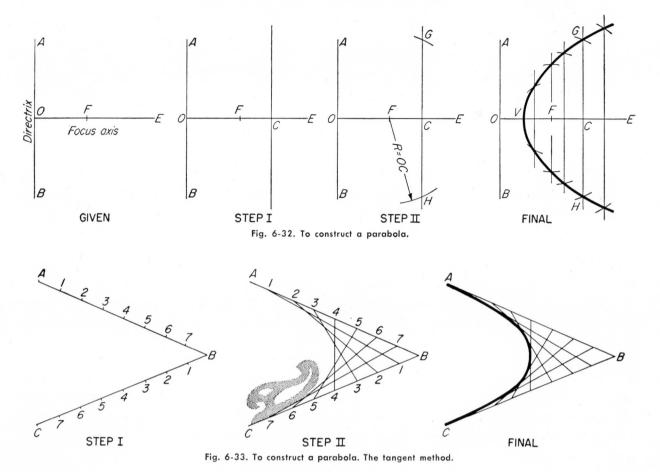

Fig. 6-32. To construct a parabola.

Fig. 6-33. To construct a parabola. The tangent method.

bolic curve. A french curve will develop the contour.

6-34. To draw a parabola through two given points (Fig. 6-34). *a.* Given the points *A* and *B*; assume the point *O*. Divide distance *AO* and *BO* into the same number of equal parts. Join the point *B* with the equispaced points on *AO*. From *BO* extend the numbered lines, parallel to *AO*, until they intersect the like-numbered lines. The

intersections of these lines determine the required curve.

b. Given the points *A* and *B*; assume the point *O* forming a right angle as shown in Fig. 6-34*b*. Join points *A*, *O*, and *B* to form the tangents. Divide line *AO* and *BO* into the same number of equal parts and number them as shown. The intersecting lines are the tangents that give shape to the parabolic curve desired.

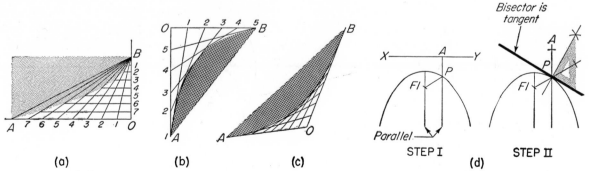

Fig. 6-34. (*a*), (*b*), and (*c*) To construct a curve of parabolic form through two given points. (*d*) To draw a tangent to a parabola.

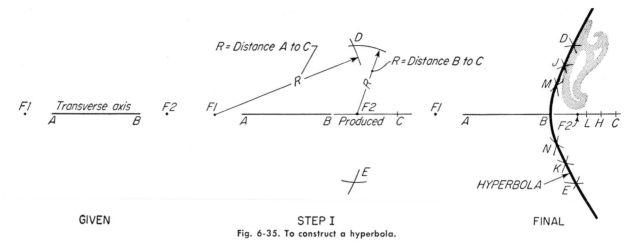

Fig. 6-35. To construct a hyperbola.

c. The procedure necessary to draw a parabola when the angle *AOB* is obtuse is shown in Fig. 6-34*c.* The construction is the same as in Fig. 6-34*b.* If the tangents *AO* and *BO* formed an acute angle, the same procedure as in Fig. 6-34*b* would also result in a curve of parabolic form.

d. Since the diameters of a parabola are at right angles to the directrix, a tangent to a parabola will bisect the angle between the focal radius and the diameter which passes through the point of tangency. The directrix *XY*, the focus *F*1, and a diameter *A* passing through the tangent point *P* are shown in Step I. *F*1 is joined to *P* to form the angle *F1PA*. The bisector of this angle is the tangent to the parabola at the point *P.*

6-35. The hyperbola. A hyperbola is a curve generated by a point that moves so that at any position the difference of its distance from two fixed points (foci) is a constant (equal to the transverse axis of the hyperbola). When a plane

cutting a cone makes a smaller angle with the axis than any of the elements, the line of intersection between the plane and the cone is known as a hyperbola. The hyperbola is a conic section (see Fig. 15-5*d*).

6-36. To construct a hyperbola (Fig. 6-35). The transverse axis *AB* and the foci *F*1 and *F*2 are given. With *F*1 as a center and a radius (greater than *F*1*B*) equal to *AC*, strike arcs at *D* and *E*. (*C* is one of a series of points selected on *AB* extended.) With *F*2 as a center and a radius equal to *BC*, strike arcs intersecting the other arcs at points *D* and *E*. These two points are on the hyperbola. By repeating this procedure, enough points may be secured to permit the drawing of the smooth curve of the hyperbola. Points *L* and *H* on the transverse axis were used in locating points *J*, *K*, *M*, and *N* on the curve.

6-37. To draw a tangent to a hyperbola (Fig. 6-36). The hyperbola, the two foci, and the point

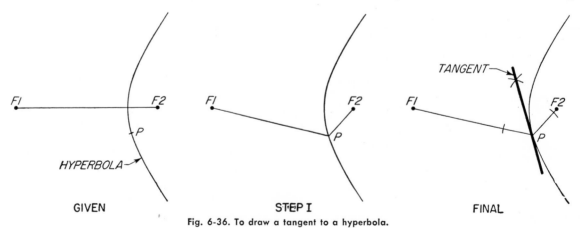

Fig. 6-36. To draw a tangent to a hyperbola.

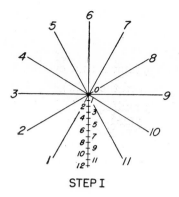

STEP I

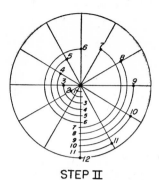

STEP II

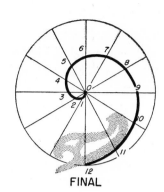

FINAL

Fig. 6-37. To draw a spiral of Archimedes.

P on the curve are given. Join the two foci *F*1 and *F*2 with *P*. The tangent to the hyperbola bisects the angle between the two focal radii *F*1*P* and *F*2*P*, which intersect at the point of tangency *P*.

6-38. The construction of a spiral of Archimedes (Fig. 6-37). If a point moves about a fixed point (the pole) and away from it in such a manner that its distance increases uniformly with the angle, the curve developed by its path produces a spiral of Archimedes. Start at the pole, point *O*, and lay out equal angles of, say, 30°, represented by the radial lines *O*-1, *O*-2, *O*-3, etc. On one of the radial lines lay out equal distances representing the movement of the point. Twelve angles require twelve equal distances. Rotate the distances on the radial line to the corresponding position on the angle line as shown in Step II. After locating the points, use the french curve for completion of the curve.

6-39. To draw the involute of a polygon (Fig.

6-38). An involute is the path made by a point on a taut string as it unwinds from a geometric shape such as a circle or polygon. In Step I extend the side *AB* of the polygon *ABCD*. With *A* as a center and side *AD* as a radius, strike an arc that intersects *AB* extended at 1. With *B* as a center and *B*1 as a radius, strike an arc intersecting *BC* extended at 2. Continue the procedure until all four points have been located, and then draw in the curve. The first radius is always equal to the length of the side of the polygon where the operation is started. Each succeeding arc always starts at the termination of the previously drawn arc, and has a radius equal to the distance from the end of the preceding arc to the furthest extremity of the side.

6-40. To draw the involute of an arc (Fig. 6-39). The arc *AB* is given. Divide *AB* into a convenient number of parts and number the points as shown. Draw a tangent to each division point.

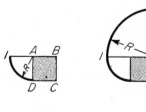

STEP I

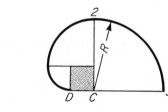

STEP II

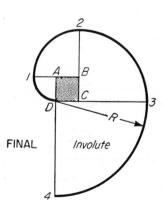

STEP III

FINAL

Involute

Fig. 6-38. To draw the involute of a polygon.

Mark off on each tangent the length of the corresponding arc (the distances O-1, O-2, O-3 etc.). A french curve will aid in securing a smooth line through the points that form the involute.

6-41. To draw the involute of a circle (Fig. 6-40).
Divide the circumference of the circle into any number of equal parts. Draw the tangents to the circle at these division points. Mark off on each tangent the length of the corresponding arc and then proceed as outlined in the preceding section.

6-42. The construction of a cycloid (Fig. 6-41).
The curve generated by a point on the circumference of a circle as the circle rolls on a plane along a straight line is known as a cycloid. Given the circle (moving toward the right) and its path, line AB, tangent to it and equal in length to the circumference of the circle. Divide the circumference and the line into the same number of equal parts. Draw the center line CL parallel to AB. Extend the numbered points on AB perpendicularly

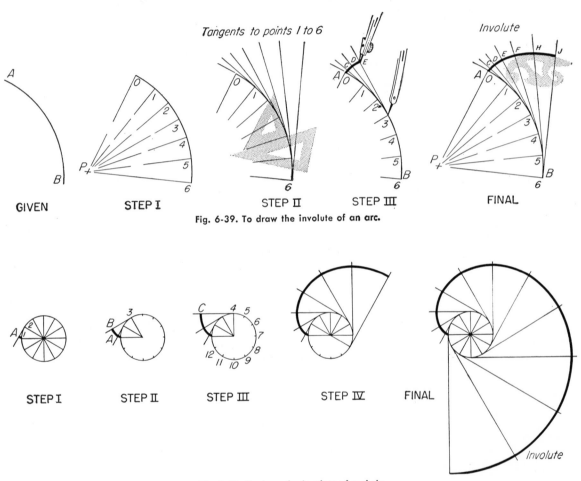

Fig. 6-39. To draw the involute of an arc.

Fig. 6-40. To draw the involute of a circle.

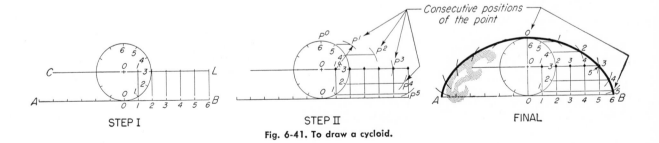

Fig. 6-41. To draw a cycloid.

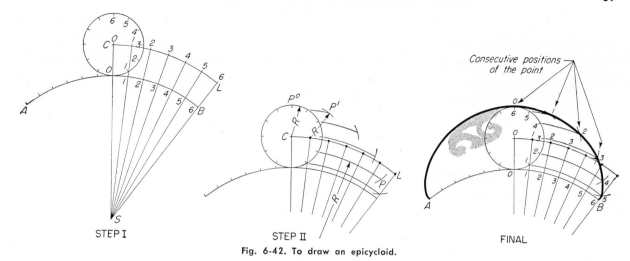

STEP I STEP II FINAL

Fig. 6-42. To draw an epicycloid.

to CL. Draw lines parallel to AB through the points on the circle. (These points represent successive positions of the original starting point P^0.) From the points located on CL and with a radius equal to the radius of the circle, strike arcs intersecting the parallel lines at points P^1, P^2, P^3, P^4, and P^5, with point B locating the final position of the point P when it touches the line. When the center of the circle has reached point 1 on CL, point P has reached P^1 on the cycloid, etc. Draw a smooth curve through the points. Repeat the process for the portion on the left to complete the cycloid.

6-43. The construction of an epicycloid (Fig. 6-42). The curve generated by a point on the circumference of a circle as the circle rolls on a plane on the circumference of another circle is known as an epicycloid. The construction necessary is similar to that used for the cycloid. Line AB, a part of the circumference of a large circle, is equal in length to the circumference of the small circle. The small circle is divided into the same number of parts as AB, its path. The circular center line CL is drawn through C. Radial lines are drawn from S, the center of the large circle, through the points on AB to locate the points on CL that show the successive positions of the center of the small circle. With S as a center, swing circular arcs through the points 1, 2, 3, etc., on the small circle. With the points on CL as centers and radii equal to the radius of the small circle, strike arcs intersecting those just previously drawn. The intersections of these arcs outline the form of the epicycloid.

6-44. The construction of a hypocycloid (Fig. 6-43). The curve generated by a point on the circumference of a circle as the circle rolls on a plane on the inside of another circle is called a hypocycloid. To draw the hypocycloid, follow the same general procedure used in the construction of the epicycloid.

6-45. The helix. The helix traces the curved path of a point as it revolves uniformly in both directions, around and up or down, on the surface of a cylinder or a cone. The *lead* is the vertical distance between the starting and finishing points after one complete revolution. It is always measured parallel to the axis of the cone or cylinder. When the word helix is used alone, it always refers to a cylindrical helix. The helix of a

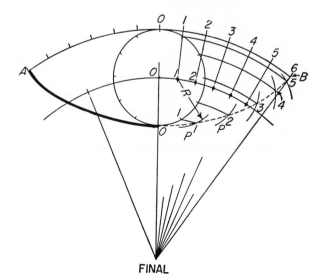

FINAL

Fig. 6-43. To draw a hypocycloid.

cone form is always referred to as a conical helix.

6-46. To draw a helix (Fig. 6-44). Draw the profile front view and the circular half top view of the cylinder. Divide the circular view into a convenient number of parts (say, 12) to locate the base points for the elements that will show the successive positions of the generating point as it moves around the cylinder. (In the half top view shown in the illustration only 7 points are shown, since the other five would project on points already indicated by numbers 2, 3, 4, 5, and 6.) Divide and number the lead (shown in the front view along the left extreme element) into the same number of 12 parts. These show the successive positions of the point as it moves upward parallel to the axis of the cylinder. Since the generating point will move across one unit as it moves upward one unit, projection of the points on the lead to intersect the same numbered elements will locate the points that trace the curved path of the helix. The development of the surface of the cylinder will show the helix as a straight line. Notice that the path of the conical helix (top view, Fig. 6-44b) resembles the spiral of Archimedes (Fig. 6-37).

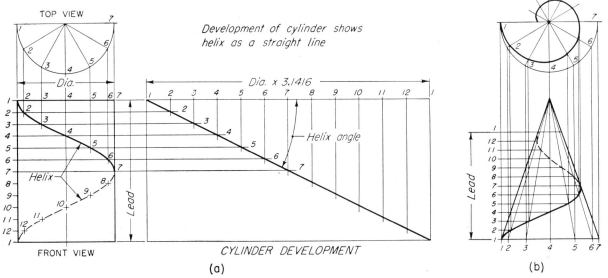

Fig. 6-44. (a) To draw the cylindrical helix. (b) To draw the conical helix.

PROBLEMS

The following problems are intended to give the student practice in applying the geometrical constructions discussed in this chapter and to help him to become familiar with the use of the drawing instruments. All drawings should be executed with utmost accuracy, and the line work must conform to the alphabet of lines as shown in Fig. 4-6. Problems 6-1 to 6-6 and 6-7 to 6-10 are located as shown on the standard 8½- by 11-in. sheet, and all dimensions are to be omitted. All other problems are also drawn on an 8½- by 11-in. sheet. Construction lines should be very lightly drawn. Points of tangency should be marked with a ⅛-in. line drawn across the points. Show all dimensions except those that serve to locate the views on the drawing sheet.

6-1. Bisect the given line.

6-2. Bisect the given angle.

6-3. Divide the given line into five equal parts.

6-4. Construct a triangle of the three given lines.

6-5. Construct a regular hexagon within the given 2-in. circle.

6-6. Construct a regular pentagon with the given 1-in. line as the length of one of its sides. (Total time for Probs. 6-1 to 6-6: 3 hr.)

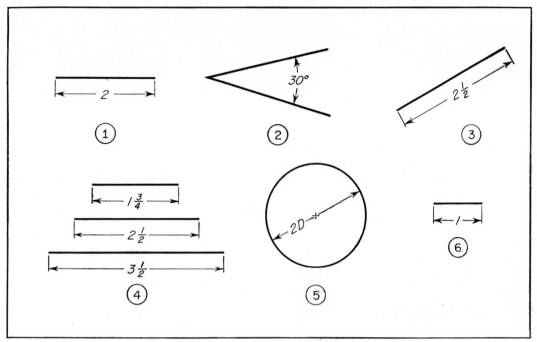

Probs. 6-1 to 6-6.

6-7. Divide the area of the given triangle into five equal parts.

6-8. Construct a line tangent to the given arc from the given point *x*.

6-9. Construct a line tangent to the two given circles.

6-10. Construct an ellipse with the given long and short diameters. (Total time for Probs. 6-7 to 6-10: 2 hr.)

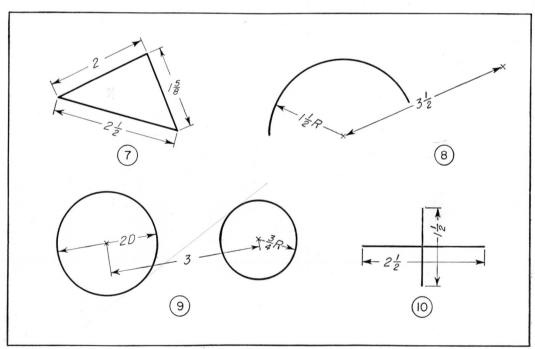

Probs. 6-7 to 6-10.

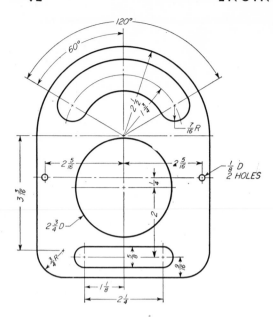

Prob. 6-11. Meter Cover.

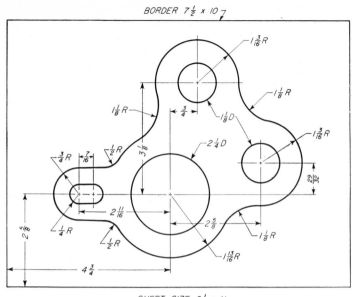

SHEET SIZE 8½ x 11
Prob. 6-12. Gasket.

6-11. *Meter cover.* Redraw the given view in its entirety. (Time: 2 hr.)

6-12. *Gasket.* Redraw the gasket shown in the figure. (Time: 3 hr.)

6-13. *Gasket.* Redraw the given view. (Time: 2½ hr.)

6-14. *Gasket.* Redraw the given view. (Time: 3 hr.)

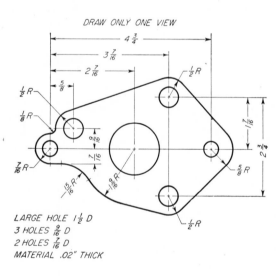

Prob. 6-13. Gasket.

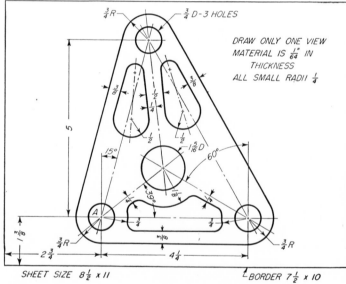

SHEET SIZE 8½ x 11
Prob. 6-14. Gasket.

6-15. *Adjusting center device.* Redraw the given view. (Time: 3 hr.)

6-16. *Adjusting fork.* Redraw the given view. (Time: 2½ hr.)

6-17. *Radio dial.* Redraw the given view. (Time: 5 hr.)

6-18. *Heart cam.* Redraw the given front and side views of the cam. (Time: 2 hr.)

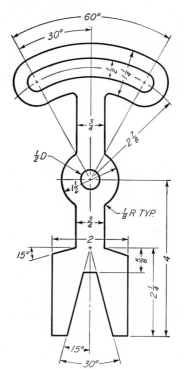

Prob. 6-16. Adjusting fork.

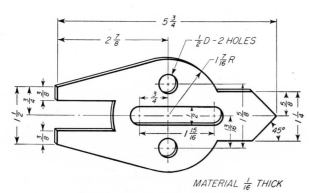

MATERIAL 1/16 THICK

Prob. 6-15. Adjusting center device.

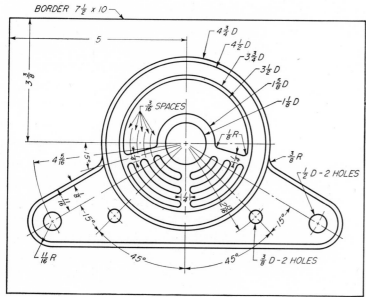

Prob. 6-17. Radio dial.

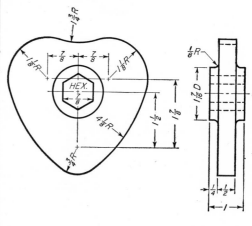

Prob. 6-18. Heart cam.

Chapter 7

SHOP PROCESSES

In order to prepare working drawings that can be readily followed by the workmen in the shop, the draftsman should be familiar with the various shop processes and equipment. An accurate knowledge of the operations performed in the pattern, foundry, forge, and machine shops will frequently enable the draftsman to simplify the worker's job by means of helpful notes concerning the particular tools required and the manner in which they should be used. The most successful drawings are those in which the manufacturing requirements have been carefully analyzed, the proper and sufficient number of views have been selected, and well-chosen dimensions and explicit notes have been supplied so as to allow the shop men to perform the necessary operations with a minimum of time, labor, and material. Whenever the draftsman is positive of the operation or procedure employed in the development or manufacture of a part, he should give such information as part of the dimensioning notes. The draftsman should always keep in mind the manufacturing processes required as he develops the notes.

Although a complete understanding of the various manufacturing procedures is obtainable only through actual experience in the shop, a description of the different processes will serve to familiarize the draftsman with the methods employed and allow him to prepare his drawings with an understanding of the basic principles involved in the manufacturing process.

Most manufactured objects and machine parts are produced by one of the following basic processes: casting, machining, forging, welding, or forming. Each process produces characteristic properties, and the manufacturing method selected is therefore directly related to the design of the part and the function it is to serve. Each of these manufacturing operations gives a distinctive appearance to a part, and these distinguishing features are shown on the drawings the draftsman prepares. Sometimes these features are shown in the line work of the drawing, but more often they appear in the dimensioning and notes describing the part.

Special drawings are sometimes prepared for the different procedures of planning, estimating, patternmaking, casting, welding, forging, machining, and assembling. However, a single general-purpose detail drawing in combination with an explicit assembly drawing can often give the necessary information for the performance of all these tasks provided that the various operations and procedures in manufacture are specifically indicated as part of the dimensioning notes.

7-1. Castings. Castings are made by the cooling of molten metal in a specially constructed mold that has been made in the shape of the desired part. There are three basic casting processes: sand casting, permanent-mold casting, and die casting. Parts made of cast iron, steel, or alloys of the nonferrous metals are produced by sand casting, while the white metals (aluminum, zinc, etc.) and copper alloys are generally produced by permanent-mold casting or by die casting. In sand and permanent-mold casting the molten material is poured freely into the forming mold; in die casting the molten metal is forced into a mold or "die" under great pressure, which is maintained until the material has cooled and hardened.

7-2. Patterns and the pattern shop. Before a mold can be constructed, a pattern (which is really a model of the object) must be made in the pattern shop (see Fig. 7-1). Patterns are generally made from the soft woods. If they are to be used repeatedly (as in permanent-mold casting) they are made of zinc, aluminum, or plastic. In the preparation of the pattern, a slight taper is given to all surfaces to permit its easy removal from the mold. The pattern is also made slightly larger than the final desired size of the casting in order to allow for shrinkage of the cooling metal and for the machining of surfaces. Cast iron may shrink as

much as ⅛ in. per ft although 1/16 in. allowance is usually sufficient for small pieces. Shrinkage in white metals varies but is less than that of the ferrous metals. Allowance for shrinkage is taken care of by the patternmaker and is not the concern of the draftsman. Occasionally the draftsman may prepare a drawing especially for the patternmaker's use, although in most instances the standard detail drawing will suffice.

When only a few castings are required, a single-piece pattern, or "loose pattern," is prepared. The most common and the easiest pattern to work with is the "split pattern," which is made in two halves. If the object is complicated, the pattern may consist of a group of partial patterns combined with "match plates" that serve as a framework that holds the partial patterns together in proper relation to one another. This type is known as a "match-plate pattern." The material of which the casting is to be made and the number of castings required generally govern the type of pattern that should be constructed.

7-3. Molding. Molding is usually done in a sand base, although plaster, steel, wood, and paper may also be used. Where great accuracy is desired, either permanent-mold casting or die casting is employed. These processes produce castings with smoother surfaces and more accurate dimensions,

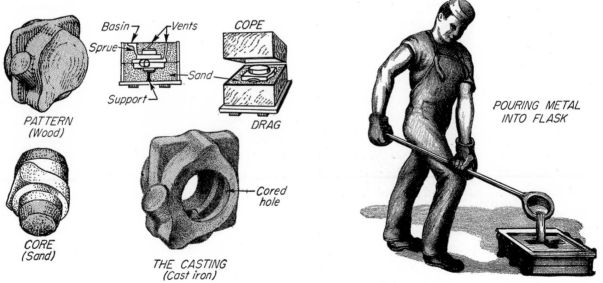

PATTERN
(Wood)

Basin   Vents   COPE
Sprue
Sand
Support   DRAG

CORE
(Sand)

THE CASTING
(Cast iron)

Cored hole

POURING METAL
INTO FLASK

Fig. 7-1. Sand casting: the pattern, mold, core, and casting.

and thus fewer machining operations are required to finish the product (Fig. 7-2). Permanent molds and dies are most often made of metal. They are used many times over and are expensive to produce. Sand casting is better adapted to a great many objects and is particularly suitable when the object to be cast contains a great many holes and other voids that require coring. Any product that can be cast can also be produced by forging.

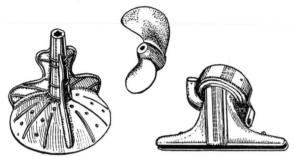

Fig. 7-2. Permanent mold and die castings.

In sand molding, the body of the mold is made with what is known as *green sand,* which is a mixture of silica sand, clay, and water that is allowed to air-harden. Castings often contain holes or voids that are usually produced by *cores.* Cores are made with *dry sand,* a mixture of silica sand and linseed oil that is baked for extra hardness. The pattern is placed in a *flask,* which is the metal box that holds the green sand. It is usually made in two parts, the upper part being called the *cope* and the lower part the *drag.* Additional pieces may be placed between the cope and the drag for more complicated work.

After the green sand has hardened slightly, the pattern is removed from the flask. If the casting is to contain holes, hard dry-sand cores of the proper shape are set in position in the green-sand mold. The metal is then poured into the remaining void. When the metal has hardened completely, the flask is opened to reveal the sand-encased casting. The sand is broken, air-blasted, and washed from the surfaces of the casting. Upon inspection, a casting will always reveal various surface imperfections occurring at seams, at points where the metal has been poured (*gates*), at air and gas escape vents (*risers*), at air pockets, etc. The larger excess metal

formations may be removed on a band saw or with the chisel of a pneumatic chipping hammer, Fig. 7-3. Smaller surface imperfections may be smoothed down with portable abrasive wheels.

Fig. 7-3. The pneumatic chipping hammer.

7-4. Fillets and rounds. In making a casting, the natural tendency of metal is to draw away from sharp corners during the cooling process and to leave a round edge instead. The rounded intersection of surfaces at an inside corner is called a *fillet;* the rounded intersection of surfaces at an outside corner is known as a *round* (see Fig. 4-14). Properly proportioned fillets and rounds are desirable features in a casting since they provide greater strength than sharp edges and permit ease of handling. Rounding of corners may also be intentionally formed on the pattern by the patternmaker to permit easy handling of the finished product (see Secs. 4-14 and 4-15).

7-5. Machine-shop processes. The draftsman should become thoroughly familiar with the various machine-shop operations, and the machines on which they are performed, because in dimensioning a part the draftsman frequently must specify the exact operation required. Although there are a great many different operations employed in the machine shop, in general, machining processes may be classified as those that (1) make holes, (2) remove metal, (3) shape to close accuracy, or (4) further refine surfaces by the use of manual or power-driven tools.

A few common machining operations and the tools that perform them are shown in Fig. 7-4. In the sections that follow, the important machine-shop processes are discussed in detail.

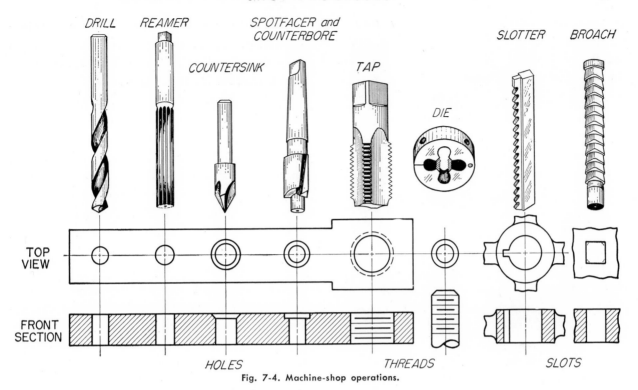

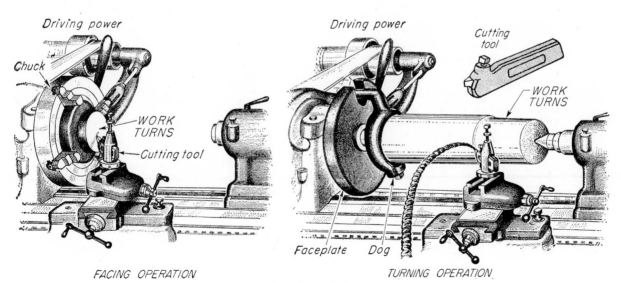

Fig. 7-4. Machine-shop operations.

7-6. Facing and turning. Facing and turning are operations that are performed on the lathe. Usually, in the operation of a lathe, the piece to be worked is held and turned by a rotating vise called a *chuck,* and the metal is removed by a non-rotating cutter. When the cutter moves perpendicular to the axis of the workpiece, the operation is known as *facing;* when it moves parallel to the workpiece axis, the operation is called *turning* (see Fig. 7-5).

7-7. Drilling. Drilling may be accomplished on a lathe or a milling machine, but the drill press is the machine designed for this operation. In this machine the tool turns and can be raised and lowered while the work is held in a fixed position (see Figs. 7-4 and 7-6).

Fig. 7-5. The lathe.

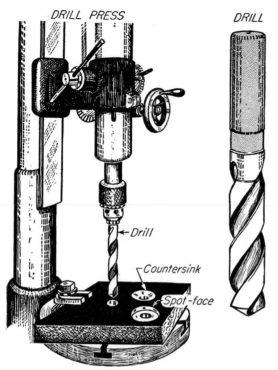

DRILL PRESS

DRILL

←Drill

←Countersink

←Spot-face

WORK REMAINS FIXED

Fig. 7-6. The drill press.

hole, boring should be indicated when great accuracy is required. The boring of small holes can be accomplished on a lathe (Fig. 7-7). A boring mill is used for the larger tasks.

7-10. Milling. Milling-machine operations are among the most comprehensive accomplished in a machine shop. Gear cutting and shaping are perhaps the most common jobs done on a milling machine. The milling-machine cutter is usually shaped to the desired appearance of the cut required and it turns until the cut is completed. The work is then moved to the next position for the succeeding cutting operation (see Fig. 7-8).

7-11. Shaping. This operation is performed on a machine called a *shaper*. The work is surfaced by a reciprocating cutting tool that moves at regular intervals across the face of the material that is being shaped. The work remains stationary while the cutting tool is engaged, but it can be raised toward the tool if a second or third operation is required (see Fig. 7-9).

7-8. Reaming. Drilled holes are rarely absolutely straight, cylindrical, or accurate in size. To "true" them they are reamed out by a tool that removes the riflings left by the drill. This operation can be performed on any machine that can be used for drilling (see Fig. 7-4).

7-9. Boring. Because reaming does not always "true" the straightness or roundness of a drilled

7-12. Planing. Large or heavy surfacing operations are accomplished on a planer (Fig. 7-10). The work is fastened to a reciprocating table that passes beneath a cutting tool that is fed into the material as the operation progresses. Some planers have cutting tools mounted at various positions on their large frames that can perform other machining operations. The planer and the shaper are designed primarily for cutting plane surfaces, however.

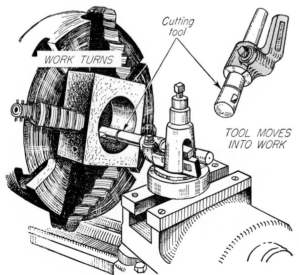

WORK TURNS

Cutting tool

TOOL MOVES INTO WORK

Fig. 7-7. Boring on a lathe.

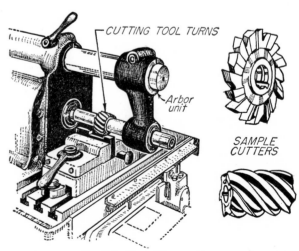

CUTTING TOOL TURNS

Arbor unit

SAMPLE CUTTERS

Fig. 7-8. The milling machine.

7-13. Broaching. Broaching is a single-stroke operation used to cut keyways and square, hexagonal, and other shaped holes (see Fig. 7-4). The cutting tool, called a broach, is either pushed or pulled through the workpiece, and it bites deeper into the metal with each succeeding tooth. A previously drilled or cored hole must be prepared, and a special machine that produces precision results is needed for this rapid operation.

7-14. Threading. Threads are cut on a milling machine or a lathe, or by the use of collapsible or fixed taps and dies (see Fig. 7-4). Expediency and sometimes the material to be worked suggests the best method. The screw thread is one of the important fastener devices. It is made by a turning operation, and when cut on the lathe the work turns while the tool moves parallel to the axis of the material. When additional cuts are required, the tool is moved perpendicular to this axis to the depth of the next required cut, and then it moves parallel to the axis to finish the operation. If taps and dies are employed, the work usually remains in a fixed position.

7-15. Grinding. This operation, intended to bring surfaces to a fine finish, is accomplished by the removal of a very small amount of the material

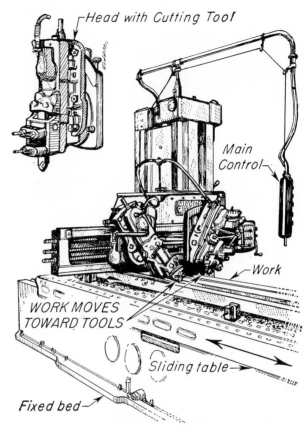

Fig. 7-10. The planer.

as both the work and the grinder turn at high speeds, or as the grinder wheel turns while the work is moved only at intervals. Grinding machines fall into four groups known as surface, cylindrical, tool, and centerless grinders (see Fig. 7-11).

7-16. Sawing. Sawing operations must often be performed on rods, bars, or thick flat pieces to cut them to the desired size as preparation for later machining operations with other tools. If the pieces are small, a hand hacksaw may be used. If many

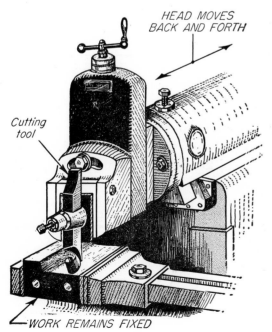

Fig. 7-9. The shaper.

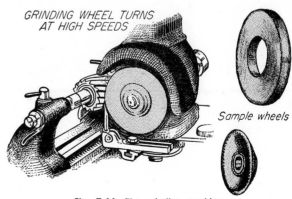

Fig. 7-11. The grinding machine.

Fig. 7-12. High-speed friction saw.

pieces are to be cut, hand-sawing can be a time-consuming and expensive operation. Therefore, large or numerous pieces are more economically handled by using a power-driven metal-sawing machine of the circular, reciprocating, or band types. Figure 7-12 shows a power-driven circular saw in which the work is clamped between the viselike jaws on the bed and is fed into a toothed disk which revolves at a speed selected for the material being worked.

7-17. Shearing. The simple trimming, slitting, and parting operations may be performed with a tinner's shears or a power-driven machine having cutting features similar to the one shown in Fig. 7-13. Certain other operations, where machines equipped with specially shaped dies that are forced through thin material to stamp out or "shear" required designs are used, may be included, in a broader sense, under this heading.

7-18. Rolling. Sheet metal may be rolled on hand-operated or power-driven machines designed to produce cylindrical forms such as cans, pails,

drums, corrugations, etc. The roll forming machine in Fig. 7-14 is manipulated by hand. Its forming mechanism consists of three rollers, two of which lie in a horizontal and parallel position, while the third rests above the lower two. The sheet metal is fed between the upper and one of the lower rollers and as the metal moves through the machine it is shaped by the action and pressure of the other lower roller. A complete cylindrical form will encircle the upper roller. It is removed from the machine by removing both the roller and the formed metal.

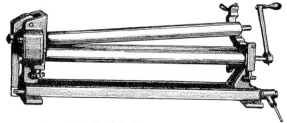

Fig. 7-14. Roll forming machine.

7-19. Folding and bending. Sheet metal is folded or bent in a simply constructed machine consisting of two flat metal straight-edges placed one above the other (see Fig. 7-15). The upper straightedge blade remains fixed, while the lower one, the jaw, bends or folds the material over the blade edge when force is applied by means of a geared hand-manipulated transmission. Flanging, seaming, and crimping are performed on special hand-manipulated or power-driven tools, but may be classified as rolling, folding, and bending operations.

7-20. Punching. Many of the large tools found in a quantity-production machine shop can be adapted to a number of different operations. The punch press, for example, is a machine that may be used for bending, folding, seaming, cupping, embossing, flattening, riveting, shearing,

Fig. 7-13. Heavy-duty shears.

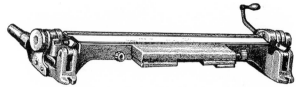

Fig. 7-15. Folding and bending machine.

notching, punching, and many other tasks which depend upon the selection of a suitable combination of punches and dies. In the operation of the punch press, the die rests on the press bed and the material is placed on it. The punch, which is fastened to the head, is lowered and forced against (or through) the material while the die cavity transmits its shape to the work. To ensure successful operation, the tool and die must be firmly attached to the machine frame and in perfect alignment with each other. Figure 7-16 shows a heavy-duty punch press.

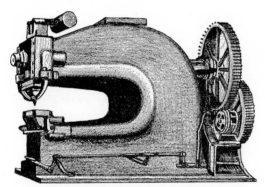

Fig. 7-16. Geared punch press.

7-21. Lapping. If very accurate fits are required, lapping will serve to bring the mating surfaces to a true finish. In this process a very fine abrasive is mixed with oil or kerosene and applied to the mating surfaces. The adjacent parts are then rubbed together until the desired smoothness and fit are obtained.

7-22. Honing. Honing is similar to the sharpening of a razor. An extremely fine abrasive is applied to the finishing tool which often takes the shape of the form that is to be finished. For example, the honing tool used to finish automobile block cylinders resembles a piston on which an abrasive material has been mounted. A very fine smooth finish is the result of a honing operation.

7-23. Buffing. Buffing is primarily a cleaning process. The pliable buffing-wheel surface is covered with wax and soft abrasives. As the work is pressed against the wheel, the high spots are smoothed down and the surface is given a glossy finish. Not enough material is removed to bring

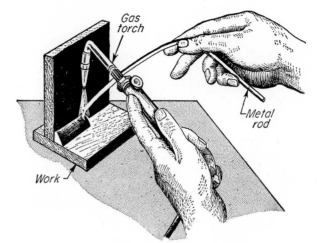

Fig. 7-17. Gas welding—hand technique.

about the accurate finish desired for machine parts.

7-24. Welding. The draftsman may be called upon to show welded forms. Welding brings about the permanent joining of several pieces of metal and is one of the most effective ways of obtaining gas or liquid-tight seams. In the simplest procedure an acetylene or hydrogen flame is used as the heating agent and a suitable filler material is required. No pressure is needed to bring the forms together (see Figs. 7-17 and 7-18).

Fig. 7-18. Hand torch welding.

Seam and spot welding are examples of electric resistance welding (see Fig. 7-19). These methods are ideally suited to the fabrication of small subassemblies that can be handled by one or two operators. The electric current passing through the welding electrodes brings the material to the fusion point. Pressure is then applied and the parts are permanently joined. Electric welding results in

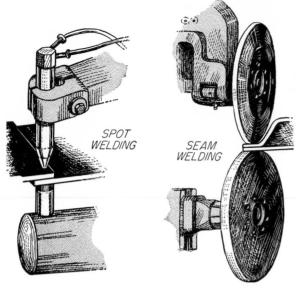

Fig. 7-19. Electric resistance welding.

7-25. Forging. The aforementioned operations, with the exception of welding, are classified as cold-working processes. Forging, however, may be accomplished by either cold- or hot-working the material. A press or heavy hammer (Fig. 7-20) is used to exert great pressure and to force the metal to "flow" into the desired shape. The use of dies depends on the type of forming desired. Few metals lend themselves to cold forming because of the breakdown of the basic structure of the component elements while being forced into shape; consequently most forging is done with hot or molten metal. Forgings are classified as drop, press, extrusion, smith, and machine forgings, according to the type of forging press used.

7-26. Jigs and fixtures. These special tools are useful in operations of many kinds, especially in the manufacture of duplicate or interchangeable parts. They facilitate production and lead to economical use of time and manpower. A jig is a device that both holds the work and guides the tool (see Figs. 7-21 and 7-22). A fixture (Fig. 7-23) simply holds the part as it is being worked. Most jigs and fixtures found in small shops are of the type shown in Figs. 7-21 and 7-23 and are usually employed in the cutting operations such as drilling and reaming. In the very large manufacturing plants the

smoother finishes than gas welding or riveting, and in many cases proves more economical.

See Secs. 13-31 to 13-34 for a more detailed discussion of welding, types of welds, and welding symbols.

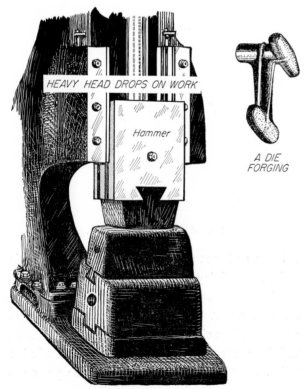

Fig. 7-20. Forging press.

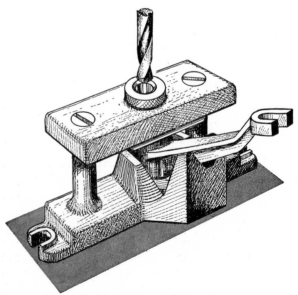

Fig. 7-21. A drill jig.

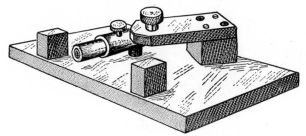

Fig. 7-22. Jig used on an automatic machine.

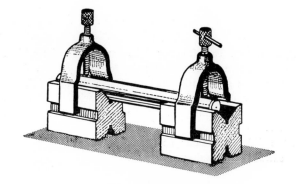

Fig. 7-23. Fixtures.

terms jigs and fixtures would also refer to the huge tooling docks and other directing and positioning structures necessary to the manufacture of large and complicated units and assemblies.

7-27. Automatic machines. Practically all the operations mentioned in the preceding sections in this chapter can be performed in any well-organized jobbing shop. When great numbers of the same pieces are required, the task of producing them is accomplished with greater all-around economy in the large production shops, where many complicated jigs, fixtures, and automatic machines, such as turret lathes, multiple-spindle drills, and automatic screw machines, are usually assembled under the one management. The special machines perform certain particular operations without the necessity of being under constant surveillance or requiring continuous manipulation by the worker.

7-28. Measuring tools. The draftsman must keep in mind that although the man in the shop tries to work as accurately as possible, no job is

ever exact or perfect. To aid the worker to reach near-perfection he has available various types of gages that enable him to check his dimensions while the work is in progress. If required, air and light gages will point out errors of a hundred-thousandth or even a millionth of an inch. For ordinary precision work, however, it is permissible to maintain tolerances to thousandths or ten-thousandths of an inch. Some of the simpler measuring devices are shown in Fig. 7-24. Most measuring tools have a scale by means of which the dimensions can be read directly; when this is not the case, the settings can be referred to a separate scale for the readings.

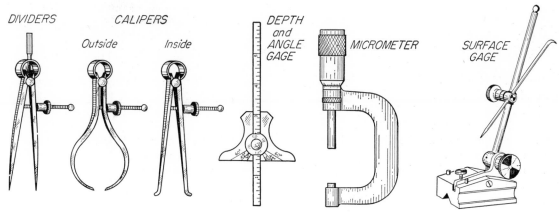

Fig. 7-24. Measuring tools.

GLOSSARY OF COMMON SHOP TERMS

Anneal (*v*). To soften metal by heating it to its critical temperature and allowing it to cool slowly. This operation removes internal stresses in the material.

Bore (*v*). To enlarge or "true" a hole with the use of a boring bar mounted on a lathe or boring mill. See Fig. 7-7.

Boss (*n*). A circular projection extending beyond the surface of a casting or forging.

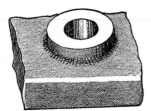

Boss

Braze (*v*). To join together by a hard solder usually consisting of a copper and zinc alloy.

Broach (*n*). A cutting tool with transverse serrated edges that is pushed or pulled in a hole to cut it to a desired shape. See Fig. 7-4.

(*v*). Machining or enlarging a hole to a desired shape, usually other than round.

Buff (*v*). To smooth and polish with a soft wheel carrying an abrasive.

Burnish (*v*). To smooth to a brilliant finish with a tool applied with great pressure.

Bushing (*n*). A cylindrical sleeve that serves as a bearing surface or as a guide for a tool in a jig or fixture.

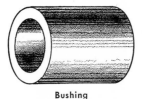

Bushing

Carburize (*v*). To harden the surface of a soft steel by heating in carbonizing material and permitting to cool slowly.

Caseharden (*v*). To harden a carburized steel by heating and quenching in oil or lead.

Chamfer (*v*). To bevel an external edge.

(*n*). A beveled edge or corner. See Fig. 8-27a.

Chase (*v*). To cut threads on a lathe with a tool shaped to form the desired thread.

Chill (*v*). To harden the surface of cast iron by placing in contact with a cool mold.

Chip (*v*). To cut, trim, or clean with a chisel. See Fig. 7-3.

Coin (*v*). To stamp into shape with the use of a design-containing die.

Core (*v*). To form the hollow parts of a casting by using a sand core that is easily broken away after the casting has cooled. See Fig. 7-1.

Counterbore (*v*). To enlarge the end of a drilled or bored hole to a certain depth. See also Fig. 7-4.

(*n*). The tool used for a counterboring operation. The pilot end is equal to the size of the hole to be enlarged.

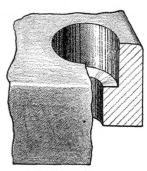

Counterbore

Countersink (*v*). To form a conical depression in a hole, usually to accommodate the head of a screw. See also Fig. 7-4.

(*n*). the conical tool used for this operation.

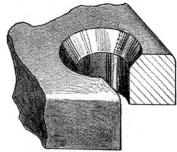

Countersink

Crown (*n*). The angular or rounded contour of a circular form as may be seen on the face of a pulley. See Fig. 8-30.

Die (*n*). A tool used for cutting external threads. See Fig. 7-4. A metal block used in forging and stamping operations to give the desired shape to the metal.

Die casting (*n*). A smooth and accurate casting produced by forcing molten metal between the two halves of a pair of dies.

Draw (*v*). To temper steel by quenching gradually or intermittently. To produce a desired shape in metal by stretching or distorting it.

Drill (*v*). To form a cylindrical hole in a part.

(*n*). A pointed cutting tool that produces a cylindrical hole as it is revolved under pressure. See Fig. 7-6.

Drop forging (*n*). A piece that has been shaped while hot between dies acted upon by a heavy hammer. See Fig. 7-20.

Face (*v*). To machine a flat surface on a piece as it turns in the headstock of a lathe or rests on the bed of a shaper. See Figs. 7-5 and 7-9.

Feather (*n*). A rectangular key which permits the hub to slide parallel to the axis of the shaft. See Fig. 13-31.

File (*v*). To cut, trim, shape, or finish by hand with a file.

Fillet (*n*). A rounded inside corner of a part tending to give added strength to the angle formed by the sides. See Fig. 4-14.

Fin (*n*). A thin projecting rib.

Fit (*n*). The tightness or looseness between the mating surfaces of mating parts.

Flange (*n*). The projecting rim, or edge, of a part that serves to strengthen it or permit connection to another part.

Flange

Forge (*v*). To shape hot or cold metal by hand or machine. See Fig. 7-20.

Galvanize (*v*). To coat with lead or zinc to prevent rusting.

Graduate (*v*). To mark off into measured intervals.

Grind (*v*). To bring to a smooth finish by means of an abrasive. See Fig. 7-11.

Kerf (*n*). A channel or groove.

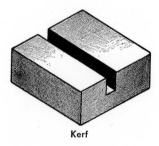

Kerf

Key (*n*). A wedge of any desired shape which prevents movement circumferentially between a hub and shaft. See Fig. 13-31.

Keyway or keyseat (*n*). The groove or slot in which the key is placed. The key slides in a keyway and rests in a keyseat. See Fig. 13-32.

Knurl (*v*). To roughen or score a cylindrical surface so that it may be more easily gripped by the hand. See Fig. 8-28.

Lap (*v*). To finish or polish with cloth, leather, or wood impregnated with abrasive material.

Lug (*n*). A projecting "ear" which permits attaching one part to another.

Lug

Malleable casting (*n*). A casting that has been toughened by annealing.

Mill (*v*). To machine with rotating cutters on a milling machine. See Fig. 7-8.

Neck (*n*). A groove cut into a shaft; often located at or near the point where the diameters change. See Fig. 8-27*a*.

Pack-harden (*v*). To carburize and caseharden.

Pad (*n*). A low projection usually rectangular in shape.

Pad

Peen (*v*). To expand or bend metal with the round head of a peen hammer.

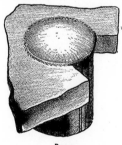

Peen

Pickle (*v*). To clean castings and forgings by immersing in a weak sulfuric acid bath.

Plane (*v*). To machine a flat surface on a planer. See Fig. 7-10.

Plate (*v*). To coat a metal with a thin layer of another.

Polish (*v*). To smooth and give luster to a surface by use of a very fine abrasive.

Punch (*v*). To perforate with a nonrotating tool.

Ream (v). To smooth or slightly enlarge a hole by the use of a fluted rotating tool of the required diameter. See Fig. 7-4.

Rivet (v). To fasten together with rivets. See Fig. 13-34.

Round (n). A rounded external corner at the intersection of two surfaces. See Fig. 4-14.

Sandblast (v). To clean a surface with sand blown through a nozzle under extremely high pressure.

Shape (v). To machine a surface with a shaper. See Fig. 7-9.

Shear (v). To cut off bar metal or sheet iron with a two-bladed shearing tool. See Fig. 7-13.

Shim (n). A thin piece of metal placed between surfaces for purposes of adjustment.

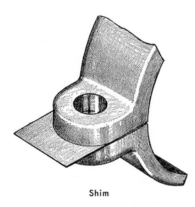

Shim

Spin (v). To shape sheet metal into a desired shape by forcing it against the shaping tool as it revolves.

Spline (v). A long keyway.

Splines

Spotface (v). To clean or indent a round finish on a hole to permit accurate seating of the head of a fastener. See also Fig. 7-4.

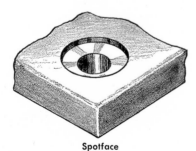

Spotface

Spot-weld (v). To weld in spots by means of electrodes employed in the electric resistance-welding processes. See Fig. 7-19.

Steel casting (n). A casting made of a suitable mixture of cast iron and scrap steel. See Fig. 7-1.

Swage (v). To shape or form metal by pressure or hammering with the aid of an anvil known as a "swage block."

Sweat (v). To join together by placing solder between the pieces and applying heat.

Tack-weld (n). A weld consisting of short and intermittent sections.

Tap (n). A tapered tool with fluted cutting edges for forming an internal thread. See Fig. 7-4.

(v). To cut internal threads with a tap.

Temper (v). To change the hardness of steel by reheating and permitting it to cool.

Template (n). A pattern that is used as a guide for tracing shapes, locating holes, etc.

Trepan (v). To cut an angular groove around a hole.

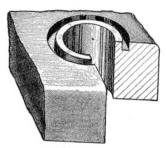

Trepan

Tumble (v). To clean and smooth castings through contact with each other while being spun in a drum containing scraps of other metals.

Turn (v). To machine on a lathe. See Fig. 7-5.

Undercut (v). To machine a part so as to provide an overhanging edge.

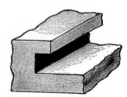

Undercut

Upset (v). A forging operation employed to enlarge a diameter or form a shoulder on a bar.

Weld (v). To join together by heating and pressing or by adding fusing material at the joint. See Fig. 7-18.

Chapter 8

DIMENSIONING

In our treatment of engineering drawing we have thus far been concerned primarily with means of representing the shape of an object. A description of shape is valueless, however, without proper and complete indication of size. The shopworker must know the exact length, height, and depth of a piece, the diameters and precise location of holes or shafts, the amount of tolerance that can be allowed in machining, and many other important details relating to the manufacture of the particular part shown in the drawing. Such information should be supplied by the draftsman on the drawing and is called *dimensioning*.

The shopworker is required to follow the instructions that appear on his working drawing and is limited to the tools and other facilities that are available to him in the shop. Therefore, the draftsman, as well as the engineer, should become thoroughly familiar with the materials used and the fundamental processes of construction and manufacturing, for the essence of proper dimensioning stems from an intimate knowledge of the methods employed in making and assembling the parts. Much valuable information on manufacturing operations can be found in books and periodicals, but observation and practical experience in a shop are an even better source.

If the draftsman keeps in mind the shop processes that will be used in the manufacture of a part, its machining requirements, and its manner of assembly with mating parts, he may, through skilled dimensioning, reduce the number of operations needed. Careful dimensioning will also help to ensure fabrication of the piece exactly as intended by the designer and the draftsman. A properly dimensioned drawing should make it possible for each worker to complete his own specialized task without the necessity of making calculations, attempting to scale the drawing, or calling on his associates for suggestions and assumptions concerning missing information or dimensions. A common error of the beginning draftsman is to show the dimensions he used to make his drawing instead of those necessary for the fabrication of the part.

8-1. Dimensioning elements: The dimension line. Figure 8-1 illustrates the basic dimensioning elements and how they are commonly used. Since dimensions must not be placed on the outlines of the object being drawn, distances or angles that are to be measured are indicated by dimension lines. The dimension line is light and firm and is broken at or near the center to allow for the insertion of the dimension figures. In structural prac-

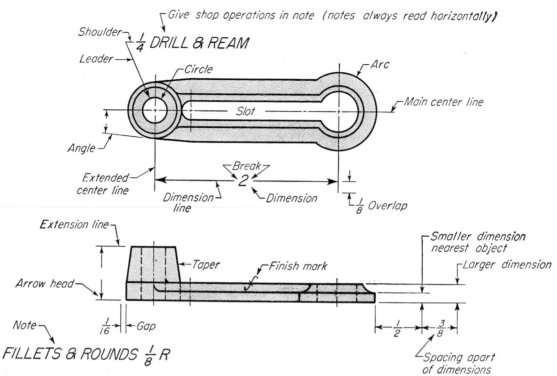

Fig. 8-1. Dimensioning elements.

tice, and at times in architectural drawing, dimension line is left unbroken while figures are placed above it. Dimension lines should not cross, or cross extension lines, unless absolutely necessary. Never use center lines as dimension lines.

8-2. Extension lines. Extension lines are thin unbroken lines used to indicate the extremities of the distance measured by the dimension line. An extension line does not touch the outline of the feature from which it extends but starts about $\frac{1}{16}$ from it and reaches to a point about $\frac{1}{8}$ in. beyond the last dimension line. Extension lines may cross an outline line of the object or another exten-

sion line wherever necessary (see Fig. 8-30, for example). Whenever practicable extension lines should extend beyond the outlines of the part to allow for dimensioning outside the view (see Fig. 8-34). Center lines representing the axes of symmetrical features, holes, etc., may be extended as necessary to serve as extension lines.

8-3. Arrowheads. The dimension line terminates in arrowheads that touch the extension lines. An arrowhead should be drawn freehand with two concave strokes made in the direction of the point (see Fig. 8-2). The length may vary from $\frac{1}{8}$ in. on small drawings to $\frac{3}{16}$ in. on larger ones. The width of the base of the arrowhead should be approximately one-third the length. Arrowheads should be drawn the same size throughout a drawing, except in restricted spaces where they may have to be made smaller.

8-4. Dimension figures. The dimension figure is placed in the break of the dimension line, as shown in Fig. 8-2. Note that the numerals in the numerator and denominator of the fraction are smaller than the whole number, but that the overall height of the fraction is twice that of the whole

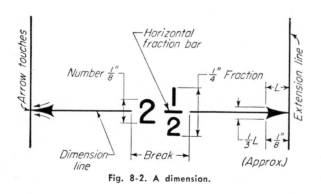

Fig. 8-2. A dimension.

number. In general, when all dimensions are given in inches, the inch mark (") is omitted entirely.

8-5. Notes. Instructions and basic information relating to the manufacture of a part that are not put in the title block or record strip are included on the drawing as notes. General notes, such as "Fillets and Rounds ⅛" or "Finish All Over," are placed along the lower border of the drawing sheet or are centered below the view to which they pertain. Notes relating to specific operations, such as "¼ Drill and Ream" or "Chamfer ⅛ × 45°," are called local notes and should be placed adjacent to the features to which they apply and be connected to them by leaders. Notes should always be placed to read horizontally. The width of the letter strokes of a note or dimension should be slightly finer than the outline of the object. Figure 8-17 shows a number of typical notes used in dimensioning holes.

8-6. Leaders. The leader is a fine line that extends from a dimension number or note toward the form to which it applies, where it ends in an arrowhead that touches the outline (see Fig. 8-3).

At the figure or note end, the leader terminates with a shoulder about ⅛ in. long which should lie even with an imaginary mid-line drawn through the figure or note and 1/16 in. from it. If the leader extends from a lengthy note, the shoulder should start at the mid-height of the first or last line, never from the middle. There should be about 1/16 in. space between the shoulder end of the leader and the note or dimension.

Curved leaders should never be used on engineering drawings. Also, to avoid confusion with lines of the object, leaders are never drawn horizontally or vertically. Instead, angles of 30°, 45°, 60°, etc., should be used, as shown in Fig. 8-3. As a general rule, leaders should never cross.

8-7. Finish marks. In dimensioning a drawing, the draftsman should mark all surfaces of a casting or forging that are to be machined. In addition to indicating the machining operation, finish marks suggest to the patternmaker where to provide extra metal on the rough casting or forging to allow for the finishing process. Figure 8-4 shows the two types of finish marks in use and

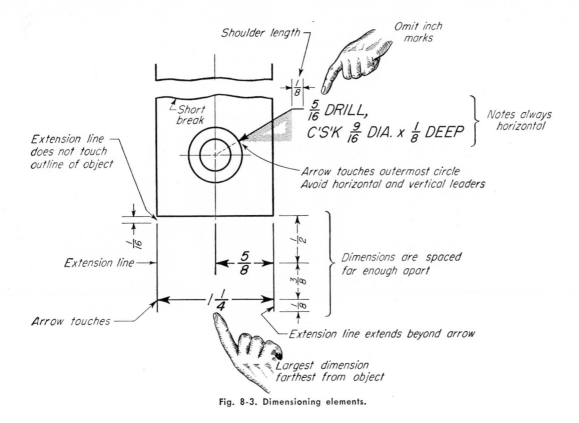

Fig. 8-3. Dimensioning elements.

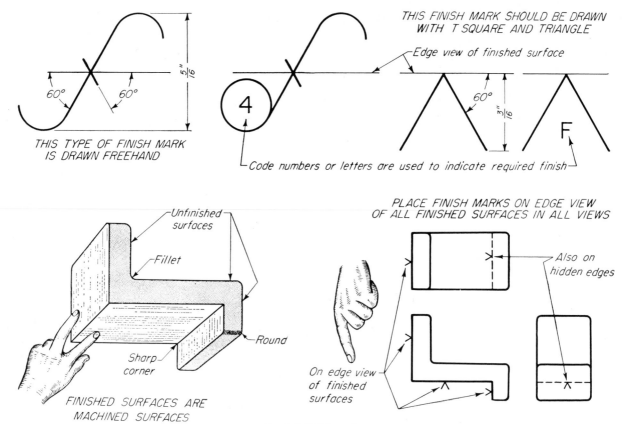

THIS TYPE OF FINISH MARK IS DRAWN FREEHAND

THIS FINISH MARK SHOULD BE DRAWN WITH T SQUARE AND TRIANGLE

Edge view of finished surface

Code numbers or letters are used to indicate required finish

Unfinished surfaces

Fillet

Round

Sharp corner

FINISHED SURFACES ARE MACHINED SURFACES

PLACE FINISH MARKS ON EDGE VIEW OF ALL FINISHED SURFACES IN ALL VIEWS

Also on hidden edges

On edge view of finished surfaces

Fig. 8-4. Finish marks.

illustrates the principles of their construction and placement. The oldest one, f, is still used by some of the larger manufacturing companies. The mark V is now more common, however, and is the one recommended by the ASA. The finish mark is always placed on the edge view of the surface to be machined and is indicated in all views where the surface shows as a line, even if the line is a dotted line. In the case of the V mark, the point touches the surface while the wings are in the air (away from the object).

If required, a code number may be added to indicate the quality of finish desired. The ASA has developed a Standard (ASA B46) that lists recommended symbols and specifications for indicating specific surface quality and finish. Part of this Standard is reproduced in "Standards for Drawings and Drafting Room Practice" (ASA Z14.1—1946). When a piece is to be finished all over, the letters "FAO" or the words "Finish All Over" are used and the finish marks are omitted entirely. Finish marks are never used on rolled stocks such

as shafts, or on holes that are to be drilled, reamed, bored, etc., because these are already understood to be finishing operations.

8-8. Fractional and decimal dimensions. There are three basic systems for giving size dimensions that are in common use in industry: (1) the fractional system, (2) the combined fractional and decimal system, and (3) the complete decimal system.

The fractional system is used in manufacturing plants where the accuracy need be only to $\frac{1}{64}$ in. Dimensions are given in units and fractional parts of an inch, such as $2\frac{3}{4}$, $3\frac{1}{8}$, $2\frac{9}{32}$, $1\frac{1}{64}$ in. In some industries dimensions greater than 72 in. are given in feet and inches, for example, 9'-7" or 12'-0".

Ordinarily it is impractical to use fractions smaller than $\frac{1}{64}$ in., and so when greater accuracy is required, dimensions are given in decimal parts of an inch, for example, 2.36 or 3.120 in. The combined system therefore employs decimal dimensions where accuracy is important and fractional

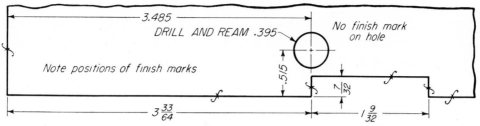

Fig. 8-5. Use of fractional and decimal dimensions.

dimensions for less critical dimensions (see Fig. 8-5).

In recent years the complete decimal system, in which all dimensions are given as decimal parts of an inch, has gained wide usage. This system not only assures accuracy and uniformity but also facilitates computations and limit dimensioning. The ASA recommends that two-place even decimals (such as .02, .10, .84) be used wherever possible (see Figs. 8-37, 8-38, and 8-40). The advantage of an even two-place decimal (for instance, a diameter of .50) lies in the fact that it results in a two-place decimal when halved (.25 for the radius). Odd decimals or decimals of three or more places may of course be used where extremely precise dimensions are necessary.

When converting common fractions to decimals, it is often necessary to round off the significant decimal places. The ASA suggests (in Z25.1—1940) the following procedure for rounding off decimals:

When the figure beyond the last figure to be retained is less than 5, the last figure retained should not be changed. *Example:* 3.46325, if cut off to three places, should be 3.463.

When the figures beyond the last place to be retained amount to more than 5, the last figure retained should be increased by 1. *Example:* 8.37652, if cut off to three places, should be 8.377.

When the figure beyond the last place to be retained is exactly 5 with only zeros following, the preceding number, if even should be unchanged; if odd, it should be increased by 1. *Example:* 4.365 becomes 4.36 when cut off to two places. Also 4.355 becomes 4.36 when cut off to two places.

8-9. Reading direction of dimensions. The ASA has approved two methods of placing dimensions on a drawing: the aligned system and the unidirectional system (see Fig. 8-6). In the aligned system the dimension figures are always placed at right angles to the dimension line and are orientated so that they are readable either from the bottom or from the right-hand side of the drawing. In the unidirectional system the dimension figures are arranged so that they may invariably be read

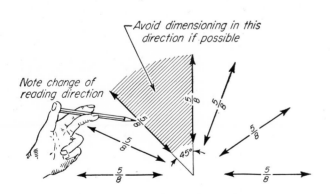

IN THE ALIGNED SYSTEM THE FIGURES ARE ALIGNED PERPENDICULAR TO THE LEADERS AND ARROWS

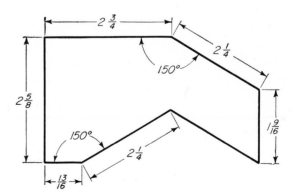

IN THE UNIDIRECTIONAL SYSTEM ALL FIGURES ARE READ FROM THE BOTTOM OF THE DRAWING SHEET

Fig. 8-6. Reading direction for dimensions.

from the bottom of the drawing. This system was devised to facilitate reading large drawings and is used extensively in the aircraft and automotive industries.

When the aligned system is used, dimensioning in the shaded area shown in the figure should be avoided wherever possible, since dimensions in this area violate the principle of bottom or right-side readability. Note the change in the reading direction of the dimension figures as they are rotated through the 180° arc.

Regardless of the system that is used for the placement of dimension figures, notes should always be located so that they read from the bottom of the drawing sheet.

8-10. Placing dimensions. Dimensions and notes should be placed outside the outlines of the piece whenever practicable (see Figs. 8-3 and 8-23, for example). In dimensioning complicated objects, however, the dimensions may have to be

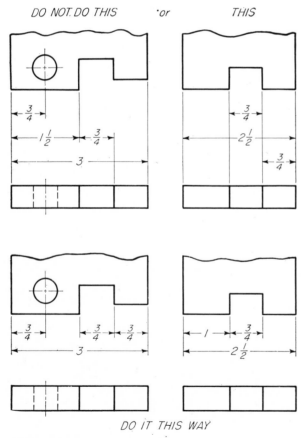

Fig. 8-7. Dimensions apply to one view only.

placed on or near the features, thus falling within the outline of the object but adding to the directness and clarity of the presentation (see Fig. 8-24). In so far as it is possible dimensions should be placed between views. When dimensions are placed between views, however, they should apply to one view only (see Fig. 8-7).

Dimension lines should be located about ½ in. from the outlines of the object. In a group of dimensions, the smallest is always placed nearest the piece and is followed by progressively larger dimensions uniformly spaced at a minimum of ⅜ in. apart (Fig. 8-3). This procedure minimizes the likelihood of crossed extension lines.

Continuous dimensions are preferable to staggered dimensions because of the ease with which they may be read (see Fig. 8-8). Staggered dimensions (Fig. 8-8) may sometimes be necessary, however, to facilitate proper placement of figures and notes.

As a general rule, dimension figures should be located at the center of the dimension line except when another line interferes. If a number of parallel dimension lines occur together, dimension figures are staggered for readability (see Fig. 8-8).

Dimensions should never be crowded into limited spaces. The use of notes is often a suitable way to avoid crowding of dimensions. If notes are not appropriate, a portion of the part may be enlarged as a separate partial view, or the methods shown in Fig. 8-9 may be used.

8-11. The theory of dimensioning. No matter how complicated in appearance an engineering form may be, it can be broken down into a group of assembled simple geometric shapes such as prisms, cylinders, cones, pyramids, spheres, etc., in their positive or negative states. (A shaft is a positive cylinder; a hole is a negative cylinder; etc.) It is then a relatively simple matter to dimension these geometric forms in a manner that will show their individual sizes and their location relative to each other. The dimensions of the contours of each geometric shape show its size and are known as *size dimensions*. The dimensions that locate these geometric shapes in relation to each other are

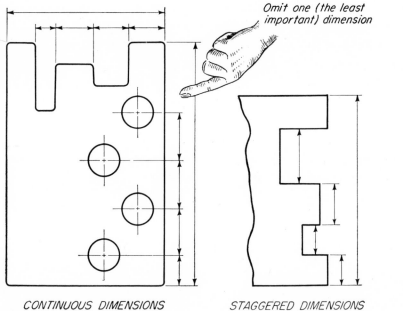

Omit one (the least important) dimension

CONTINUOUS DIMENSIONS   STAGGERED DIMENSIONS   STAGGERED FIGURES

Fig. 8-8. Placing dimensions.

known as *location dimensions*. The two types of dimensions cannot always be sharply distinguished, however, since in some instances size dimensions also serve as location dimensions.

8-12. Size dimensions and location dimensions. The geometric breakdown of a simple machine form is shown in Fig. 8-10. In the figure,

NEVER CROWD DIMENSIONS IN LIMITED SPACES
ALWAYS MAKE FIGURES LEGIBLE

Fig. 8-9. Dimensioning in limited spaces.

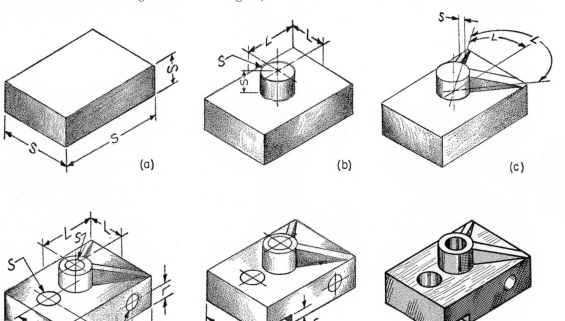

(a)   (b)   (c)

(d)   (e)

Fig. 8-10. Size and location dimensions.

S indicates a size dimension and *L* a location dimension. In (*a*) the dimensions shown give the size of the prism. In (*b*) the dimensions give the size of the cylinder and its location on the prism. In (*c*) the dimensions indicate the size and locations of the ribs. The size and location dimensions given in (*a*), (*b*), and (*c*) interest the worker who will make the pattern for the casting. The size and location dimensions of the holes and slot in (*d*) and (*e*) are necessary for the machine-shop worker who will fashion these with the proper tools. Note

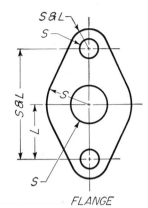

Fig. 8-11. Size and location given by one dimension.

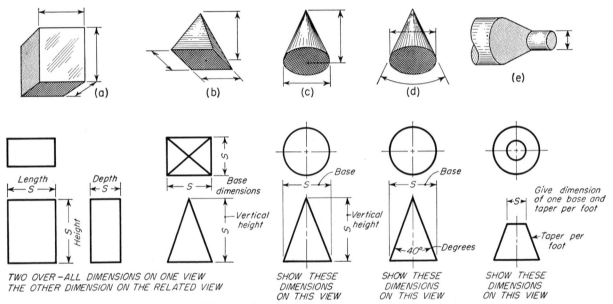

Fig. 8-12. Size dimensions of common geometric forms.

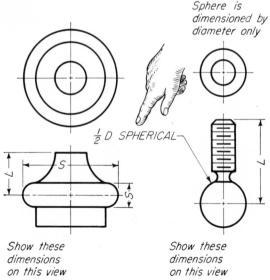

Fig. 8-13. Dimensioning the torus and the sphere.

that a location dimension serves to locate the entire geometric element and not merely a side, surface, or line of the element.

The dimensioning of the flange in Fig. 8-11 illustrates how, in some cases, one dimension serves as both a size and a location dimension.

Figure 8-12 illustrates the manner in which the size dimensions of certain basic forms are given: (*a*) a rectangular prism, (*b*) a pyramid, (*c*) and (*d*) cones, and (*e*) a cone frustum illustrating a taper. The manner in which the torus (a round ring or protuberance) and the sphere are dimensioned is shown in Fig. 8-13.

Over-all dimensions (the principal size dimensions that give the entire length, height, and thickness of the object) should always be shown outside (or beyond) all other dimensions, avoiding as far as possible the crossing of extension lines. They should be placed so that two over-all dimensions appear on one view and the third on an adjacent view.

8-13. The principle of contour dimensioning. Typical features of objects such as holes, round ends, angles, slots, etc., may be seen and dimensioned more clearly in views where their contour shapes appear, rather than in other views where they may appear as dotted lines or be otherwise obscured. In some cases, a note may be used to dimension a single hidden detail in order to avoid drawing extra views. Nevertheless, the general rule

is to give the size and location dimensions of a feature in the view which shows it in its true size and shape (see Fig. 8-14).

8-14. Shafts, holes, and arcs. As shown in Fig. 8-15, a complete circle, whether a hole or a solid shaft, is dimensioned by giving its diameter. An incomplete circle, such as a curve or arc, on the other hand, is dimensioned by radius only. Where necessary the abbreviations "D" and "R," for "diameter" and "radius," respectively, should be used to avoid misinterpretations.

The length and diameter of a positive cylinder (a shaft) should be given in the view where these

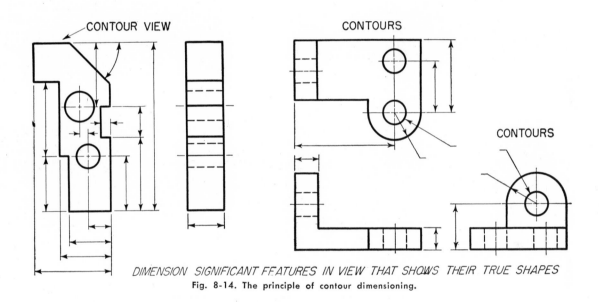

Fig. 8-14. The principle of contour dimensioning.

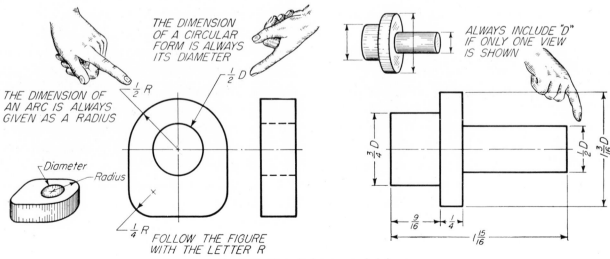

Fig. 8-15. Dimensioning arcs and circles.

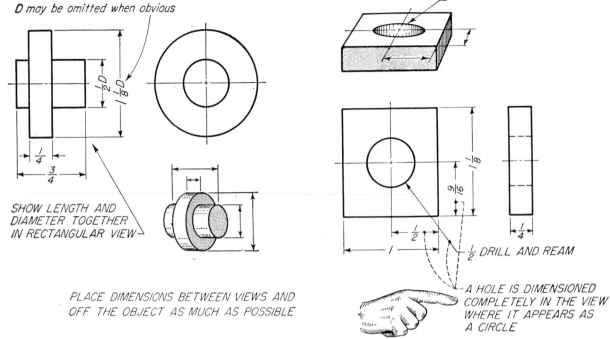

Fig. 8-16. Dimensioning a hole and a shaft.

dimensions are seen together (see Fig. 8-16). Simple cylindrical forms may be drawn and dimensioned completely in one view (see the right side of Fig. 8-15). For limit dimensioning of a shaft, see Fig. 8-40.

Dimension a negative cylinder (a hole) completely in the view where it is seen as a circle. If a hole goes through a piece, which is usually the case, the depth of the hole is not given in the circular view inasmuch as this information appears on the related view. Figure 8-17 shows the manner in which various types of holes are dimensioned by shop notes.

Holes in one surface should be located in reference to holes in another surface (see Fig. 8-18a). The location dimensions should be given decimally to three places if they are actually important to the accurate functioning of one part with its mating piece. Cylindrical shapes, whether holes or shafts, are located by dimensioning to their center lines, never to the perimeters of the circles (see Fig. 8-18b). Location dimensions for unfinished parts may be given fractionally. Location dimensions for finished features should be given decimally.

8-15. Dimensioning holes on a bolt circle. When holes are *equally spaced* in a circular flange, one hole should be located on either the vertical or horizontal main center line. Then the holes may be dimensioned as shown in Fig. 8-19a. The diameter dimension of the bolt circle should always be given in the circular view.

8-16. Locating holes by rectangular coordinates. When extremely precise location dimensions for holes are required, locate the holes by the use of rectangular coordinates, and give the dimensions as decimals (see Fig. 8-19b).

8-17. Unequally spaced holes. Unequally spaced holes may be located by rectangular coordinates or by the method shown in Fig. 8-20. One hole on the bolt circle is located from one of the main center lines (if one is not already located on a center line) by giving the angle in degrees; then the other holes are located from the first hole by angular dimensions.

8-18. Arcs and round-end shapes. An arc is dimensioned by giving the radius of the circle of which it is a part. The center of the circle is shown by crossed lines from which the dimension line for the arc is extended. The dimension line is always

½ DRILL

½ DRILL,
¾ DEEP, 3 HOLES

.4040 DRILL
.4070 REAM

½ DRILL
82° C'S'K TO 15/16 DIA.

¼ DRILL
82° C'S'K - 5/32 DEEP

½ DRILL
SPOT-FACE 15/16 D. x
1/16 DEEP
5 EQUISPACED HOLES

½ DRILL
SPOT-FACE
TO CLEAN

5/16 DRILL
C'BORE ½ DIA. x
3/16 DEEP
7 HOLES

¼ -20 NC -3
6 HOLES

Give fraction dimension
for cores

Give decimal dimensions
for close tolerances

CORE 2 DIA. x ½ DEEP
.750 DRILL THROUGH
C'BORE 1.500 DIA. x
.2500 DEEP

Numbered and lettered drills

#10 DRILL
3 HOLES

K DRILL
5 HOLES

.2660 DRILL
SPOT-FACE ½ D.
TO CLEAN - 7 HOLES

DRILL AND REAM FOR
#4 TAPER PIN WITH
PIECE #8 IN POSITION

Giving all required shop information as one note on circular view prevents confusion, needless repetition, and overloading of the drawing. Make notes brief but explicit.

Fig. 8-17. Dimensioning particular types of holes by use of notes.

drawn at an angle and has an arrowhead only at the end touching the arc. Figure 8-21 shows the manner in which arcs of various sizes are dimensioned. Note that as the arc becomes progressively smaller first the dimension figure, and then the dimension figure and dimension line are placed out-

side the arc. If an arc is very flat and its center lies outside the boundaries of the drawing, the broken dimension line is shown in a zigzag form starting from the point of the center of the arc (see Fig. 8-25).

Round-end shapes are dimensioned as shown in

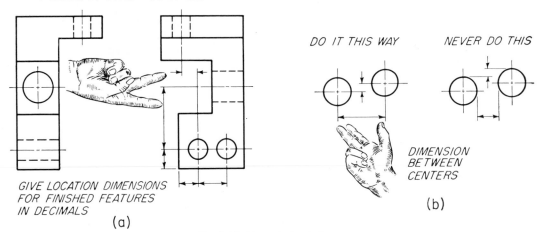

Fig. 8-18. Dimensioning holes.

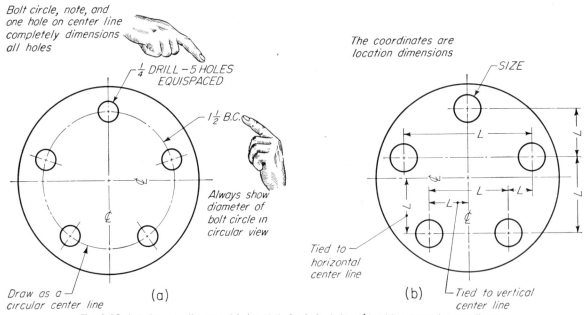

Fig. 8-19. Locating equally spaced holes. (*a*) On bolt circle; (*b*) with rectangular coordinates.

Fig. 8-22. If the arcs on opposite ends of a piece are the same, the center lines for both circles should be drawn, but only one arc need be dimensioned. When the radii of the arcs are less than ½ in., the size dimension of the piece is given from end to end; when the radii are ½ in. or more, the size dimension from center to center is given.

Slots are dimensioned according to the methods used in their manufacture. Figure 8-23 shows the dimensioning of straight and curved round-end slots. Figure 8-24 illustrates the size and location dimensions necessary for drawing a piece containing various types of slots. The general note "Fillets and Rounds ⅛" is sufficient dimensioning for all arcs of this size that appear on the object being drawn.

8-19. Irregular curves. Irregular curves are always dimensioned in the contour view that shows their true shape. The irregular curve may be broken up into a series of circle arcs, which can

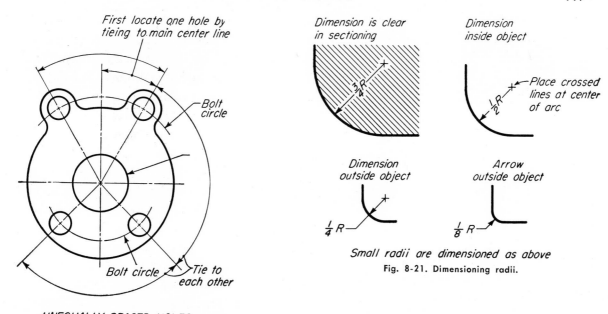

First locate one hole by tieing to main center line

Bolt circle

Bolt circle

Tie to each other

UNEQUALLY SPACED HOLES

Fig. 8-20. Dimensioning of unequally spaced holes.

Dimension is clear in sectioning

Dimension inside object

Place crossed lines at center of arc

Dimension outside object

Arrow outside object

Small radii are dimensioned as above

Fig. 8-21. Dimensioning radii.

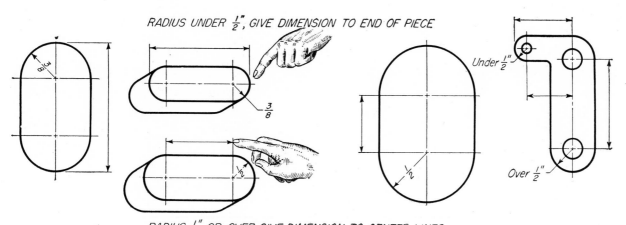

RADIUS UNDER ½", GIVE DIMENSION TO END OF PIECE

Under ½"

Over ½"

RADIUS ½" OR OVER, GIVE DIMENSION TO CENTER LINES

Fig. 8-22. Dimensioning of round-end shapes.

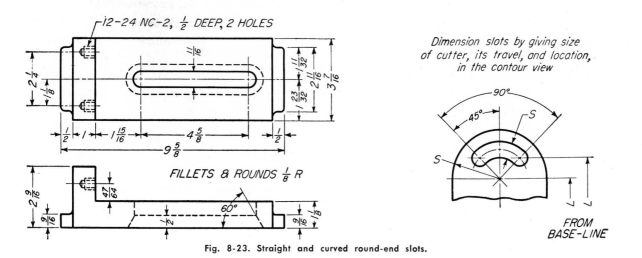

12-24 NC-2, ½ DEEP, 2 HOLES

FILLETS & ROUNDS ⅛ R

Dimension slots by giving size of cutter, its travel, and location, in the contour view

FROM BASE-LINE

Fig. 8-23. Straight and curved round-end slots.

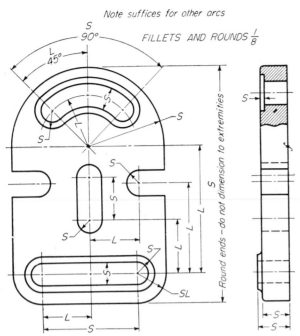

Fig. 8-24. Slot location and size dimensions.

by a series of offset dimensions originating in a base line and terminating in points on the curve, which also are dimensioned laterally. These points are actually spaced and dimensioned on a series of rectangular coordinates.

8-20. Angles. The arrowheads of the dimension for an angle are placed on an arc struck from the point of intersection of the sides (see Fig. 8-26). For small angles the figures are placed to read vertically; for the larger angles the figures are placed radially. An angle may also be dimensioned by either of the methods shown at the right in Fig. 8-26. When angles are given in degrees and minutes, the two figures are shown closed up without a dash, for example, 45°17′.

8-21. The chamfer, countersink, and counterbore. Chamfers are dimensioned as shown in Fig. 8-27A. A 45° chamfer is dimensioned by giving the angle and its width as a note. If the angle is other than 45°, the angle and the width should not be given as a note but should appear at the point of the chamfer as shown at the lower right in the illustration. Figure 8-27B shows the

then be dimensioned by their radii, much as shown in Fig. 8-25. If the center of a radius falls too far from the drawing, the leader is broken as illustrated. Irregular curves may also be dimensioned

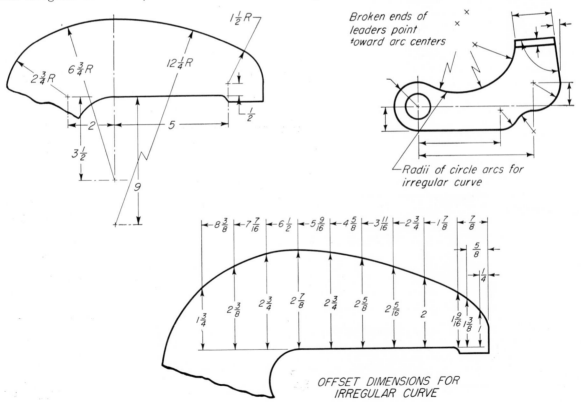

Fig. 8-25. Dimensioning circle arcs and irregular curves. (*From ASA Z14.1—1946.*)

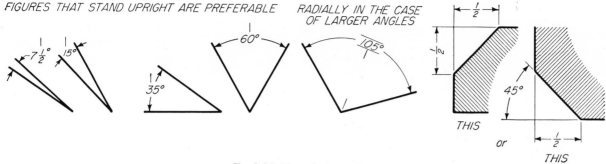

Fig. 8-26. Dimensioning angles.

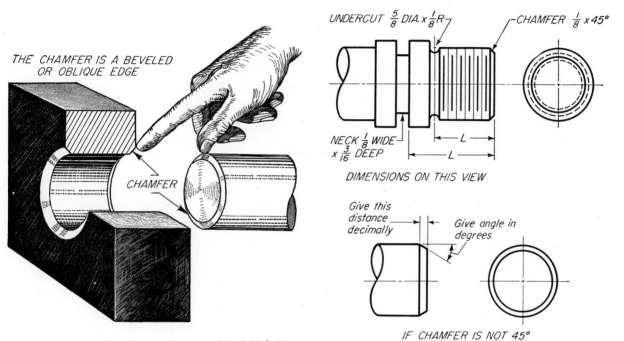

THE CHAMFER IS A BEVELED OR OBLIQUE EDGE

CHAMFER

UNDERCUT $\frac{5}{8}$ DIA. x $\frac{1}{8}$ R — CHAMFER $\frac{1}{8}$ x 45°

NECK $\frac{1}{8}$ WIDE x $\frac{3}{16}$ DEEP

DIMENSIONS ON THIS VIEW

Give this distance decimally   Give angle in degrees

IF CHAMFER IS NOT 45°

Fig. 8-27A. Dimensioning the chamfer.

manner in which countersinks and counterbores are drawn (for dimensioning, see Fig. 8-17).

8-22. Threads, tapers, springs, bushings, etc. Figure 8-28 illustrates the manner in which screw threads, tapers, compression springs, and other common features are dimensioned by notes. The dimensioning of bushings is shown in Fig. 8-29. Figure 8-30 illustrates the dimensioning of pulleys. The manner in which a spline key is dimensioned is shown in Fig. 8-31.

8-23. Half sections. Although dimensioning a half section (see Sec. 9-12) is occasionally difficult, the proper use of hidden lines in the external portion of the half-section view will generally allow the draftsman to dimension such views satisfactorily. In half-section views it is permissible, and even

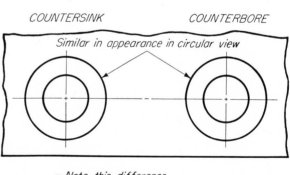

COUNTERSINK   COUNTERBORE

Similar in appearance in circular view

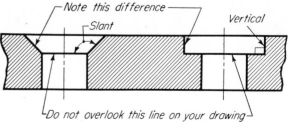

Note this difference

Slant   Vertical

Do not overlook this line on your drawing

Fig. 8-27B. Drawing of the countersink and the counterbore.

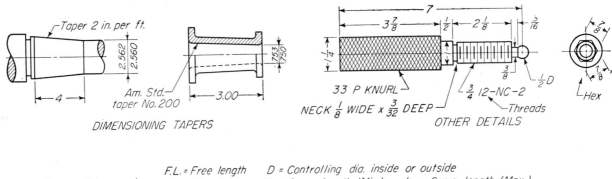

DIMENSIONING TAPERS   OTHER DETAILS

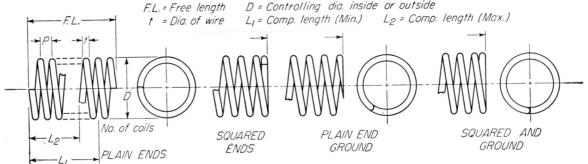

REPRESENTING AND DIMENSIONING COMPRESSION SPRINGS.

Fig. 8-28. Dimensioning various details. (*From ASA Z14.1—1946.*)

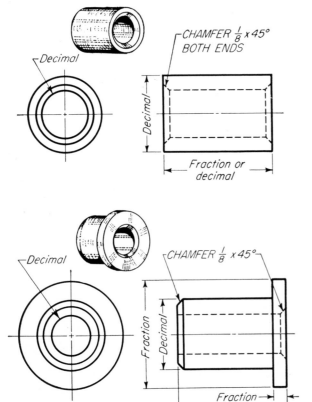

Fig. 8-29. Dimensioning bushings.

advisable, to dimension to hidden lines (see Fig. 8-32) in order to avoid confusion and possible misinterpretations. Dimensioning such views requires great care in the placement of dimension and extension lines and usually calls for extensive notes. The draftsman should be careful to follow the rule that requires a hole to be dimensioned in the view where it appears as a circle and a shaft where its length and diameter appear together.

8-24. Standard parts. Bolts, screws, keys, pins, wire, rolled shapes, nails, pipes, chains, ropes, etc., are usually standardized features. They are shown symbolically on the drawing and are listed in the bill of materials of an assembly drawing as standard parts. Their actual dimensions, if required, are available in pamphlets published by the ASA or in manufacturers' manuals.

8-25. Base-line dimensioning. To avoid the accumulation of errors that is likely to occur with the use of continuous dimensions (see Fig. 8-8), base-line dimensioning is used for precision work. Base-line dimensioning means that wherever possible all dimensions are referred to a common reference line. A center line or a finished surface

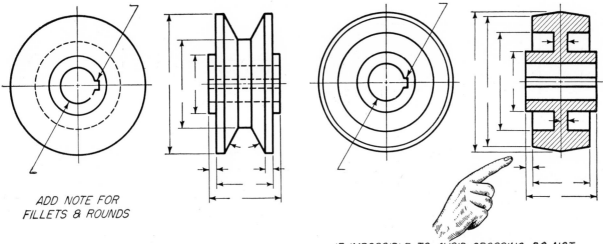

ADD NOTE FOR
FILLETS & ROUNDS

IF IMPOSSIBLE TO AVOID CROSSING, DO NOT
BREAK EXTENSION OR DIMENSION LINES

Fig. 8-30. Dimensioning pulleys.

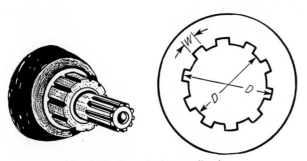

Fig. 8-31. Dimensioning a spline key.

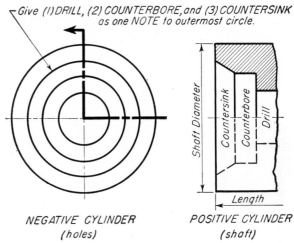

Give (I) DRILL, (2) COUNTERBORE, and (3) COUNTERSINK
as one NOTE to outermost circle.

NEGATIVE CYLINDER
(holes)

POSITIVE CYLINDER
(shaft)

Fig. 8-32. Dimensioning half sections.

is generally used as the reference point for each independent dimension (see Figs. 8-33 and 8-34). Note in the illustrations that the last dimension is superfluous and may be omitted, since the over-all dimension gives the distance from end to end for the piece. The dimension omitted should always be the least necessary. If desired for checking or reference, the extra dimension may be included and marked with the abbreviation "Ref." Note in Fig. 8-34 that dimensioning within a view is always permissible if doing so helps to clarify the presentation.

8-26. Importance and preference in dimensions. Dimensioning practice should always be considered in light of the manufacturing processes required in making a part, and wherever possible a dimension or note should indicate the specific procedure to be followed by the worker. Notes should be used freely to convey any information that a figured dimension alone cannot supply.

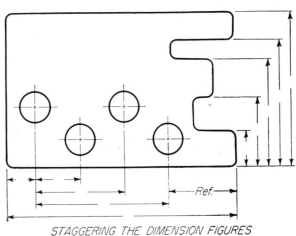

STAGGERING THE DIMENSION FIGURES
IS MORE PLEASING

Fig. 8-33. Base-line dimensioning.

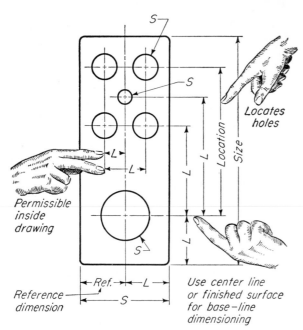

CENTER LINES MAY BE USED FOR DIMENSIONING

Fig. 8-34. Base-line dimensioning for strict accuracy.

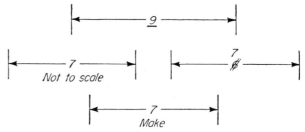

WHEN CHANGE IN DIMENSION IS MADE NOTE *IT* IN TITLE BLOCK OR RECORD STRIP

Fig. 8-35. Changes and corrections in dimensions.

The draftsman can help the worker in the shop to produce accurately the part shown in the drawing by following a recognized sequence of importance and preference when specifying dimensions. For the highest degree of accuracy, the sequence of importance in giving size dimensions is as follows:

1. Finished surface to finished surface
2. Finished surface to unfinished surface
3. Unfinished surface to unfinished surface

For location dimensions, the preferred sequence is:

1. Center line to center line
2. Center line to finished surface
3. Finished surface to finished surface
4. Center line to unfinished surface
5. Finished surface to unfinished surface
6. Unfinished surface to unfinished surface

When dimensioning drawings for the shop, the draftsman should take particular care to be certain that the dimensions are direct and do not require calculations on the part of the worker.

8-27. Changes and corrections of dimensions. When it is necessary to alter or correct a dimension, and the change is not sufficiently important to warrant remaking the entire drawing, the dimen-

sion figure may be altered by one of the methods shown in Fig. 8-35 and a note with the date of the change added in the title block (or just above it, if no space is allotted for this in the block). Of course, if the change radically alters the appearance and design of the part, a new drawing must be prepared.

8-28. Final check. A suitable application of the dimensioning principles discussed in this chapter will enable the draftsman to dimension any object adequately. As a final step, the drawing should be checked to make sure that all over-all, size, and location dimensions have been given and that the dimensions shown are those necessary for the manufacture of the part and not those used to make the drawing. Check also to be certain that dimensions have been placed on the view showing the true size or shape of a particular feature and that no line of the object or center line has been used as a dimension line. Although unnecessary dimensions should be avoided, make sure that the dimensions given are sufficient for the manufacture, assembly, and inspection of the part. The scale, material, number of pieces required, and all other pertinent information listed in the bill of materials, the title block, and the record strip must be checked to be sure that sufficient data has been supplied to allow the workman in the shop to do his job accurately and efficiently.

8-29. Interchangeable manufacture and selective assembly. In industrial practice it has proved feasible to manufacture each of several mating parts in plants remote from each other and still assure suitable functioning when the pieces are brought together in assembly. This has been made possible by setting up standards that specify allowable variations in size for mating parts under various specific conditions. This permitted variation in size is known as "tolerance." It is the function of the designer to specify the desired tolerances on mating parts, which the draftsman then expresses as dimensions on the drawing. The draftsman can make his own computations for these dimensions from standard tables if he knows the required mating conditions, or "fit," which are discussed in Sec. 8-31. The tolerance of mating parts is given on a drawing by specifying the maximum and minimum size limits of each of the mating members. This phase of dimensioning practice is known as *limit dimensioning*, and is of vital importance in the quantity manufacture of parts for interchangeable and selective assembly.

8-30. Definition of terms. The terms used in limit dimensioning and their definitions are as follows:

Nominal size. The approximate standard size of a part, usually indicated by a fractional dimension.

Basic size. The exact theoretical size, given as a decimal dimension from which the limits are computed.

Limits. The maximum and minimum permissible sizes of a part given as decimal dimensions.

Tolerance. The permissible variation in the final size of a part, given as a decimal dimension.

Allowance. The minimum acceptable clearance (for clearance fits) or the maximum acceptable interference (for interference fits) between two mating members. It is the decimal dimension that indicates the loosest or the tightest fit between parts. For clearance fits the allowance is positive; for interference fits it is negative.

8-31. Classes of fits. Fits on machine parts are of three general types: the clearance fit, the interference fit, and the transition fit (see Fig. 8-36).

In the *clearance fit,* the internal member is smaller than the external member, and the mating parts move rather freely. The space between the parts allowing this freedom is termed the "allowance" and is indicated as positive.

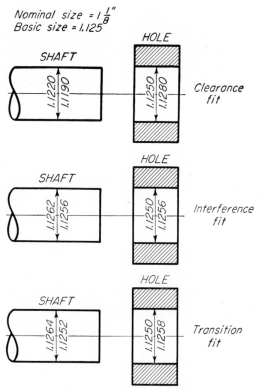

Fig. 8-36. The three types of fits.

In the *interference fit* there is interference of metal because the internal member is larger than the external member, and the allowance is negative.

A *transition fit* is one in which the parts are made to allow either a clearance or an interference fit—a maximum external member and a minimum internal member will give a clearance fit; a minimum external member and a maximum internal member will give an interference fit. The transition fit requires *selective assembly* for the mating parts, whereas with clearance or interference fits *interchangeable assembly* may be used. With transition fits, however, the parts are graded in size, and it is often possible to obtain a closer fit.

8-32. ASA cylindrical fits. The ASA has classified cylindrical fits into eight numbered classes, as follows:

Class 1: Loose fit (large allowance)

Class 2: Free fit (liberal allowance)

Class 3: Medium fit (medium allowance)

Class 4: Snug fit (zero allowance)

Class 5: Wringing fit (zero to negative allowance)

Class 6: Tight fit (slight negative allowance)

Class 7: Medium force fit (negative allowance)

Class 8: Heavy force and shrink fit (considerable negative allowance)

The first three are free fits, the fourth allows no clearance yet can be assembled by hand, and the last four are interference fits required by different types of assembly procedures. The ASA has also compiled a set of tables that give the limits for various sizes of external and internal members in each of the different classes of fit. These tables are reproduced in the Appendix.

8-33. Computations of limit dimensions. The ASA has designated two systems whereby the correct fit between engaging surfaces of parts may be found. These are designated the *basic-hole* and the *basic-shaft* systems. In the basic-hole system, the size of the hole is taken as the basic dimension and the size of the shaft is determined by the dimensions of the hole and the type of fit desired. The nominal size (fractional dimension) of the hole is converted to the basic size (decimal dimension), and the limit dimensions for both hole and shaft are derived by subtracting or adding, whichever the case may be, the limit figures taken from the proper fit chart. When the basic-shaft system is used, the maximum dimension of the shaft is taken as the basic size. However, by adding (for a clearance fit) or subtracting (for an interference fit) the permissible allowance to this basic shaft size, the basic size of the hole can be found. The procedure is then reduced to finding the limits for both shaft and hole according to the basic-hole system.

8-34. Limit dimensions, basic-hole system. To show how the tables in the Appendix are applied, let us find the limits for the hole and shaft shown in Fig. 8-37. The nominal size of each of the parts is ¾ in. They are to work with a free medium fit (Class 3), which provides for a medium allowance with interchangeable assembly. Refer to that part of the table headed "Class 3, Medium fit," under the column for hole size and find the fractional dimension indicating the size of the hole; in this case it is the item in the left-hand column reading "1¼₆ to ¹³⁄₁₆." Now read across horizontally and note that the size of the hole may vary from the basic size by +0.0007 and 0.0000. The limits for the shaft are —0.0007 and —0.0014. These limits are added and subtracted from the basic size dimension 0.7500 to give the absolute limits in size for the largest and smallest hole and the largest and smallest shaft. The allowance is determined by subtracting the dimension for the largest shaft from the figures for the smallest hole. In this case it is found to be 0.0007 in. When assembled, no matter where the size of the parts may range between these limits, they will perform the task for which they are intended.

8-35. Ways of indicating tolerance. Tolerances are indicated on a drawing either by a general note or by specific limits on the parts affected. A general note indicating tolerance, such as, "All fractional dimensions to ±¹⁄₃₂ in.," is assumed to apply to all features on which the tolerance has not been specifically indicated. In the absence of specific tolerances or a general note, the worker in the shop will, in general, assume a tolerance of ±¹⁄₆₄ in. for fractional dimensions and ±0.01 for a two-place decimal dimension, ±0.001 for a three-place decimal, etc. Angles for which no limits have been specified are assumed to have a tolerance of ±½°.

Specific tolerances may be either *unilateral* or *bilateral*. A unilateral tolerance is one in which the variation from the basic size is in one direction (plus or minus), but not both. Unilateral tolerances are preferably indicated as shown in Fig. 8-38, with the two limits given one above the other, but they may also be expressed by giving one limit size and the tolerance, for example, $0.7500 + 0.0007$ or $0.7500 {+ 0.0007 \atop - 0.0000}$. Bilateral tolerances are used when the variation from the basic size may be either plus or minus, for example, $0.100 ± 0.002$ or $0.100 {+ 0.002 \atop - 0.002}$. As a general rule, nonmating members are toleranced bilaterally, while mating surfaces are toleranced unilaterally.

In specifying tolerances, the draftsman should keep in mind the method that will be used to re-

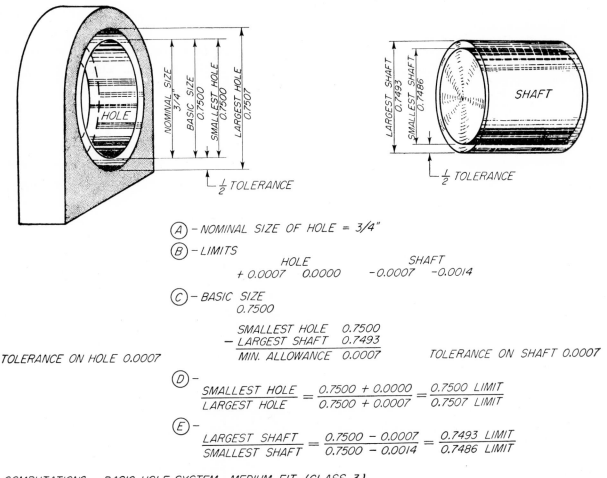

A – NOMINAL SIZE OF HOLE = 3/4"

B – LIMITS

	HOLE		SHAFT	
	+ 0.0007	0.0000	− 0.0007	− 0.0014

C – BASIC SIZE
0.7500

TOLERANCE ON HOLE 0.0007

	SMALLEST HOLE	0.7500
−	LARGEST SHAFT	0.7493
	MIN. ALLOWANCE	0.0007

TOLERANCE ON SHAFT 0.0007

D –
$$\frac{SMALLEST\ HOLE}{LARGEST\ HOLE} = \frac{0.7500 + 0.0000}{0.7500 + 0.0007} = \frac{0.7500\ LIMIT}{0.7507\ LIMIT}$$

E –
$$\frac{LARGEST\ SHAFT}{SMALLEST\ SHAFT} = \frac{0.7500 - 0.0007}{0.7500 - 0.0014} = \frac{0.7493\ LIMIT}{0.7486\ LIMIT}$$

COMPUTATIONS: BASIC HOLE SYSTEM, MEDIUM FIT (CLASS 3)
MEDIUM ALLOWANCE – INTERCHANGEABLE

Fig. 8-37. Computing limit dimensions.

move excess material in the machining operation and should place the dimension limits accordingly. In the case of a hole, for example, the machinist will reach the smallest size first, and so the small dimension is placed over the dimension for the largest hole. A shaft, on the other hand, is turned down from the larger to the smaller dimension; thus the larger limit is placed over the smaller limit (see Fig. 8-38).

8-36. Allowances. Although technically the term *allowance* means the minimum clearance between mating parts, in shop practice it is common to speak of minimum and maximum allowance. The minimum allowance between two pieces in assembly is the difference between the smallest hole and the largest shaft (see Fig. 8-39). For clearance fits, it represents the tightest permissible fit between the two parts in assembly; for interference fits, it is the maximum permissible interference between the two members. The maximum allowance is the difference between the largest hole and the smallest shaft and represents the loosest permissible fit (or minimum interference in the case of interference fits) between the two parts in assembly.

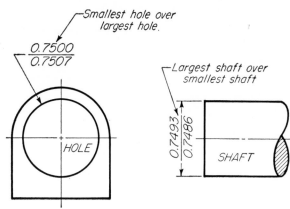

Fig. 8-38. Placing limits in the dimension.

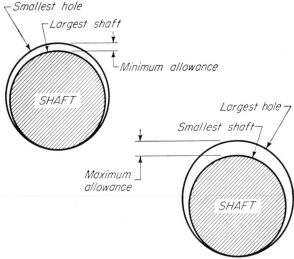

Fig. 8-39. Minimum and maximum allowance for clearance fit.

8-37. Cumulative tolerances. The shaft shown in Fig. 8-40 has been dimensioned to function with various types of bearings and bearing surfaces. The tolerances on the various diameters have been computed and specified according to the desired fits with the mating forms. Superfluous dimensions should be avoided, and errors in cumulative tolerances held down to an absolute minimum by using base-line dimensioning whenever possible. Continuous dimensions always tend to build up inaccuracies in tolerances. Note in the illustration that a critical surface at about the center of the shaft has been used as the base line from which the length dimensions are given, thus nullifying the possibility of cumulative errors. Note the manner in which the thread at the right end of the shaft has been dimensioned.

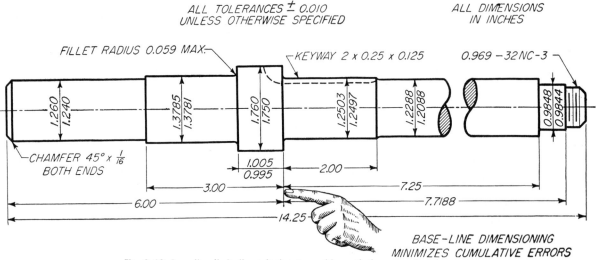

Fig. 8-40. Base-line limit dimensioning to avoid cumulative errors in tolerance.

PROBLEMS

Although these problems have been selected primarily to provide practice in applying correct dimensioning procedures, they also afford training in the selection of views, in the choice of a suitable scale for the object, and in the spacing of the views so as to permit the placement of dimensions and notes without crowding.

A preliminary thumbnail sketch (to be submitted to the instructor) will aid in visualizing and solving these problems. In working from the pictorial illustrations, the student should keep in mind that the dimensions given are intended only to make it possible to prepare the necessary orthographics and are not necessarily the ones he will place on his drawing sheet. Also, it should be pointed out that pictorials of machine forms do not always permit dimensions to be shown according to the rules of good practice.

All drawings are to be prepared on standard 8½- by 11-in. or 11- by 17-in. sheets. A simple title form containing only the name of the object, the scale, and the material it is made of may be used instead of a complete title block with parts list and record strip (unless a printed form appears on your sheet).

Other dimensioning problems may be selected from the large number of details that make up the assemblies shown in the problem section of Chap. 14.

Until the student has read the discussions in Chaps. 10, 11, and 13, however, care should be taken to avoid assigning problems which contain fastener details, such as screw threads, or require auxiliary views for complete description.

8-1. Make a suitable shop drawing of the cast-iron base. (Time: 2½ hr.)

8-2. Make a suitable shop drawing of the brass swivel frame. Show all dimensions in decimals with the exception of the drilled hole and, of course, the angles. (Time: 3 hr.)

8-3. Make a suitable shop drawing of the aluminum hanger bracket. (Time: 3 hr.)

8-4. The scale shown on the illustration indicates ⅛-in. divisions. With dividers transfer the orthographic views of the cast-iron pulley to the drawing sheet and dimension the part suitably for manufacture. (Time: 1½ hr.)

8-5. Transfer to the drawing sheet the two views of the steel clevis, using the scale shown as ⅛-in. divisions. The holes are drilled and counterbored. Dimension your drawing to serve as a working drawing for the shop. (Time: 2 hr.)

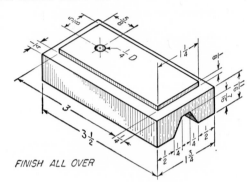

Prob. 8-1. Base, cast iron.

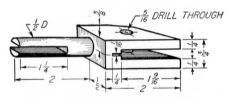

Prob. 8-2. Swivel frame, brass.

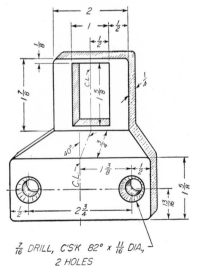

Prob. 8-3. Hanger bracket, aluminum.

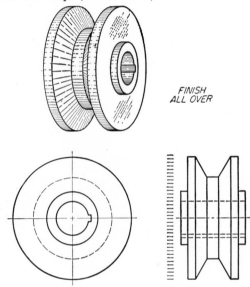

Prob. 8-4. Pulley, cast iron.

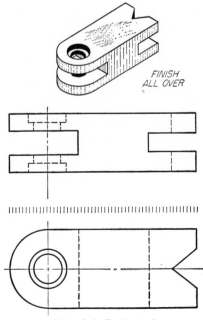

Prob. 8-5. Clevis, steel.

8-6. Make a suitable working drawing of the brass oarlock mounting. Portions of the object have been cut away to show the shape of the holes. (Time: 2 hr.)

8-7. Make a suitable working drawing of the brass oarlock. (Time: 2 hr.)

8-8. Make a suitable working drawing of the cast-iron rod support. (Time: 2 hr.)

8-9. Make a suitable working drawing of the cast-iron rod guide. (Time: 2½ hr.)

8-10. Make a suitable working drawing of the cast-iron rod guide. (Time: 1½ hr.)

8-11. Make a suitable working drawing of the steel clamp. (Time: 1½ hr.)

8-12. Make a suitable working drawing of the cast-iron bearing cap. (Time: 1½ hr.)

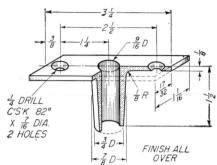

Prob. 8-6. Oarlock mounting, brass.

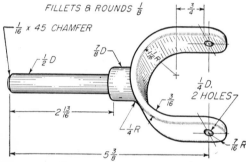

Prob. 8-7. Oarlock, brass.

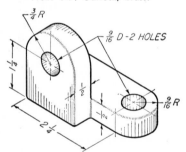

Prob. 8-8. Rod support, cast iron.

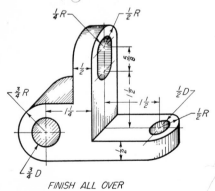

Prob. 8-9. Rod guide, cast iron.

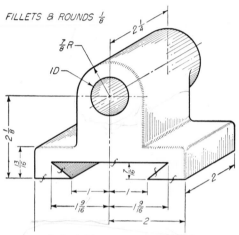

Prob. 8-10. Rod guide, cast iron.

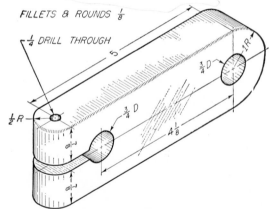

Prob. 8-11. Clamp, steel.

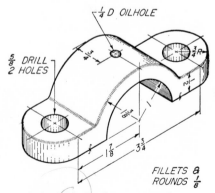

Prob. 8-12. Bearing cap, cast iron.

8-13. Make a suitable working drawing of the steel chassis lift. (Time: 2 hr.)

8-14. Make a suitable working drawing of the steel vise jaw. (Time: 3 hr.)

8-15. Make a suitable working drawing of the brass lever. (Time: 2 hr.)

8-16. Transfer the two views of the cast-iron base to your drawing sheet, adding the notes and dimensions required for a suitable working drawing. The scale shown on the illustration indicates ⅛-in. divisions. (Time: 2 hr.)

8-17. Make a suitable working drawing of the cast-iron adjusting bracket. (Time: 4 hr.)

8-18. Redraw the given views of the steel yoke,

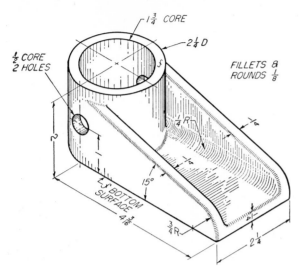

Prob. 8-13. Chassis lift, steel.

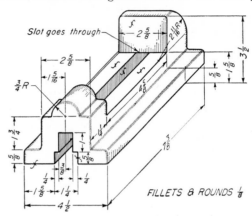

Prob. 8-14. Vise jaw, steel

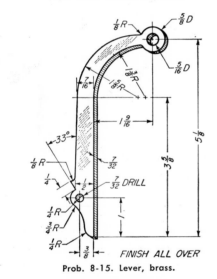

Prob. 8-15. Lever, brass.

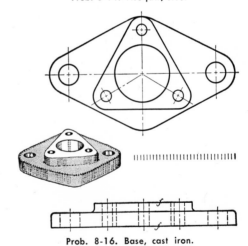

Prob. 8-16. Base, cast iron.

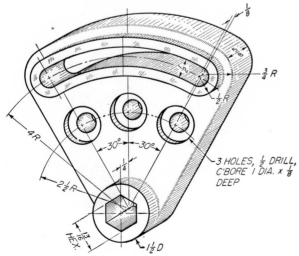

Prob. 8-17. Adjusting bracket, cast iron.

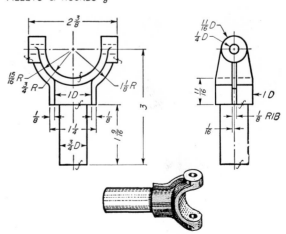

Prob. 8-18. Yoke, steel.

rearranging the dimensions you feel are improperly placed so as to satisfy the principles of proper dimensioning procedure and present a suitable working drawing. (Time: 2 hr.)

8-19. Make a suitable working drawing of the cast-iron clamp bracket. (Time: 3 hr.)

8-20. Make a suitable working drawing of the brass brake arm. (Time: 3 hr.)

8-21. With dividers, transfer the two views of the steel tool support to the drawing sheet. Add dimensions and notes to produce a suitable working drawing. The scale shown on the illustration indicates ⅛-in. divisions. (Time: 3½ hr.)

8-22. Make a suitable working drawing of the steel adjusting lever. (Time: 2½ hr.)

8-23. Make a working drawing of the cast-iron tool support. (Time: 3½ hr.)

8-24. Make a suitable working drawing of the steel hinge. (Time: 2 hr.)

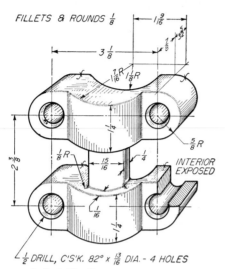

FILLETS & ROUNDS ⅛

Prob. 8-19. Clamp bracket, cast iron.

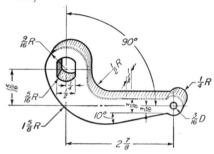

FILLETS & ROUNDS ⅛
Prob. 8-20. Brake arm, brass.

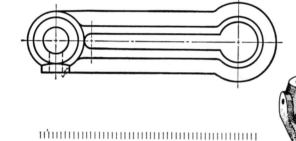

Prob. 8-21. Tool support, steel.

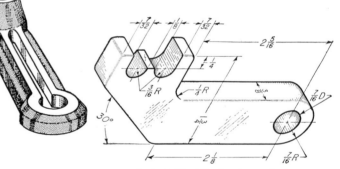

Prob. 8-22. Adjusting lever, steel.

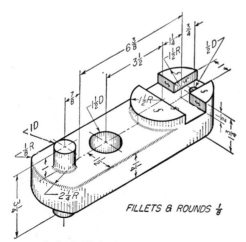

FILLETS & ROUNDS ⅛

Prob. 8-23. Tool support, cast iron.

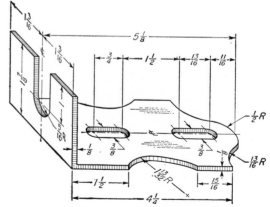

Prob. 8-24. Hinge, steel.

8-25. Change the fractional dimensions to decimal dimensions reduced to two places and make a suitable working drawing of the wedge block. (Time: 2 hr.)

8-26. Change all dimensions with the exception of the necks and chamfers to decimals of four places and make a suitable working drawing of the steel shaft. (Time: 1¾ hr.)

8-27. Make suitable working drawings of the steel stud shaft and bronze bushing on the same sheet. Change all dimensions with the exception of the necks and chamfers to decimals of four places. Compute the dimensions for the classes of fits from the tables in the Appendix. (Time: 4½ hr.)

8-28. Make a suitable working drawing of the brass lock base. (Time: 2½ hr.)

8-29. Make a suitable working drawing of the cast-iron rocker arm. (Time: 2½ hr.)

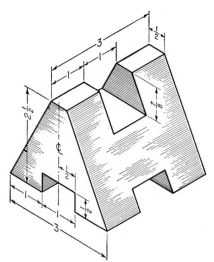

Prob. 8-25. Wedge block.

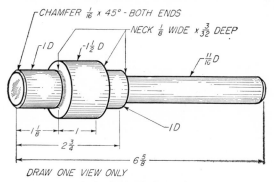

DRAW ONE VIEW ONLY

Prob. 8-26. Shaft, steel.

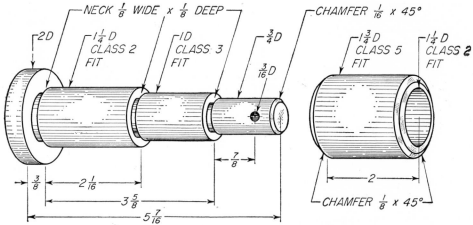

Prob. 8-27. Steel stud shaft with bronze bushing.

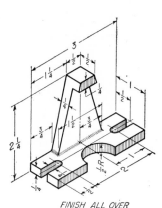

FINISH ALL OVER

Prob. 8-28. Lock base, brass.

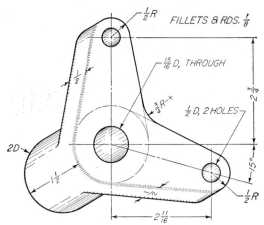

Prob. 8-29. Rocker arm, cast iron.

8-30. Make a suitable working drawing of the steel clevis. (Time: 2½ hr.)

8-31. Make a suitable working drawing of the brass valve handle. (Time: 2½ hr.)

8-32. Make a suitable working drawing of the aluminum pulley bracket. (Time: 3 hr.)

8-33. Make a suitable working drawing of the brass lock catch. (Time: 2 hr.)

8-34. Make a suitable drawing of the steel arm spindle. (Time: 3 hr.)

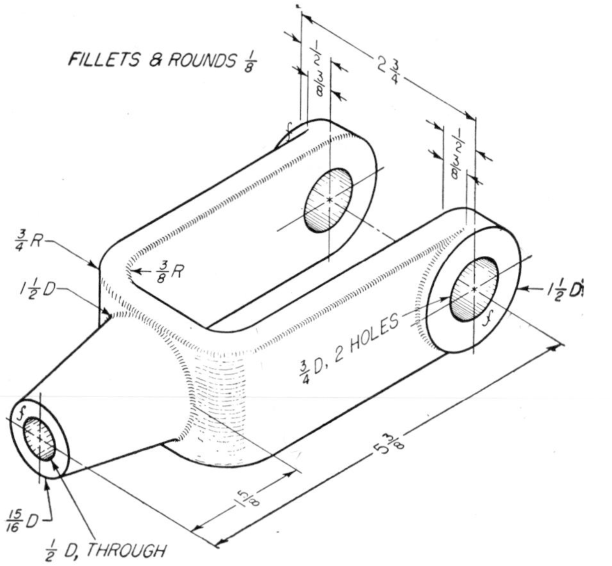

FILLETS & ROUNDS 1/8
3/4 R
1 1/2 D
3/8 R
3/4 D, 2 HOLES
1 1/2 D
2 3/4
5 3/8
15/16 D
1/2 D, THROUGH

Prob. 8-30. Clevis, steel.

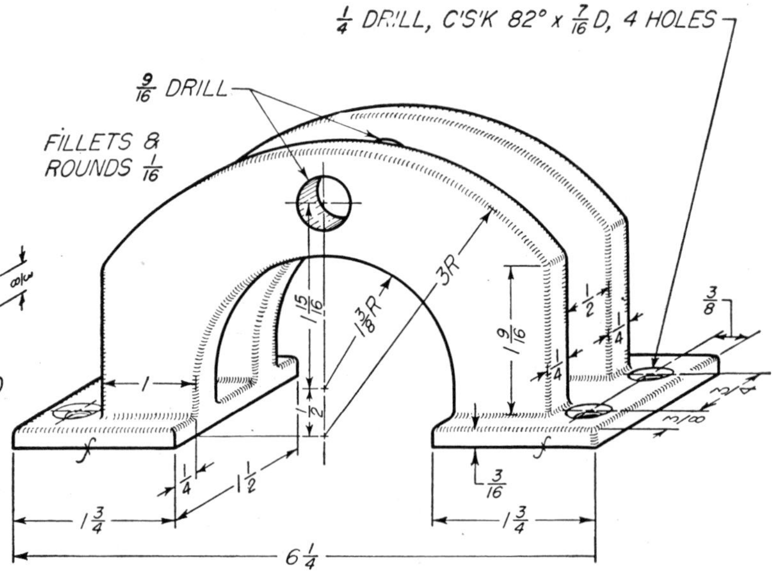

1/4 DRILL, C'S'K 82° x 7/16 D, 4 HOLES
9/16 DRILL
FILLETS & ROUNDS 1/16
3R
1 3/8 R
1 15/16
1 9/16
6 1/4
1 3/4
1 3/4
3/16

Prob. 8-32. Pulley bracket, aluminum.

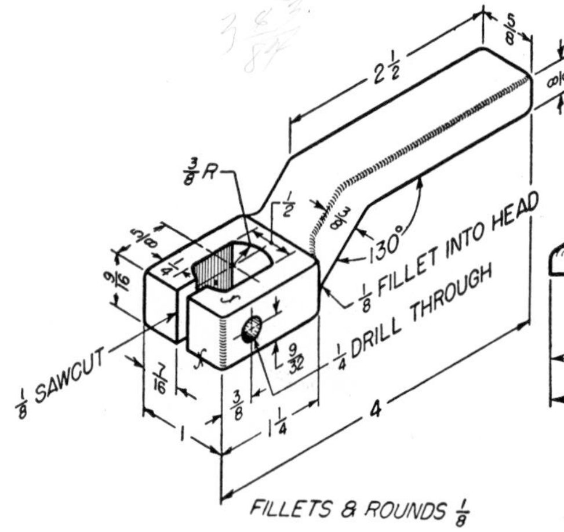

3/8 R
2 1/2
130°
1/8 FILLET INTO HEAD
1/4 DRILL THROUGH
1/8 SAWCUT
4
1 1/4
FILLETS & ROUNDS 1/8

Prob. 8-31. Valve handle, brass.

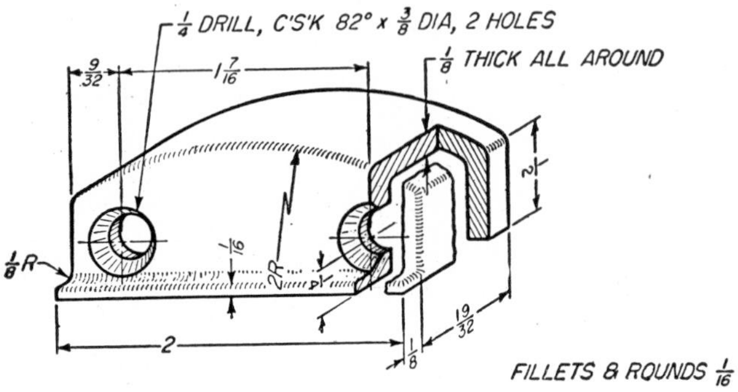

1/4 DRILL, C'S'K 82° x 3/8 DIA, 2 HOLES
1/8 THICK ALL AROUND
9/32
1 7/16
1/8 R
2R
2
19/32
FILLETS & ROUNDS 1/16

Prob. 8-33. Lock catch, brass.

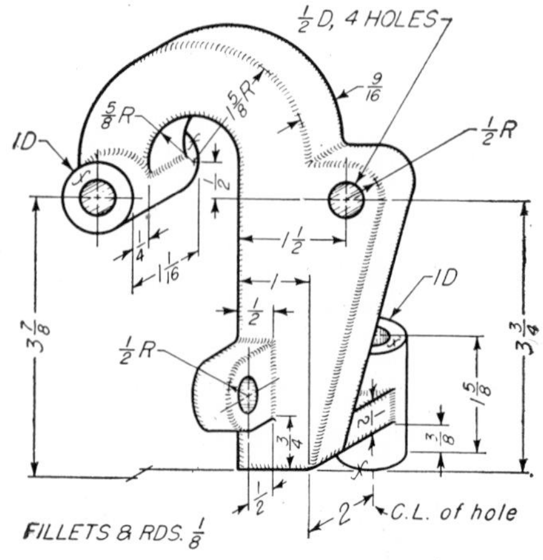

1/2 D, 4 HOLES
1D
5/8 R
1 5/8 R
1/2 R
1 1/2
1D
1/2 R
3 7/8
3 3/4
1 5/8
C.L. of hole
FILLETS & RDS. 1/8

Prob. 8-34. Arm spindle, steel.

Chapter 9

SECTIONING AND CONVENTIONAL PRACTICES

Sometimes an object is so complicated that its ordinary orthographic representation would result in a bewildering conglomeration of dotted lines representing hidden details. The draftsman can avoid this confusing situation by making a drawing "in section" which reveals the interior features while preserving a portion of the significant external lines of the piece. To obtain a section view an imaginary cutting plane is passed through the object in a selected position and direction. The portion shown in the section drawing is the part of the object that would be seen if the segment nearest the observer had been cut away and discarded. The other views are drawn in the ordinary manner, the only change being the inclusion of the symbolic cutting-plane line, which shows the position of the imaginary cutting plane.

A longitudinal section cuts an object lengthwise; a cross section cuts an object crosswise. The former is termed a sectional view; the latter is known as a cross section. Section views are helpful in detail drawing and are practically indispensable in assembly drawing, where the great number of hidden lines encountered would defeat any worthwhile purpose of the representations.

9-1. Full sections. When a longitudinal imaginary cutting plane extends through an entire object showing the whole object in section, as in **Fig.** 9-1, the result is known as a full section. In the front view, note that not only the cut surface but also any visible lines behind the sectioning plane are shown. Note also that the top view, with the exception of the inclusion of the cutting-plane line, is represented in the ordinary manner.

9-2. The cutting-plane line. The construction of the symbolic cutting-plane line is shown in **Fig.** 9-2. It is placed on the view related (adjacent) to the section view and indicates the path of the cutting plane. The line consists of two short and one long dash repeated as required for **its** length, terminating in arrows that point in **the** direction in which the object was viewed when **the** section was taken. A simple way to avoid confusion is to remember that the arrows always point away from the discarded portion of the object. If only one section view appears on the drawing sheet and the position of the cutting-plane line is obvious or cannot be mistaken, it may be omitted on that sheet. If two or more section views appear on the same sheet, however, the cutting-plane lines must be shown and identified by letters placed at the extremities below or behind the arrows (see Figs. 9-3 and 9-18). These letters are capitals and should be the largest letters on the

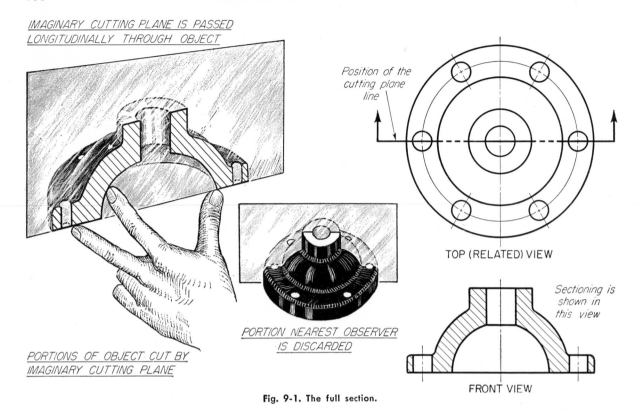

IMAGINARY CUTTING PLANE IS PASSED
LONGITUDINALLY THROUGH OBJECT

Position of the
cutting plane
line

TOP (RELATED) VIEW

PORTION NEAREST OBSERVER
IS DISCARDED

Sectioning is
shown in
this view

PORTIONS OF OBJECT CUT BY
IMAGINARY CUTTING PLANE

FRONT VIEW

Fig. 9-1. The full section.

ARROWS POINT IN SAME DIRECTION AS LINE OF SIGHT
USED FOR DRAWING OF THE SECTION VIEW

$\frac{1}{16}$ $\frac{3}{4}$

A   A

$\frac{1}{8}$ *Same weight as object line*

THE SYMBOLICAL CUTTING PLANE LINE IS PLACED
ON THE VIEW RELATED TO THE SECTION VIEW

Fig. 9-2. The cutting-plane line.

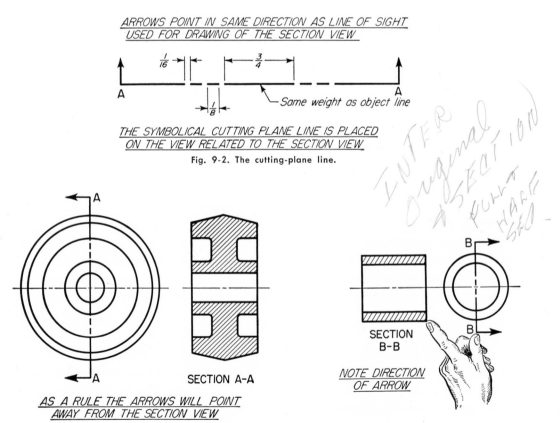

A

A

SECTION A-A

AS A RULE THE ARROWS WILL POINT
AWAY FROM THE SECTION VIEW

B

B

SECTION
B-B

NOTE DIRECTION
OF ARROW

Fig. 9-3. Use of the cutting-plane line.

drawing (¼ to ⅜ in. high). It may not always be possible or desirable to place a section view on the same sheet as the view showing its cutting-plane line. Therefore, when a cutting-plane line identifies a section view on another sheet, a fraction is used showing in the numerator the letter of the section and in the denominator the number of the sheet where the section view may be located. The fraction is placed in a circle at the intersection of the line and the shaft of the arrow, as shown in Fig. 9-4. When a cutting-plane line and a center line coincide, the cutting-plane line takes precedence and is the one shown on the drawing (see Figs. 9-13 and 9-14).

9-3. Offset sections. A full-section cutting plane need not always pass through the main axis or center line of an object. Its direction may be changed (*i.e.,* offset) in order to show other desired features and details. When an offset full section is drawn, the section view shows no lines to indicate the break, or offsetting, of the imaginary cutting plane. However, the true course of the cutting plane is always shown in the related view by the symbolic cutting-plane line. Figure 9-5 illustrates the use of an offset section plane.

9-4. Invisible lines. Ordinarily, all contours of the forms exposed, including the edges of the parts severed by the cutting plane, are shown in the section view. Since the prime reason for drawing a section view is to show the internal forms and features of a part, hidden lines should not be shown in a drawing unless they are absolutely necessary for further clarification, or their presence is indispensable for dimensioning purposes. (A section view may be used for dimensioning just like any ordinary view.) If the use of several hidden lines will save the labor of producing another complete view, the draftsman should resort to his own judgment in the matter. In Fig. 9-1, for example, no dotted lines are shown in the section view (front view).

9-5. Section lining. All section views are distinguishable by what is known as section lining (sometimes erroneously called crosshatching). In section lining, parallel lines are drawn across all surfaces cut by the sectioning plane. Since the appearance of a drawing may be marred by poor section lining, this step in making the view should be done very carefully.

9-6. Section-lining technique. The section lining for each individual part must always be drawn in the same direction with the same spacing and angle in all views showing a part in section, whether standing alone or shown in assembly with other pieces. A single piece is sectioned with sharp thin lines about ¹⁄₁₆ in. apart, with the lines making an angle of 45° with the horizontal (see Fig. 9-9). In the case of small pieces, the pitch (spacing) may be reduced to ¹⁄₃₂ in., while for large objects the section lines may be as much as ⅛ in. apart. There is no set rule governing the amount

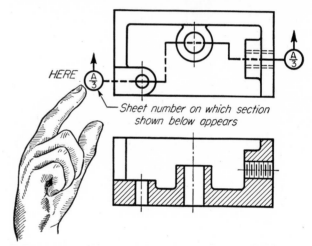
HERE
Sheet number on which section shown below appears

Fig. 9-4. Identification for section views. (*From ASA Z14.1—1946.*)

of pitch or the size of the angle. The size and contour of the part will often suggest the best spacing and angle to employ.

Section lining requires much patience and care on the part of the draftsman, since, in addition to having to maintain uniform pitch "by eye," he must make the lines regular and of even weight, with sufficient contrast between them and the lines of the object. The left-hand portion of Fig. 9-6 shows the pleasing pattern obtained when an even and proper pitch is combined with uniform lines that make a proper contrast with the outlines of the cut portion and the other contour lines of the object. The right side of the figure

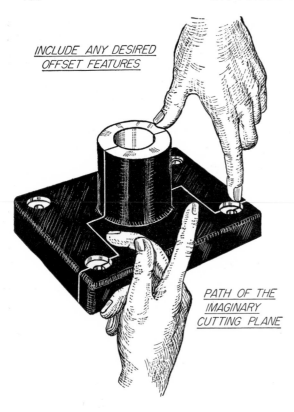

INCLUDE ANY DESIRED
OFFSET FEATURES

PATH OF THE
IMAGINARY
CUTTING PLANE

OFFSET SECTIONS MAY BE TAKEN IN ANY
DESIRED DIRECTION

OFFSET SECTIONS SAVE THE DRAWING OF
EXTRA VIEWS OF IRREGULAR OBJECTS

Fig. 9-5. The offset section.

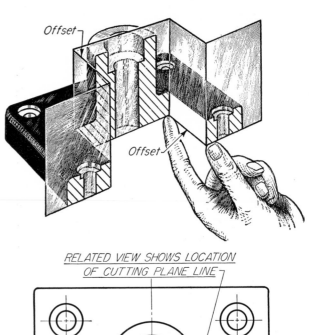

Offset

Offset

RELATED VIEW SHOWS LOCATION
OF CUTTING PLANE LINE

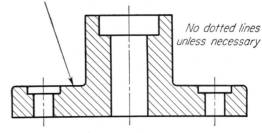

No line to show the
offset in section view

No dotted lines
unless necessary

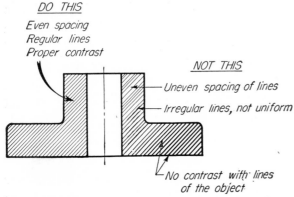

DO THIS
Even spacing
Regular lines
Proper contrast

NOT THIS
Uneven spacing of lines
Irregular lines, not uniform

No contrast with lines
of the object

Fig. 9-6. Contrast of proper and poorly done section lining.

shows the ruinous effect of poorly spaced and executed section lining. When objects whose dominant outlines are parallel to the natural 45°, 30°, and 60° angles are encountered, a 75° or 15° slant, or any odd angle, should be employed to avoid bizarre effects such as grooving and other distortions (see Fig. 9-7).

9-7. Outline sectioning. For very large areas it is permissible to show section lines just within the boundary of the surface shown sectioned, leaving the interior portions untouched. An example of outline sectioning is shown in Fig. 9-8.

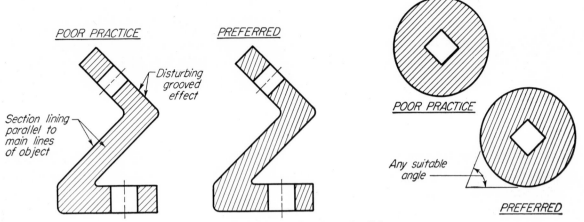

Fig. 9-7. Avoid bizarre effects in section lining.

9-8. Sections in assembly. In assembly drawings, all portions of the same piece are always shown in all views with the section lining running in the same direction, with the lines all the same weight and the same distance apart. The section lining of the part adjacent runs in an opposite direction. If two pieces are shown in assembly, the lines of each piece are drawn at 45° angles running in opposite directions (see Fig. 9-9). When three or more pieces appear in assembly, angles of 30°, 60°, or even 15° may be

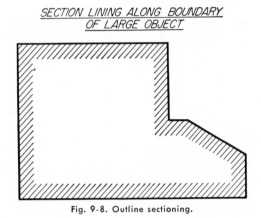

Fig. 9-8. Outline sectioning.

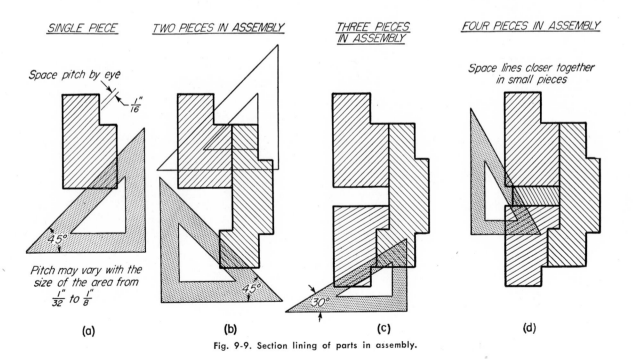

Fig. 9-9. Section lining of parts in assembly.

employed (see Fig. 9-9c and d), or the pitch of the section lining may be varied (that is, drawn slightly closer together or further apart depending on the size of the piece), taking care that the lines do not run parallel to the principal lines of the part being sectioned. Adherence to these few rules will prevent the possibility of an observer confusing one piece with another.

9-9. Section code for different materials. Different kinds of section lining may be used to indicate various materials (steel, cast iron, brass or copper, the white metals, etc.). When a drawing shows only a single detail, the exact composition of the object is shown in the title block and *code* section lining is not necessary. Where several pieces are shown in a section assembly, however, it may be helpful to identify the different parts and materials by using the sectioning code approved by the American Standards Association (Fig. 9-10). Code sectioning is not in general use in industry, however, and in most shops its use is determined by the chief draftsman. The customary practice is to use the section lining for cast iron for all objects and indicate the exact composition in the title block or bill of materials (see Figs. 9-9 and 9-14, for example).

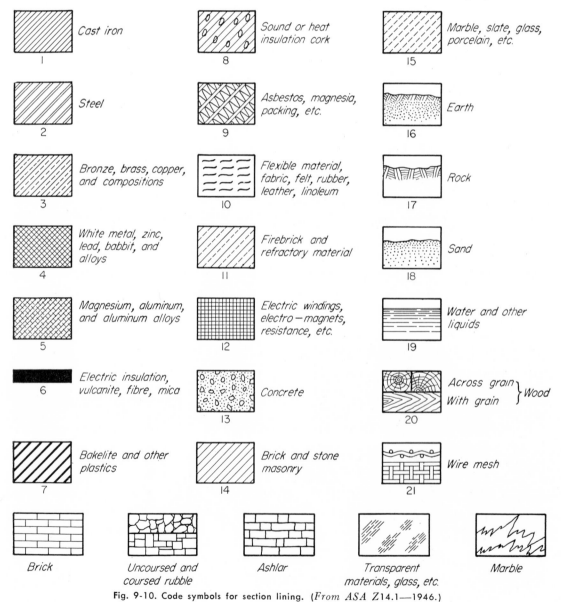

Fig. 9-10. Code symbols for section lining. (*From ASA Z14.1—1946.*)

9-10. Shafts, rods, nuts and bolts, rivets, keys, pins, etc. Pieces of this type that have no internal features are not drawn in section if seen in profile (when their axes lie parallel to the plane of the paper). However, cross sections or broken-out sections may be employed if they would prove helpful to the worker. Figure 9-11 illustrates their appearance in an assembly section.

9-11. Thin materials. The cross-section views of structural steel, sheet-metal forms, gaskets, and other thin materials are shown in solid black. If two or more thin pieces are adjacent to each other, a white line should separate the parts (see Fig. 9-12).

9-12. Half sections. A half section is produced by passing an imaginary cutting plane halfway through an object, stopping at the main axis, or center line. One-quarter of the object is discarded, and the resulting drawing shows the portion on one side of the main center line as an ordinary external view and the other half as a section revealing the internal forms and features of the object (see Fig. 9-13). Hidden lines are omitted in both halves unless absolutely necessary for further description or for dimensioning purposes. The half section is not recommended if it is necessary to dimension diameters of circular forms that extend on both sides of the main center line, since the dimensioning can rarely be done without the addition of hidden lines in the portion that shows the external features. In the case of assembly drawings, however, where often the only dimensions required are reference over-alls and those between main center lines, it is very advantageous to the draftsman to be able to show both the external and internal appearance of a

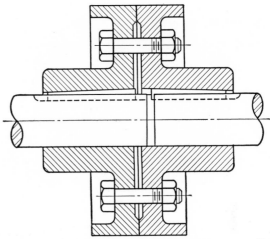

Fig. 9-11. Shafts, keys, bolts and nuts in sectional view. (*From ASA Z14.1—1946.*)

bisymmetrical group in assembly (Fig. 9-14). Note also in Figs. 9-13 and 9-14 that a center line is used at the center of the view, for if any center line and a cutting-plane edge coincide in the section view, a center line is shown instead of a solid object line, since the edge represents only the imaginary cutting plane and the parts themselves

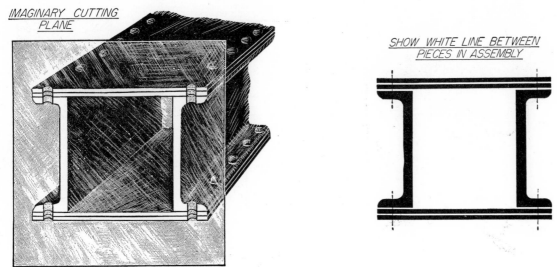

Fig. 9-12. Thin materials in section.

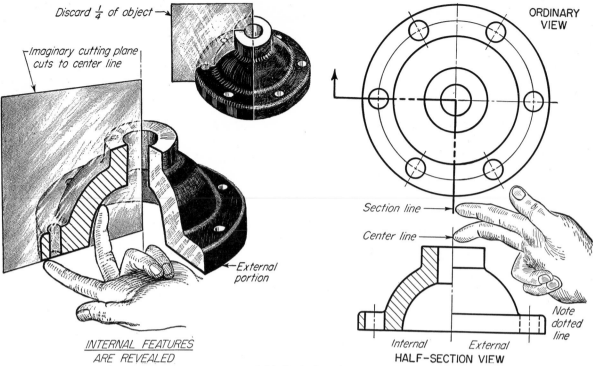

Discard ¼ of object

Imaginary cutting plane cuts to center line

External portion

INTERNAL FEATURES ARE REVEALED

ORDINARY VIEW

Section line

Center line

Note dotted line

Internal   External

HALF-SECTION VIEW

Fig. 9-13. The half section.

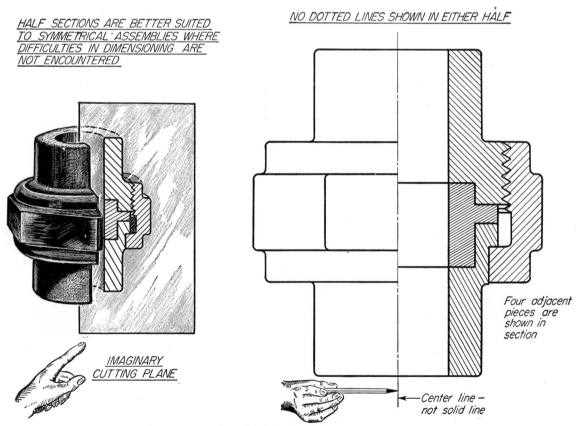

HALF SECTIONS ARE BETTER SUITED TO SYMMETRICAL ASSEMBLIES WHERE DIFFICULTIES IN DIMENSIONING ARE NOT ENCOUNTERED

IMAGINARY CUTTING PLANE

NO DOTTED LINES SHOWN IN EITHER HALF

Four adjacent pieces are shown in section

Center line — not solid line

Fig. 9-14. Half section of an assembly.

are not actually to be severed in the machine shop.

9-13. Broken-out sections. In cases where only isolated details or features need be shown, and a full or half section would serve no useful purpose, a partial, or broken-out, section is used. The imaginary cutting plane passes through some particular feature, exposing its interior to view and leaving an irregular break line as a boundary (see Figs. 9-15 and 9-16). No further identifica-

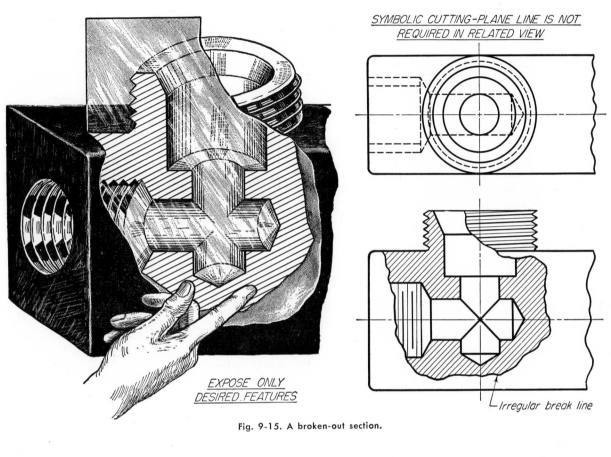

Fig. 9-15. A broken-out section.

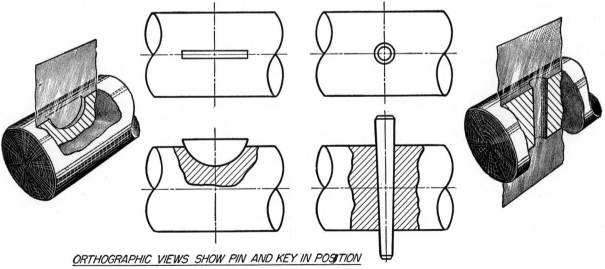

Fig. 9-16. Broken-out sections showing positions of keys, pins, etc.

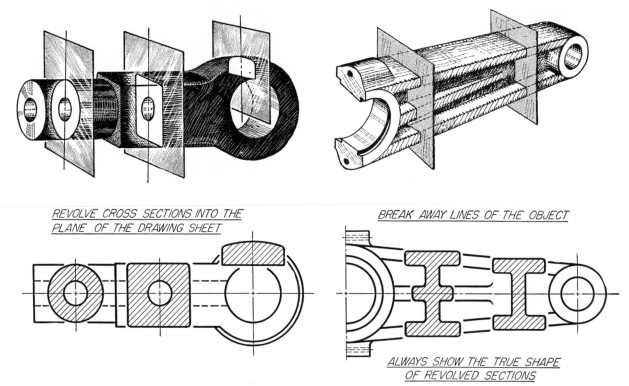

REVOLVE CROSS SECTIONS INTO THE
PLANE OF THE DRAWING SHEET

BREAK AWAY LINES OF THE OBJECT

ALWAYS SHOW THE TRUE SHAPE
OF REVOLVED SECTIONS

Fig. 9-17. Revolved sections.

tion is required, and the symbolic cutting-plane line is not shown in the related view.

9-14. Revolved sections. If the true cross-sectional appearance of a propeller blade, a rib, bar, or other like form is to be shown, a revolved section is employed (see Fig. 9-17). The imaginary cutting plane is passed through the object perpendicular to the axis in the profile view and then revolved on its center line 90° into the plane of the paper. Any lines of the object that might tend to pass through the true-shape cross-section view are omitted and in many cases broken away to leave the view clear. The section is always superimposed on an exterior view and always shows the true shape of the exposed sectioned portion, disregarding the direction of the contour lines of the object.

9-15. Detail, or removed, sections. At times, additional clarity may be attained by drawing a detail, or removed, section. This view is drawn at either the same scale as the related view or enlarged to facilitate dimensioning and emphasize the construction (see Fig. 9-18). If more than

one detail section appears on the drawing sheet, each view must be identified with a note below it, such as "section *AA*," "section *BB*," etc. The symbolic section line must always appear in the related view. Good practice suggests that detail section views be placed directly above or below the point on the related view where the section has been taken, or on the same center line at either side of the piece. The detail and revolved sections are similar, with the exception that the detail section is not superimposed on the external view. When a partial removed section is employed, the entire object need not be drawn. The judicious use of revolved and removed sections will result, in many instances, in more easily understood drawings.

9-16. Phantom sections. A phantom section shows the exterior of an object with its internal features brought out by dotted section lining (see Fig. 9-19). The phantom section is valuable in showing the relative positions of external and internal adjacent portions or complete parts. It is rarely used but at times is very helpful.

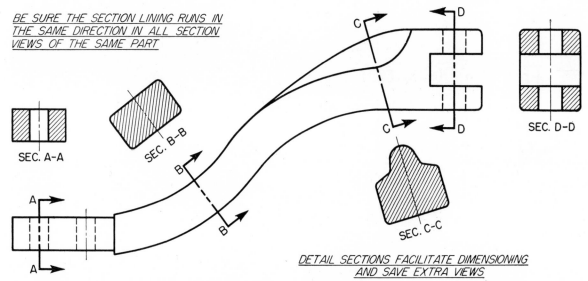

BE SURE THE SECTION LINING RUNS IN THE SAME DIRECTION IN ALL SECTION VIEWS OF THE SAME PART

SEC. A-A

SEC. B-B

SEC. C-C

SEC. D-D

DETAIL SECTIONS FACILITATE DIMENSIONING AND SAVE EXTRA VIEWS

Fig. 9-18. Detail, or removed, sections.

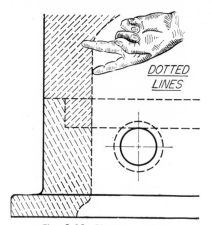

DOTTED LINES

Fig. 9-19. Phantom section.

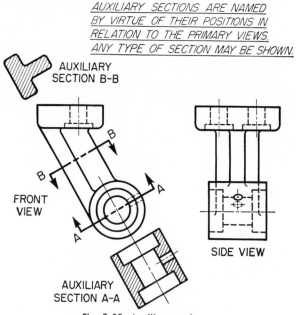

AUXILIARY SECTIONS ARE NAMED BY VIRTUE OF THEIR POSITIONS IN RELATION TO THE PRIMARY VIEWS. ANY TYPE OF SECTION MAY BE SHOWN.

AUXILIARY SECTION B-B

FRONT VIEW

SIDE VIEW

AUXILIARY SECTION A-A

Fig. 9-20. Auxiliary sections.

9-17. Auxiliary sections. A section view projected to a plane that is not one of the principal planes is called an auxiliary section (see Fig. 9-20). The principles of auxiliary projection and the selection of auxiliary views are explained in detail in Chaps. 10 and 11. An auxiliary section may be any type of section (full, half, broken-out, detail, revolved, etc.); the term auxiliary merely indicates its required position in relation to the view from which it has been projected or in relation to the principal views on the drawing sheet.

9-18. Conventional practices. It is often advisable to violate certain procedures of true projection for both sectional and ordinary views to simplify the representation or to avoid distorted or confusing drawings. Accordingly, a number of "conventional practices" have become established which enable the draftsman to clarify certain presentations. Various conventional procedures have now been adopted by the American Standards Association because their use aids materially in producing readily comprehensible drawings. A number of the more common examples follow.

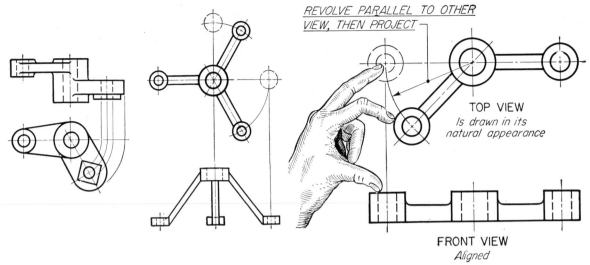

REVOLVE PARALLEL TO OTHER VIEW, THEN PROJECT

TOP VIEW
Is drawn in its natural appearance

FRONT VIEW
Aligned

Fig. 9-21. Alignment of parts. (*Part* (a) *from ASA Z14.1—1946.*)

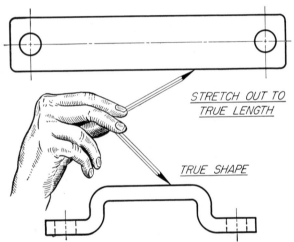

STRETCH OUT TO TRUE LENGTH

TRUE SHAPE

Fig. 9-22. Developed or stretched-out forms.

9-19. Aligned views. Parts that have features at an angle with each other, such as arms, lugs, and other like forms, may be shown straightened out, or aligned, in one view by imagining that the features at an angle are rotated into the plane of projection. Figure 9-21 shows three examples of aligned views. One of the views gives the natural appearance of each part, while in the related views the arms are shown revolved into alignment to give understandable and symmetrical representations of the objects. These straightened-out views show the true shape of the features and their true distances from the centers to which they are related—something that could not be conveyed by strict orthographic representation.

9-20. Developed views. Pieces of thin material of various shapes are drawn in their true bent-shape contours in one view and shown stretched out to their over-all length in the related view (see Fig. 9-22). In specifying over-all dimensions, extra metal must be allotted for bends. Exactly how much to allow is best determined from shop experience, although formulas are available.

9-21. Revolution of ribs and holes. Ribs and holes that are arranged radially from a common center are rotated into the plane of projection in one view in order to convey a symmetrical appearance and to show the true distance of the features from the center of the part (see Fig. 9-23). The ribs and holes are shown in their true positions in the circular view, which also shows the plane of rotation.

9-22. Conventional practices in sectioning. Web and riblike features of a part are not shown sectioned in section views. Although the cutting plane is shown passing lengthwise through the center of the ribs in the circular view, it should be imagined that the cutting plane is offset so as to pass just in front of the ribs (see Fib. 9-24). The section lining of the ribs is then omitted and the ribs appear in outline form in the section view. This procedure avoids giving the misleading impression that the object is solid. In most

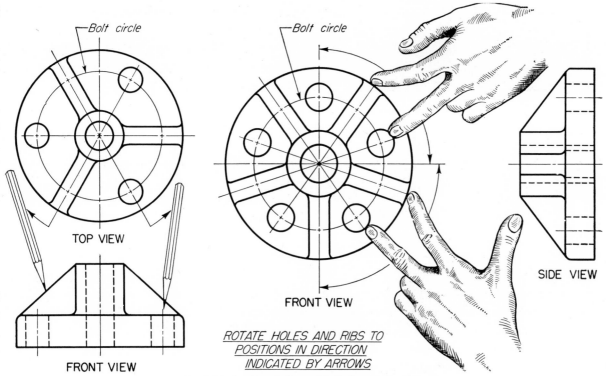

Fig. 9-23. Rotation of ribs and holes in ordinary views.

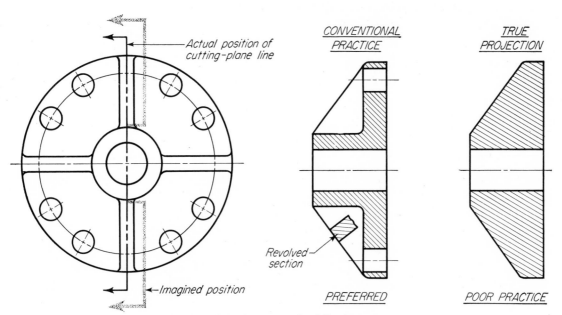

Fig. 9-24. Treatment of weblike forms.

cases the inclusion of a revolved section as shown in the figure will show all that need be known about the shape of the ribs.

If the rib or web is likely to be overlooked by the workman, its presence on the object may be emphasized by section lining in which every other line is omitted, as in Fig. 9-25. This technique is employed only on rare occasions.

Radially arranged ribs and holes located on the bolt circle are rotated into the plane of sectioning

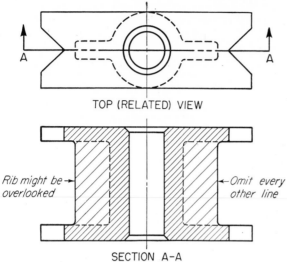

TOP (RELATED) VIEW

Rib might be → ← *Omit every*
overlooked   *other line*

SECTION A-A

Fig. 9-25. Sectioning of ribs (rarely used).

in the same manner as described in Sec. 9-21. The ribs are shown unsectioned and the holes appear outlined in the section view (see Fig. 9-26). Arms, lugs, and other similar forms on parts such as those in Fig. 9-27 are treated in the same fashion.

Note the misleading true projection and sectioning of the wheel and its spokes in Fig. 9-28 and then study the conventional treatment illustrated at the right. If the spokes were shown sectioned the implication would be that the rim's supporting structure was solid (compare this drawing with Fig. 9-24). Revolving the slot into

the position shown facilitates its dimensioning and shows the true section across the hub.

9-23. Boltheads, nuts, slots, pinholes. In the representation of boltheads and nuts strict adherence to the rules of orthographic projection would be misleading, since a hexagonal head or nut would appear to have only two sides in one view (see Fig. 9-29). The head and nut of a bolt are therefore shown "across corners," in profile views. This violation of true projection (when the head and nut are not shown in a slot assembly) is desirable, for it not only avoids confusion, but it also shows the amount of clearance needed for the fastener.

Figure 9-30 shows the conventional treatment for representing slots and pinholes. The slot in the cap screw is drawn at an angle of 45° in the circular view and in its true shape and position in the related profile view. The pinhole is shown in its true circular appearance in one view but at the attention-compelling angle of 45° in its related view.

Half views or partial views of symmetrical objects may be drawn when space is limited. When the front view is to be in section, the related partial view should show the portion behind the section plane (Fig. 9-31). If the front view is an ordinary orthographic representation, the partial

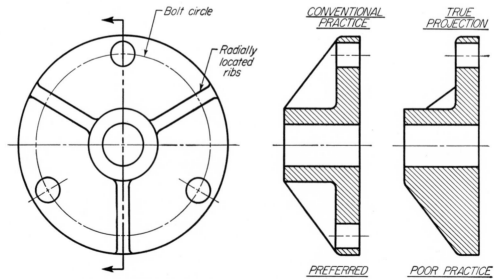

Fig. 9-26. Revolution of radially located ribs. and holes on bolt circles.

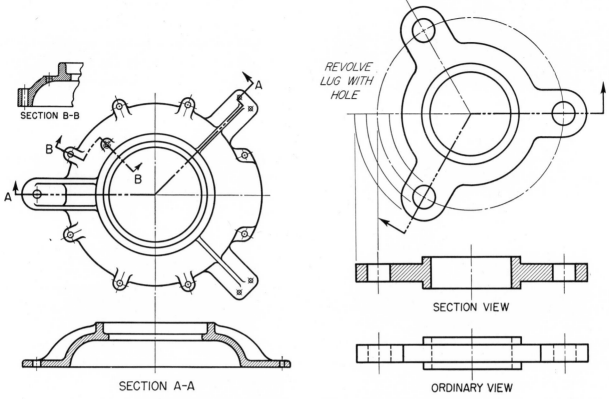

SECTION B-B

SECTION A-A

REVOLVE LUG WITH HOLE

SECTION VIEW

ORDINARY VIEW

Fig. 9-27. Rotation of arms, lugs, etc. *(From ASA Z14.1—1946.)*

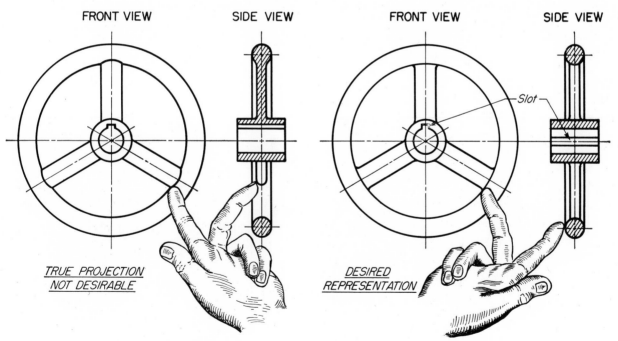

FRONT VIEW   SIDE VIEW   FRONT VIEW   SIDE VIEW

Slot

TRUE PROJECTION
NOT DESIRABLE

DESIRED
REPRESENTATION

Fig. 9-28. True and conventional representations of a wheel and its spokes.

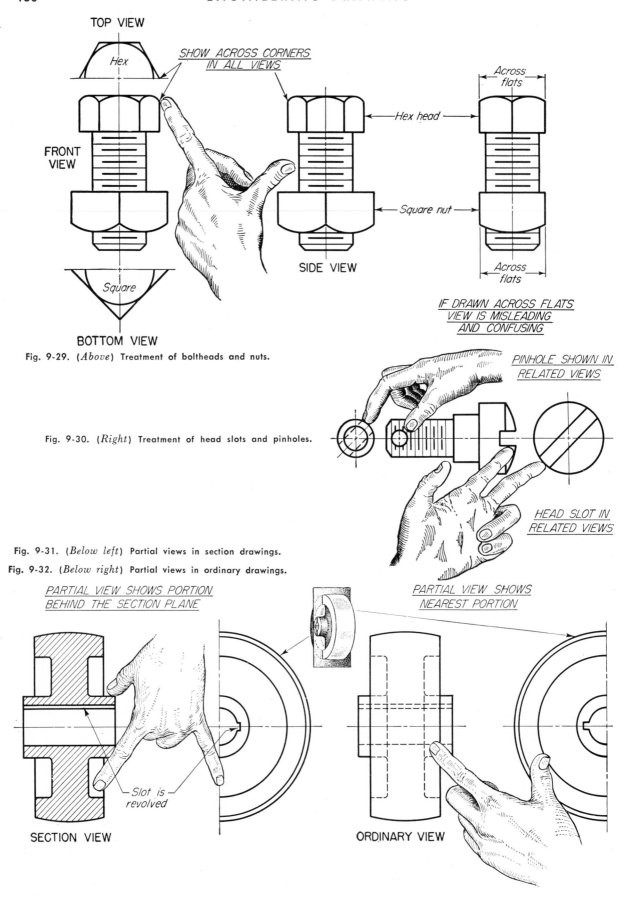

TOP VIEW

Hex

SHOW ACROSS CORNERS
IN ALL VIEWS

FRONT
VIEW

Across
flats

Hex head

Square nut

SIDE VIEW

Across
flats

Square

BOTTOM VIEW

Fig. 9-29. (*Above*) Treatment of boltheads and nuts.

IF DRAWN ACROSS FLATS
VIEW IS MISLEADING
AND CONFUSING

PINHOLE SHOWN IN
RELATED VIEWS

Fig. 9-30. (*Right*) Treatment of head slots and pinholes.

HEAD SLOT IN
RELATED VIEWS

Fig. 9-31. (*Below left*) Partial views in section drawings.

Fig. 9-32. (*Below right*) Partial views in ordinary drawings.

PARTIAL VIEW SHOWS PORTION
BEHIND THE SECTION PLANE

PARTIAL VIEW SHOWS
NEAREST PORTION

Slot is
revolved

SECTION VIEW

ORDINARY VIEW

view should show the nearest external portion of the object (Fig. 9-32).

9-24. Alternate positions. The method of showing an alternate position of a part, or the limiting position of a moving part, is shown in Fig. 9-33. The alternate or limiting-position lines of the object are drawn as long dashes finer and lighter than the lines of the object in the original position.

9-25. Unimportant intersections. Figure 9-34 shows the conventional manner of representing unimportant intersections of circular and rectangular forms. The extra work necessary for

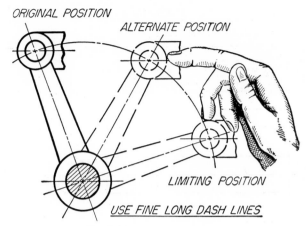

Fig. 9-33. Alternate positions.

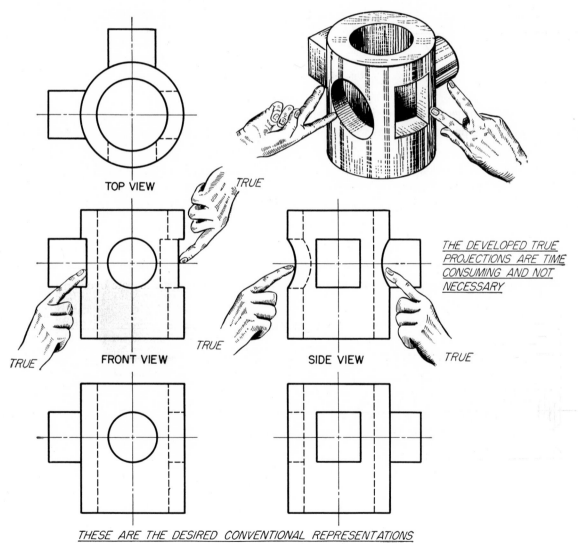

Fig. 9-34. Unimportant intersections.

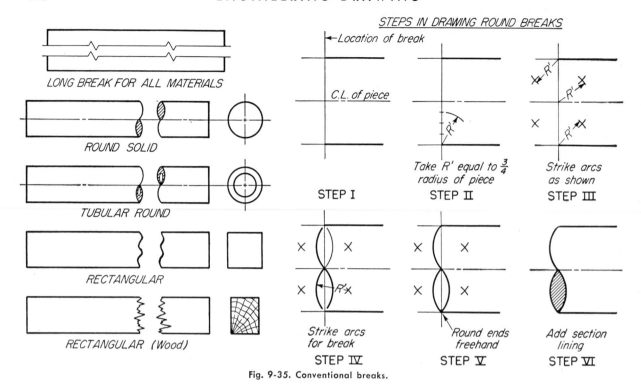

STEPS IN DRAWING ROUND BREAKS

LONG BREAK FOR ALL MATERIALS

ROUND SOLID

TUBULAR ROUND

RECTANGULAR

RECTANGULAR (Wood)

← Location of break

C.L. of piece

STEP I

Take R' equal to ¾ radius of piece
STEP II

Strike arcs as shown
STEP III

Strike arcs for break
STEP IV

Round ends freehand
STEP V

Add section lining
STEP VI

Fig. 9-35. Conventional breaks.

developing the true projected lines of intersection would serve no useful purpose, and thus this long procedure is ignored.

9-26. Conventional breaks. When unusually long, simply constructed features, such as bars, rods, shafts, tubes and arms, are to be drawn, the entire length need not be shown on the sheet. The form may be broken at a convenient position and a cross section shown at that point, or a conventional break may be used such as those recom-

mended by the American Standards Association (see Fig. 9-35). Conventional breaks may be drawn with a compass or irregular curve, or freehand, on either detail or assembly drawings (see the righthand portion of Fig. 9-35). A part having repeated similar features may be represented by the completion of several of its profiles and the use of ditto lines as shown in Fig. 9-36. Although the broken representation on the sheet is not drawn to full scale, the true over-all length of the

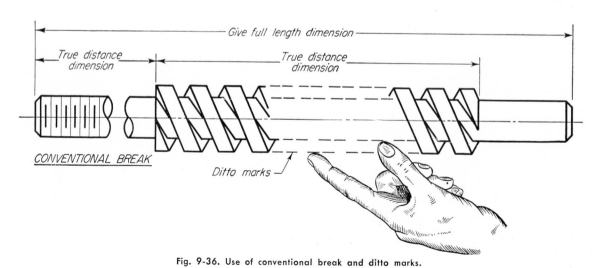

Give full length dimension

True distance dimension

True distance dimension

CONVENTIONAL BREAK

Ditto marks

Fig. 9-36. Use of conventional break and ditto marks.

piece and the true distances between features are given when the piece is dimensioned.

9-27. Fillets, rounds, runouts. The intersections formed by surfaces of objects often can be shown more clearly if a conventional treatment is adopted. The intersection of two unfinished surfaces at an inside corner of a casting is always rounded for greater strength. This small curved intersection is called a fillet (see Fig. 9-37). A fillet is either formed naturally when the metal hardens or is formed artificially by the intentional

rounding of the edges of the pattern by the patternmaker. Outside corners of castings are rounded for appearance and for ease of handling. The rounded external corners are known as rounds. Fillets and rounds should always be shown when drawing corners of unfinished castings. A sharp edge or corner should be drawn when one surface is to be machined and the other left in its original state, or when both intersecting surfaces are to be machined.

Supporting, bracing, or strengthening forms,

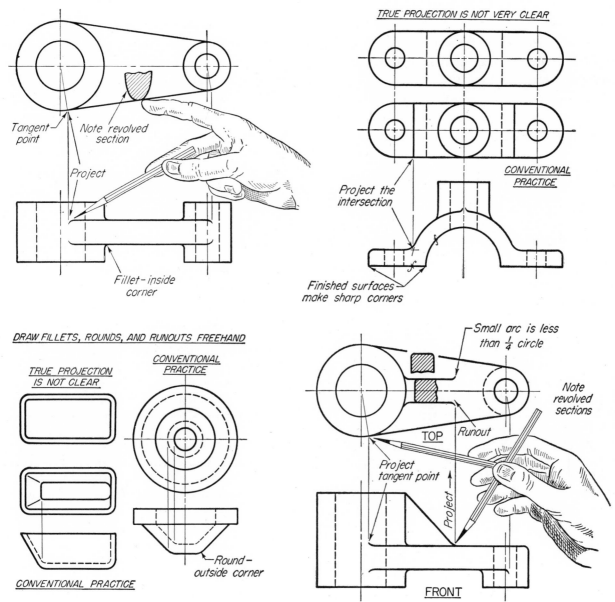

Fig. 9-37. Conventional treatment of fillets, rounds, and runouts.

such as ribs and webs, will often run smoothly into other surfaces or features and terminate in curves called runouts, which are conventional representations of filleted intersections where the change in direction is so gradual that theoretically no line should be drawn.

If iron is used in casting, the fillets and rounds are generally about $\frac{1}{8}$ in. in radius. Most of the white metals (aluminum, zinc, etc.) leave a $\frac{1}{16}$-in. fillet or round. The draftsman should indicate the size of all undimensioned fillets and rounds with a note on the drawing sheet thus: "All fillets and rounds $\frac{1}{8}$"," or "All fillets and rounds $\frac{1}{16}$" unless otherwise specified." Such a note should be placed near enough to one of the principal views so as to appear as part of the regular dimensioning of the object.

The conventional treatment used in drawing some of the types of fillets and rounds encountered in practice is shown in Fig. 9-37. Arcs are usually drawn freehand; however, some draftsmen prefer to use a compass or a french curve. In drawing fillets and runouts, the tangent point should be projected to the related view, where the representation is then shown by an arc of a radius equal to the fillet or runout. The curved segment of the runout should be noticeably less than a quarter circle. The extreme end of the arc is in direct projection with the tangent point in the other view, and the cross section of the material (web, rib, etc.) determines the direction in which the arcs turn.

On an outside surface the theoretical intersection forming a round is projected from the circular view to the related view, where it is represented by the required solid or dotted lines. The true smooth projection of the round (or fillet) is ignored in order to offer a more comprehensible representation on the drawing from which the shop man will work.

PROBLEMS

The following problems have been especially selected to give the student practice in applying his knowledge of conventional treatments as well as sectioning procedure. Most of the problems deal with objects that contain special features such as holes, ribs, and lugs that are to be treated conventionally in the related views. All the drawings should be properly and completely dimensioned according to the principles set forth in Chap. 8. The section views should be dimensioned, when necessary, along with the ordinary views. The drawings should be made on $8\frac{1}{2}$-by 11-in. sheets unless otherwise noted.

9-1. *Cover plate.* Reproduce the front view. Draw the top view as a full section. Dimension completely. (Time: $1\frac{1}{2}$ hr.)

9-2. *Gland.* Employ the scale shown, holding all dimensions to the nearest $\frac{1}{16}$ in. Reproduce the front view. Draw the side view in full section. Dimension completely. (Time: 2 hr.)

9-3. *Jack base.* Redraw the front and side views so that the side view will be a full section. The cutting plane should pass through both slots and the center hole of the front view. Dimension completely. (Time: 2 hr.)

9-4. *Bracket.* Reproduce the top and side views. Draw the front view in full section. Use all three views for dimensioning. Sheet size, 11 by 17 in. (Time: 4 hr.)

9-5. *Shifter bracket.* Employ the scale shown, holding all dimensions to the nearest $\frac{1}{16}$ in. Reproduce the top view. Show the front view in full section. Dimension completely. (Time: 2 hr.)

9-6. *Shaft yoke.* Employ the scale shown, holding all dimensions to the nearest $\frac{1}{16}$ in. Reproduce the front view. Complete the side view as a full section. Observe the rules of accepted conventional procedure in showing the ribs and holes in the section view. Dimension completely. (Time: 2 hr.)

9-7. *Cover plate.* Redraw the front view. Complete the side view as a full section, showing the proper treatment of the lugs. Dimension completely. (Time: $2\frac{1}{2}$ hr.)

9-8. *Pulley.* Redraw the front view, omitting the revolved section of the rim. Add a side view in full section showing the proper location of the slot in this view. Dimension completely. (Time: $2\frac{1}{2}$ hr.)

9-9. *Bearing bracket.* Make a three-view drawing. Show one view in full section. Offset the cutting plane so that it passes through the holes in the vertical and horizontal planes. Dimension completely. (Time: 4 hr.)

9-10. *Shaft support.* Employ the scale shown, holding all dimensions to the nearest $\frac{1}{16}$ in. Reproduce the front and top views. Add a side view in full section by employing an offset cutting plane passing through the large hole and the two nearest holes in the horizontal surface. Dimension completely. (Time: 3 hr.)

9-11. *Caster frame.* Make three views. Show one view as a full offset section. Dimension completely. (Time: 2½ hr.)

9-12. *Face plate.* Draw two views. Make one a full offset section. Dimension completely. (Time: 2½ hr.)

9-13. *Float bracket.* Draw a front and top view. Make the front view a suitable full offset section. Dimension completely. (Time: 3 hr.)

9-14. *Cover plate.* Reproduce the top view showing a broken-out section at the oil hole. Make a full-section front view. Each frame is a ¼-in. square. Dimension completely. (Time: 3 hr.)

9-15. *Die shoe.* This offers varied treatment as a sectioning problem. The choice is left to the student. Draw three views and dimension completely. Make object half size on an 8½- by 11-in. sheet. (Time: 4 hr.)

9-16. *Bearing bracket cap.* Employ the scale shown, holding all dimensions to the nearest $\frac{1}{16}$ in. Reproduce the top view. Make the front a half-section view. Dimension completely. (Time: 2½ hr.)

9-17. *End plate.* Employ the scale shown, holding all dimensions to the nearest $\frac{1}{16}$ in. Reproduce the front view. Show the side view as a half section. Dimension completely. (Time: 2½ hr.)

9-18. *Pulley.* Employ the scale shown, holding all dimensions to the nearest $\frac{1}{16}$ in. Reproduce the front view. Show the side as a half section. Dimension completely. (Time: 2½ hr.)

9-19. *Bearing bracket.* Draw a front and top view. Show the front as a half section. Dimension completely. (Time: 3 hr.)

9-20. *Link.* Reproduce the front and top views. Show revolved sections of the web structure in both top and front views. Dimension completely. (Time: 2 hr.)

9-21. *Cement breaker.* Draw one view only and show removed sections that will adequately describe the piece. Dimension completely. (Time: 2½ hr.)

9-22. *Pipe support.* Employ scale shown, holding all dimensions to the nearest $\frac{1}{16}$ in. Reproduce the top view. Show a revolved and a broken-out section in the front view. Dimension completely. Make object three-quarter size on an 8½- by 11-in. sheet. (Time: 2½ hr.)

9-23. *Cable guide.* Employ the scale shown, holding all dimensions to the nearest $\frac{1}{16}$ in. Draw the front view only. Make removed sections that will adequately describe the piece. Dimension completely. (Time: 2½ hr.)

The following problems may also be assigned as sectioning exercises if the instructor desires:

Problems 4-8, 4-9, 4-10, 4-12, 4-20, 4-21, 4-22, 8-3, 8-4, 8-6, 8-12, 8-17, 8-18, 8-33, 12-18, 12-33.

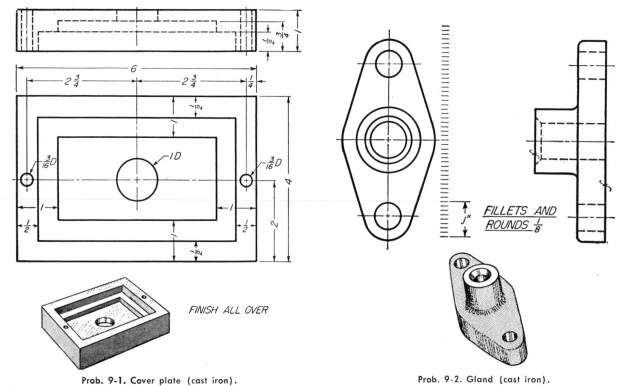

FINISH ALL OVER

Prob. 9-1. Cover plate (cast iron).

FILLETS AND
ROUNDS $\frac{1}{8}$

Prob. 9-2. Gland (cast iron).

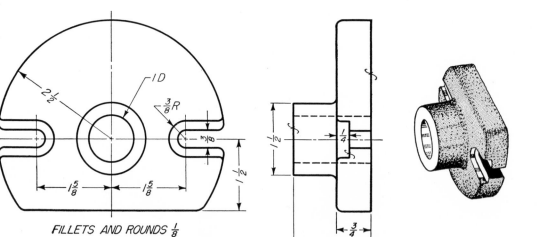

FILLETS AND ROUNDS $\frac{1}{8}$

Prob. 9-3. Jack base (cast iron).

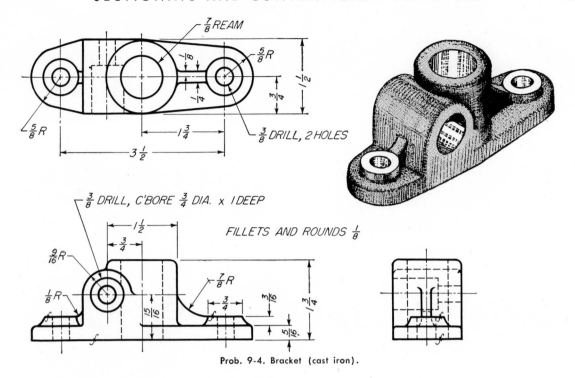

$\frac{7}{8}$ REAM

$\frac{1}{8}$

$\frac{5}{8}$ R

$\frac{1}{2}$

$\frac{3}{4}$

$\frac{1}{4}$

$\frac{5}{8}$ R

$1\frac{3}{4}$

$\frac{3}{8}$ DRILL, 2 HOLES

$3\frac{1}{2}$

$\frac{3}{8}$ DRILL, C'BORE $\frac{3}{4}$ DIA. x 1 DEEP

$1\frac{1}{2}$

$\frac{3}{4}$

FILLETS AND ROUNDS $\frac{1}{8}$

$\frac{9}{16}$ R

$\frac{7}{8}$ R

$\frac{3}{16}$

$\frac{3}{4}$

$\frac{1}{8}$ R

$\frac{15}{16}$

$\frac{3}{4}$

$\frac{5}{16}$

Prob. 9-4. Bracket (cast iron).

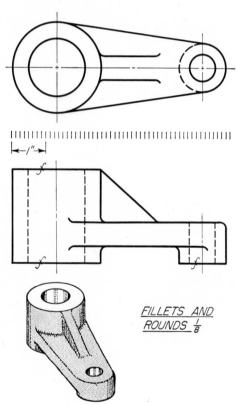

$\vdash$ $1''$ $\dashv$

FILLETS AND
ROUNDS $\frac{1}{8}$

Prob. 9-5. Shifter bracket (cast iron).

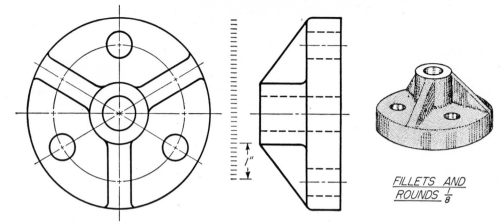

FILLETS AND ROUNDS $\frac{1}{8}$

Prob. 9-6. Shaft yoke (cast iron).

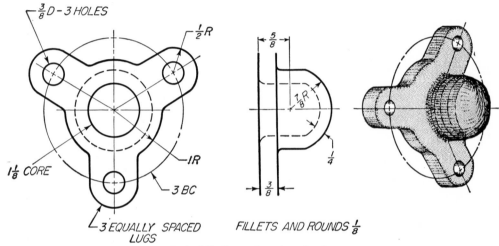

$\frac{3}{8}D$ – 3 HOLES

$\frac{1}{2}R$

$1\frac{1}{8}$ CORE

IR

3 BC

3 EQUALLY SPACED LUGS

$\frac{5}{8}$

$\frac{7}{8}R$

$\frac{1}{4}$

$\frac{3}{8}$

FILLETS AND ROUNDS $\frac{1}{8}$

Prob. 9-7. Cover plate (cast iron).

SLOT $\frac{1}{8}$ WIDE x $\frac{3}{32}$ DEEP

$\frac{1}{2}$

$4\frac{1}{8}D$

4D

$3\frac{3}{8}D$

ELLIPTICAL

$\frac{3}{16}$

$\frac{5}{16}$

$\frac{5}{8}D$

HUB $1\frac{1}{8}$ DIA. x $\frac{3}{4}$ LONG

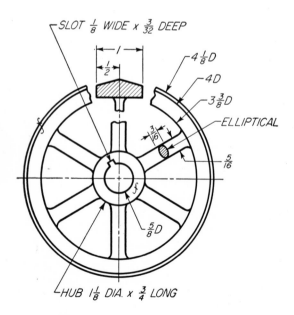

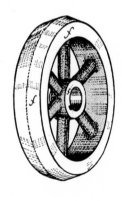

FILLETS AND ROUNDS $\frac{1}{8}$

Prob. 9-8. Pulley (cast iron).

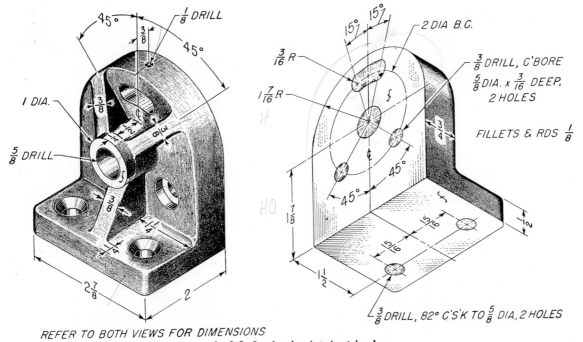

REFER TO BOTH VIEWS FOR DIMENSIONS

Prob. 9-9. Bearing bracket (cast iron).

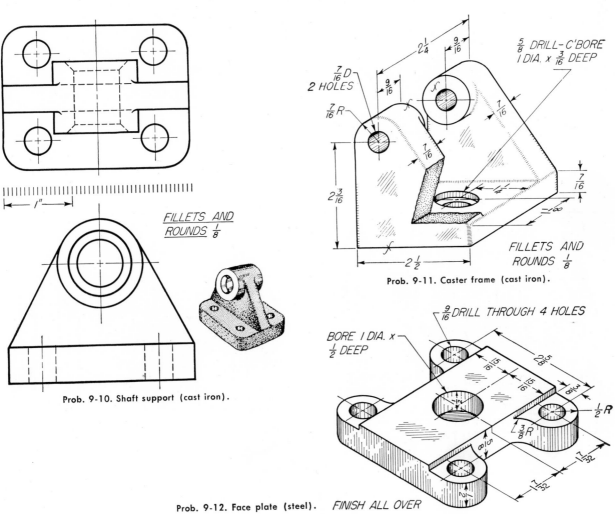

Prob. 9-10. Shaft support (cast iron).

FILLETS AND ROUNDS $\frac{1}{8}$

Prob. 9-11. Caster frame (cast iron).

Prob. 9-12. Face plate (steel). FINISH ALL OVER

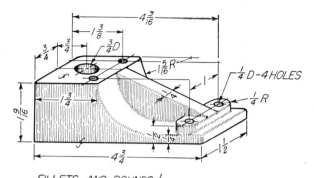

FILLETS AND ROUNDS $\frac{1}{8}$

Prob. 9-13. Float bracket (cast iron).

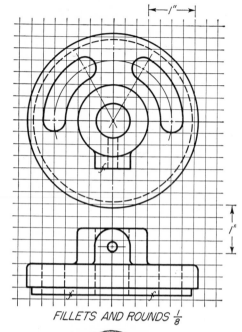

FILLETS AND ROUNDS $\frac{1}{8}$

Prob. 9-14. Cover plate (cast iron).

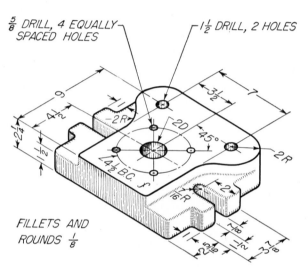

$\frac{5}{8}$ DRILL, 4 EQUALLY SPACED HOLES

$1\frac{1}{2}$ DRILL, 2 HOLES

FILLETS AND ROUNDS $\frac{1}{8}$

Prob. 9-15. Die shoe (steel casting).

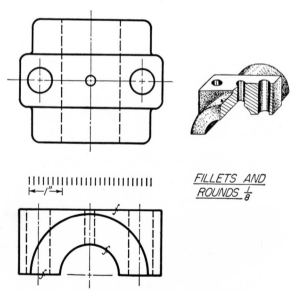

FILLETS AND ROUNDS $\frac{1}{8}$

Prob. 9-16. Bearing bracket cap (cast iron).

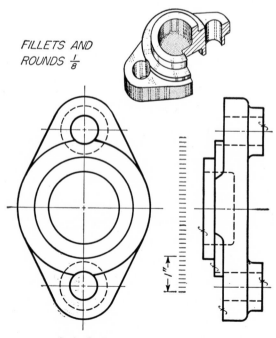

FILLETS AND ROUNDS $\frac{1}{8}$

Prob. 9-17. End plate (cast iron).

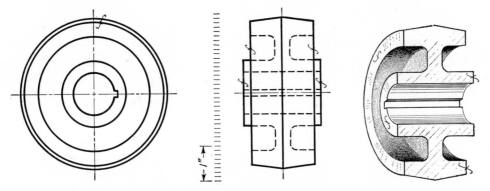

FILLETS AND ROUNDS $\frac{1}{8}$

Prob. 9-18. Pulley (cast iron).

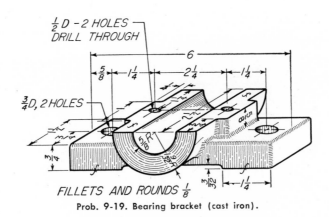

$\frac{1}{2}D$ – 2 HOLES
DRILL THROUGH

$\frac{3}{4}D$, 2 HOLES

FILLETS AND ROUNDS $\frac{1}{8}$

Prob. 9-19. Bearing bracket (cast iron).

Border $7\frac{1}{2}$ x 10

$\frac{3}{8}$

$\frac{3}{4}$

$1\frac{3}{4}$

$\frac{1}{8}R$

$1\frac{1}{4}$

$\frac{1}{8}R$

2

$3\frac{1}{4}$

$5\frac{3}{4}$

$1\frac{1}{4}D$

$\frac{5}{32}$

$\frac{3}{4}D$

$\frac{5}{16}$

$1\frac{7}{8}$

FILLETS AND ROUNDS $\frac{1}{8}$

$2\frac{1}{2}$

Prob. 9-20. Link (cast iron).

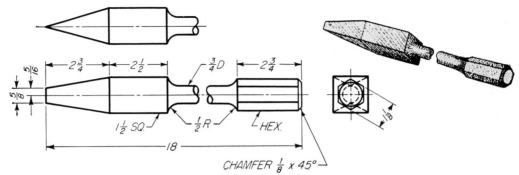

Prob. 9-21. Cement breaker (tool steel).

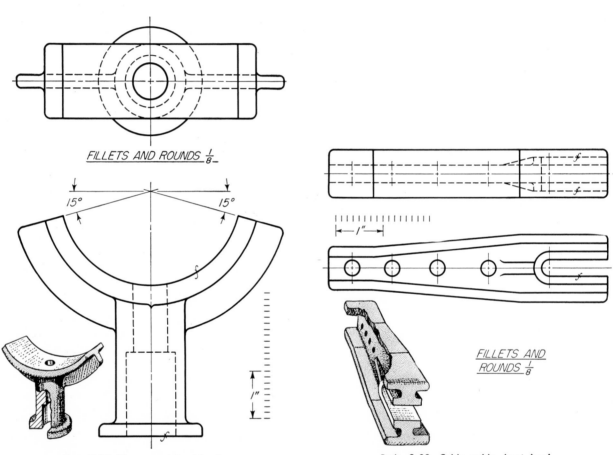

Prob. 9-22. Pipe support (cast iron).

Prob. 9-23. Cable guide (cast iron).

Chapter 10

PRIMARY AUXILIARY VIEWS

One of the basic rules of dimensioning states that a line should be dimensioned only in the view where it is seen in its true length and that a plane with its details should be dimensioned only in the view where it is seen in its true shape. Since every object that is drawn is bounded by lines and planes, and some of these may lie inclined or oblique to the principal planes of projection, it is obvious that the draftsman must be able to select and draw the view that will show the true length of a line or the true shape of a surface so that he may include on his working drawing all notes and dimensions necessary for producing the part.

A simple object may be rectangular in shape, and its lines and surfaces can be shown in their true dimensions by making use of a combination of two or more of the principal views. When an object contains an inclined surface, however, the true shape of the surface can be shown only by an auxiliary view that is drawn on a plane of projection placed parallel to the inclined surface.

10-1. Primary auxiliary views. Any view that is not projected to one of the principal planes may be classified as an auxiliary view. A *primary auxiliary view* is a view projected to a plane perpendicular to one of the three principal planes— front, top, or side—and inclined to the other two.

Such a plane is shown in Fig. 10-1 (the auxiliary plane is inclined to the top and side views and perpendicular to the front). Note that the true shape of the inclined surface can be seen only on a plane lying parallel to the inclined surface. The method of projecting the image of an object to an auxiliary plane is identical to that employed for projecting an image to one of the principal planes; the projectors are parallel and the observer is stationed an infinite distance away.

10-2. True size and shape of a plane. If a surface of an object is inclined to any one of the principal planes it will not show in its true shape in any of the principal views (see planes 1-2-3-4 and 2-5-6-7 in Fig. 10-2a). The true-shape projection of a plane surface is seen on a plane of projection passed parallel to that surface (see Fig. 10-2b).

10-3. Types of primary auxiliary views. The three types of primary auxiliaries are shown in Fig. 10-3. The auxiliary elevation (a) is inclined to the front and side views and is perpendicular to the top. The inclined auxiliary at (b) is at an angle to the top and side views and is perpendicular to the front. At (c) the auxiliary is inclined to the front and top views and is perpendicular to the side. Any number of auxiliary planes may be passed

164

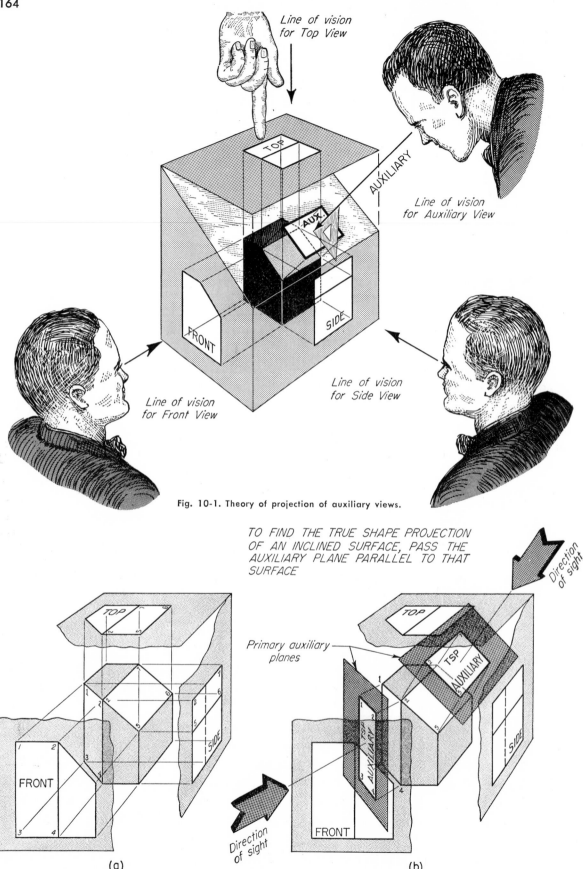

Fig. 10-1. Theory of projection of auxiliary views.

TO FIND THE TRUE SHAPE PROJECTION OF AN INCLINED SURFACE, PASS THE AUXILIARY PLANE PARALLEL TO THAT SURFACE

(a) (b)

Fig. 10-2. (*a*) Principal views and inclined plane. (*b*) Principal views and primary auxiliary views.

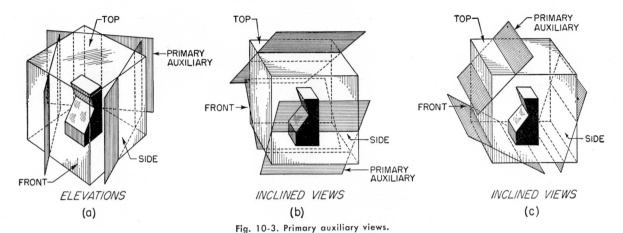

Fig. 10-3. Primary auxiliary views.

setting up these conditions with the principal planes, and still fall in the category of primary auxiliary views. It is important to bear this in mind, since in design work the draftsman often encounters conditions which require auxiliary views that solve problems other than finding the true shapes of planes.

An auxiliary elevation is used to show the true shape of a plane surface that is inclined to the front and side views and perpendicular to the top. The auxiliary plane is passed parallel to the inclined surface and perpendicular to the top, and is then rotated into the plane of the paper as if attached to the top view. This procedure is illustrated in Fig. 10-4. Note that the auxiliary view is an additional view; it is the third in the series of front, top, and auxiliary; it is perpendicular to, projected from, and thus adjacent to the top view;

and, since the front is also adjacent to and perpendicular to the top, the distance from any point in the auxiliary to its reference line (see Sec. 10-4) is the same as the distance from the identical point in the front view to the reference line between the top and front views. This is true because in any three successive related planes of projection the middle plane is always perpendicular to the two extreme planes and the depth dimension of a point will be the same in the extreme planes of the group.

If a plane surface is perpendicular to the front view and inclined to the top and side views, its true shape may be shown on a plane passed parallel to the inclined surface and perpendicular to the front view (see Fig. 10-5). Here again the auxiliary and the front are attached and adjacent; the front and the top are attached and adjacent. The

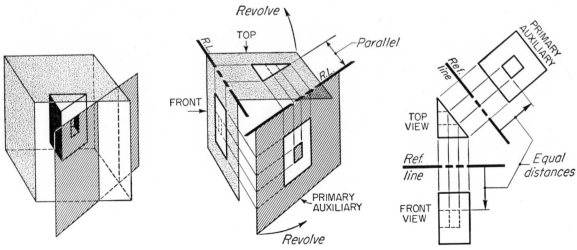

Fig. 10-4. Characteristics of auxiliary elevation views.

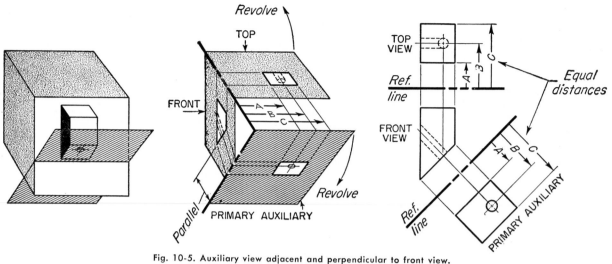

Fig. 10-5. Auxiliary view adjacent and perpendicular to front view.

auxiliary and the top are perpendicular to the front; thus any point common to the auxiliary and top views will be the same distance from their respective reference lines (that is, distances *A, B,* and *C,* for example, will be equal).

If a plane is inclined to the top and front views and is perpendicular to the side, the auxiliary showing the true shape of that plane must be passed parallel to the plane and perpendicular to the side view (see Fig. 10-6). The auxiliary is attached to the side view and passed perpendicular to it. The front is also perpendicular to the side and attached to it. Thus, as noted above, all points common to the front and auxiliary views will be the same distance from their respective reference lines.

10-4. How to draw an auxiliary view.

Figure 10-7 illustrates the general procedure followed in the construction of all types of primary auxiliary views. First draw two adjacent principal views, one of which must show the inclined plane as an edge (line projection). Then draw a line, which we shall call the *reference line,* parallel to the edge view of the inclined plane whose true shape is to be shown. A reference line is also passed between the two principal views, as shown in the illustration. The reference lines may be considered as folding lines that are placed at any convenient distance that will allow the auxiliary view to fall in a clear space on the drawing sheet. Often the reference lines can be drawn to coincide with a line on the object itself, as we shall see later. The reference lines are

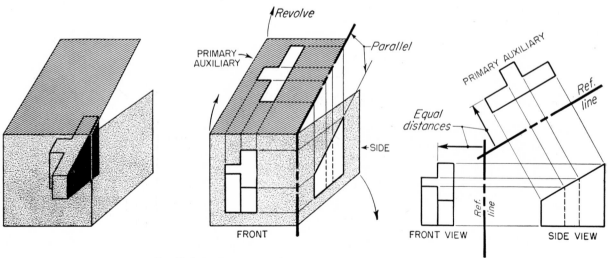

Fig. 10-6. Auxiliary view adjacent and perpendicular to side view.

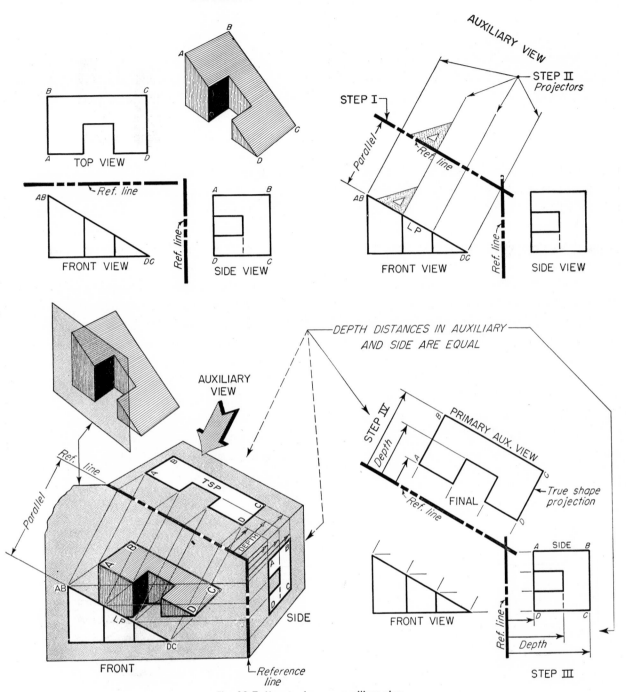

Fig. 10-7. How to draw an auxiliary view.

used to locate points in the auxiliary view, and if they have been placed between the views they are usually erased once the drawing has been completed. Therefore, they should be drawn **very** lightly.

In Fig. 10-7, the inclined plane *ABCD* is perpendicular to the front view, where it appears as a line projection. In Step I the reference line is passed parallel to the inclined plane at any convenient distance from it. Since both the top and side views show the required depth distances, the top is unnecessary and is discarded to avoid overlapping projections. Step II shows the points of the inclined plane being projected into the auxiliary.

The projectors are drawn perpendicular to the line projection of the inclined plane and perpendicular to the reference line. The missing dimensions—the locations of the points on their projectors in the auxiliary view—are the same as the depth dimensions of the points on the side view. The distances from the reference line between the two principal views to the various points in the side view are taken with a compass or dividers and are then transferred as depth distances from the auxiliary's reference line to their positions on their projectors in the auxiliary view (Steps III and IV). The pictorial view shown in Fig. 10-7 should enable the student to visualize the steps taken and to understand why the depth dimensions are transferred from the side view to the auxiliary.

In commercial practice it is more convenient and greater accuracy is possible if the reference line is passed through a plane or points on the object itself. In Fig. 10-8 the front image plane is imagined resting on the surface of the object, thus allowing the reference line to fall on the same front surface in the side and auxiliary views. The procedure in projecting the points of the object and locating them on their projectors in the auxiliary view is identical to that used for the construction of the preceding drawing.

10-5. Constructing auxiliary views of simple objects. Figure 10-9 illustrates a convenient procedure for constructing auxiliary views. It is recommended only for simple objects consisting of few details, however. Step I shows a line projection of the desired surface in the front view, while the top shows the surface in an inclined position. In the top view, pass reference line *FT* through the back surface of the object as shown. Then pass reference line *F1* parallel to the line projection of the plane in the front view so that it intersects *FT* at *O* as shown. In Step II the angle at *O* formed by the two reference lines is bisected. In Step III the points in the top view are projected to the bisector and from there are projected parallel to the reference line of the auxiliary into the auxiliary plane. The points are then projected perpendicularly from the front to the auxiliary. The intersections of the projectors from the top and front views locate the points and form the true shape of the inclined surface in the auxiliary view.

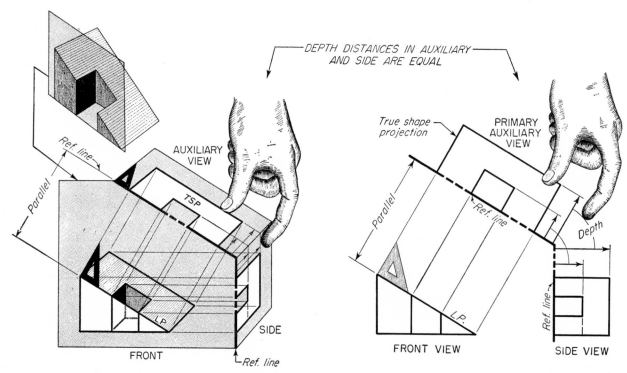

Fig. 10-8. A unilateral auxiliary view.

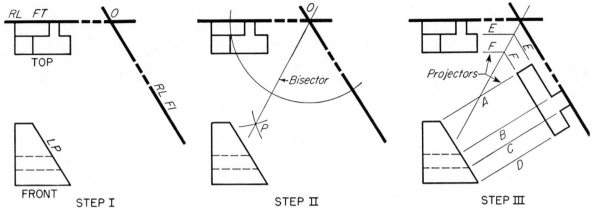

Fig. 10-9. Auxiliary view of a simple object.

10-6. Partial auxiliary views. In drawing an auxiliary view, it is customary to show only the shape and details of the inclined surface, and not a view of the entire object as seen from the position of the auxiliary plane. If practice in projection is desired, the entire object may, of course, be drawn. However, this is rarely necessary and is often confusing because of the abundance of lines that appear in the drawing. Notice in Fig. 10-10 that the partial auxiliary is much clearer and less time-consuming to draw than the complete auxiliary, and yet it gives all the necessary information concerning the inclined plane.

10-7. Auxiliary view to complete a principal view. In Fig. 10-10 it is obvious that the side view could not have been completed without having first constructed the true-shape projection shown in the auxiliary view. This situation is encountered frequently, and the draftsman should become familiar with the correct procedure to follow. The view showing the inclined surface as an edge is always constructed as a principal view. From the dimensions available, the auxiliary is drawn on a plane of projection parallel to the edge view. The points of the object are projected back from the auxiliary view to the line projection of the surface in the principal view, and then in the proper manner to the other principal view, the points in this view being located the same distance from the selected reference line on their projectors as they are shown in the auxiliary.

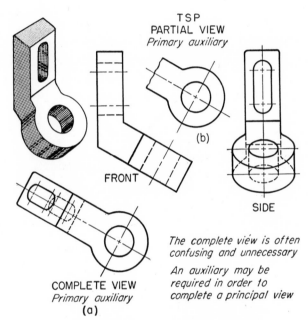

The complete view is often confusing and unnecessary

An auxiliary may be required in order to complete a principal view

Fig. 10-10. Complete and partial auxiliary views.

10-8. Circular and curved forms in auxiliary projections. The procedure used to draw the true-shape auxiliary projection of curved surfaces is shown orthographically in Fig. 10-11 and pictorially in Fig. 10-12. Note that the side view of the curve and its adjacent line-projection view are given. Locate any desired points on the curve and project these to the line projection, or edge view. These points are then projected to the auxiliary view, where the reference plane has been passed conveniently through the center line of the piece to locate the reference line that is drawn parallel to

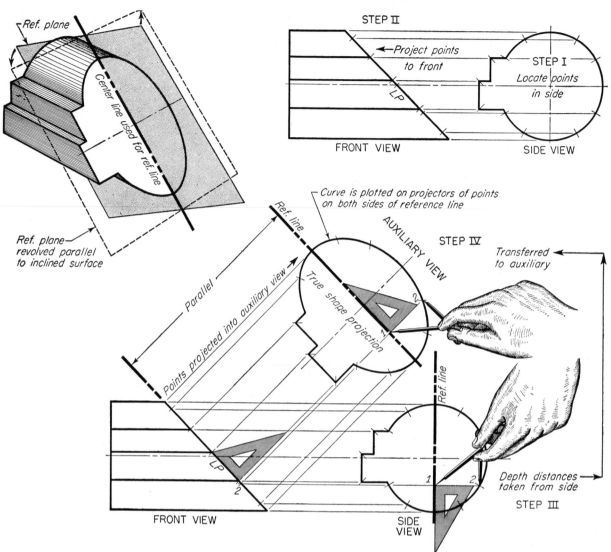

Fig. 10-11. Auxiliary of curved forms (bilateral auxiliary).

the edge view of the desired surface. In this case the points of the curve in the auxiliary view are located on their projectors on either side of the reference line as indicated by their positions in the side view, where the reference line is also passed through the center of the piece.

10-9. True length of a line. The true-length projection of a line is seen only on a plane of pro-

jection passed parallel to the line. In Fig. 10-13 the pictorials show the "in space" conditions of the oblique line *AB* and the manner of revolving the plane passed parallel to it into the plane of the paper. The last drawing, coinciding with an orthographic, shows how the dimensions locating points *A* and *B* of the line in the auxiliary are taken from the front view. The orthographic step-

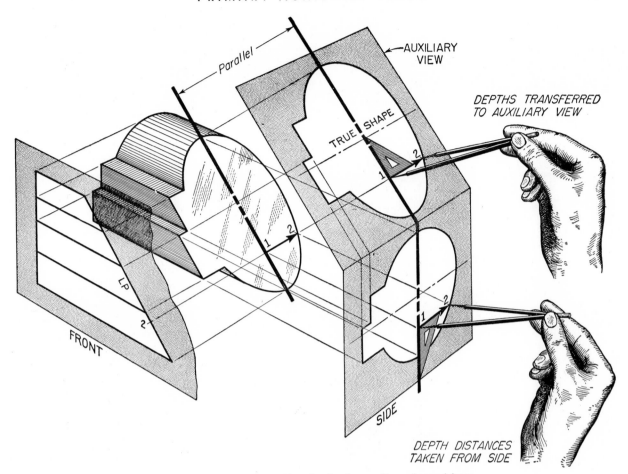

Fig. 10-12. Pictorial of procedure for drawing auxiliary of curved forms.

by-step procedure is shown below the pictorials. The very last drawing of the group shows that a reference plane could have been passed parallel to any given view of the line in order to have obtained its true-length projection.

10-10. True length of a line by revolution. Another manner in which the true length of a line may be secured, and one that is much used by draftsmen for checking purposes, is illustrated in Fig. 10-14. The line *AB* is considered as the element of a cone, shown obliquely in the principal views. When the line is revolved about the imagined apex of the cone (point *A*) parallel to

the plane of projection in the top view, and the revolved position of the point *B* is projected to the front view, the line will appear as a true-length projection because it takes the same position as an extreme element of the cone, which would be seen in true length in the front view. Note that in the act of revolution the point *A* has not moved from its original position in either view. Point *B* has been revolved to bring the line *AB* parallel to the reference line in the top view. It was projected from its revolved position to the front view, where it moved in a line parallel to the reference line to show its revolved position.

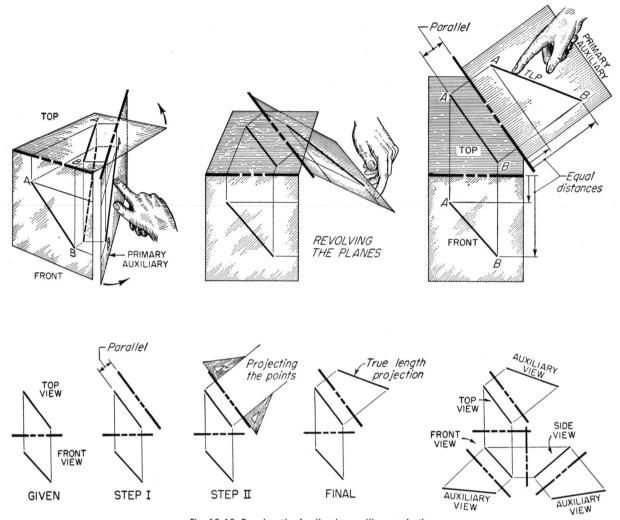

Fig. 10-13. True length of a line by auxiliary projection.

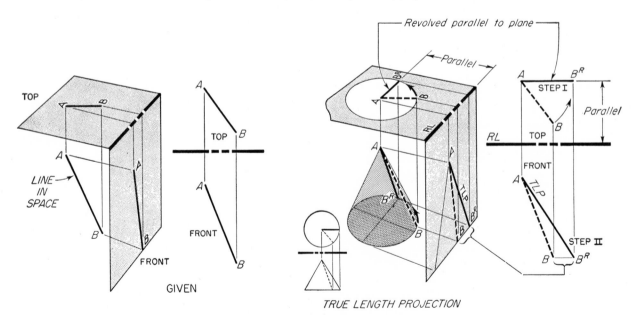

Fig. 10-14. True length of a line by revolution.

PROBLEMS

In commercial drafting practice, only that portion of an object that does not appear in its true shape in any of the principal views is projected to an auxiliary plane. Good practice requires that two complete principal views be shown in addition to the auxiliary view. The auxiliary view need not be overloaded with superfluous dotted lines which would confuse

rather than clarify the drawing. However, the instructor should require that the entire object be drawn in the auxiliary view if the problem is a simple one, for this will give the student added practice in projection. The practice of lettering points will facilitate the procedure. Use an 8½- by 11-in. drawing sheet unless otherwise noted.

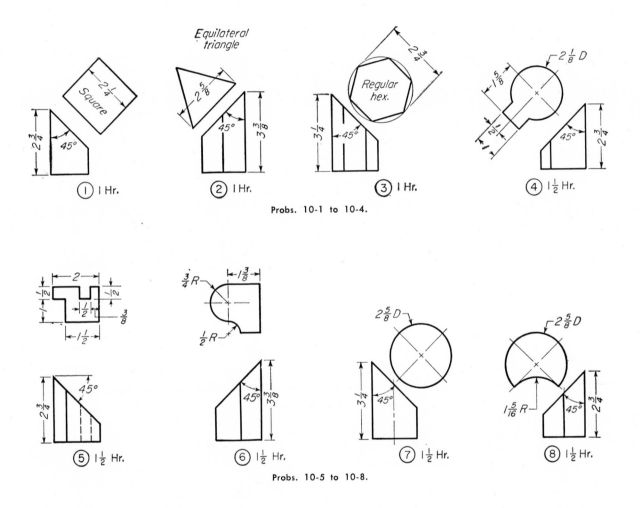

Probs. 10-1 to 10-4.

Probs. 10-5 to 10-8.

10-1 to 10-4. Redraw the given front view and the true-shape auxiliary of the inclined surface. Draw the top view. Show two problems on the sheet; omit dimensions.

10-5 and 10-6. Redraw the given front and top views. Project the entire object to the auxiliary view,

which will show the true-shape projection of the inclined surface. Omit dimensions.

10-7 and 10-8. Redraw the given front view and partial true-shape auxiliary. Show the top view. Show a complete view of the object as seen from the auxiliary plane. Omit dimensions.

10-9. Reproduce the given front and top views of the objects. Show the true shapes of the inclined surfaces in the auxiliary views. Omit all dimensions. (Time: 2½ hr.)

10-10. Reproduce the given top and front views of the objects. Show the true shape of the inclined surfaces in the auxiliary views. Omit all dimensions. (Time: 2½ hr.)

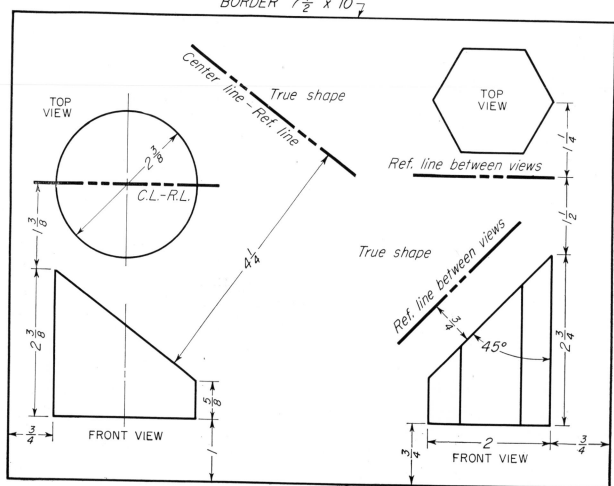

Prob. 10-9.

BORDER 7½ x 10

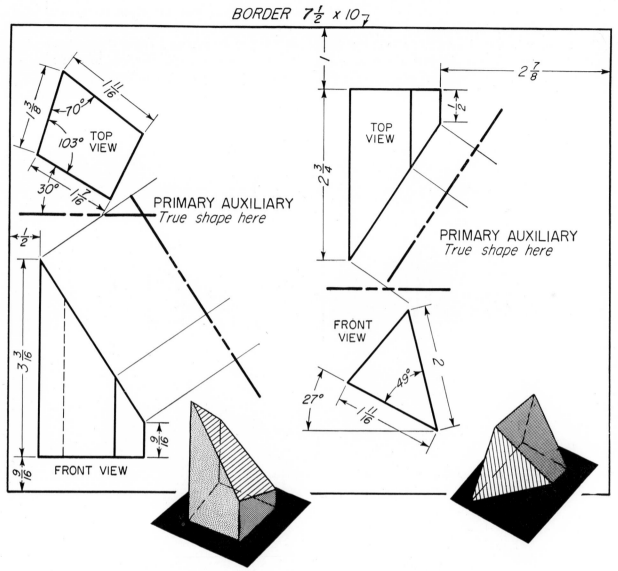

Prob. 10-10.

10-11. Reproduce the given three views of the objects. Find the true shapes of planes *A*, *B*, and *C* inclined to the principal views. Omit all dimensions. Use dividers to transfer the views to your sheet at a suitable scale. (Time: 1½ hr.)

10-12. Reproduce the given three views of the objects. Find the true shapes of planes *A*, *B*, and *C* inclined to the principal views. Omit all dimensions. Use dividers to transfer the views to your sheet at a suitable scale. (Time: 1½ hr.)

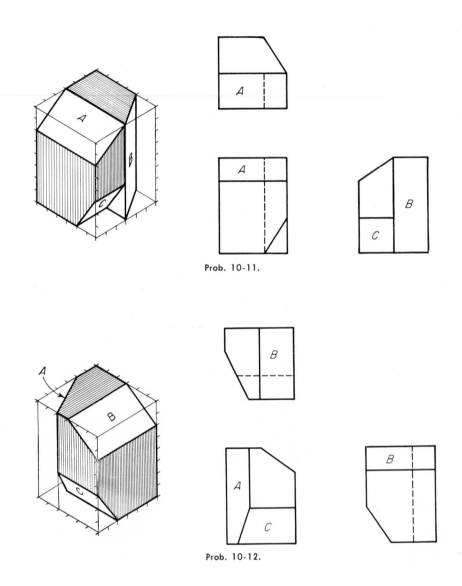

Prob. 10-11.

Prob. 10-12.

10-13. Complete the front view as a full section view. Show the side in ordinary orthographic projection. Dimension the drawing completely. (Time: 2½ hr.)

10-14. Complete the front view as an offset section view. Show the side as an ordinary orthographic projection. Dimension your drawing completely. (Omit dimensions that locate views on the drawing sheet.) (Time: 4 hr.)

FILLETS & ROUNDS $\frac{1}{8}$

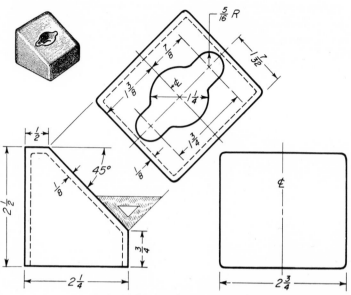

Prob. 10-13. Switch cover, cast iron.

BORDER $7\frac{1}{2}$ x 10

FILLETS & ROUNDS $\frac{1}{8}$

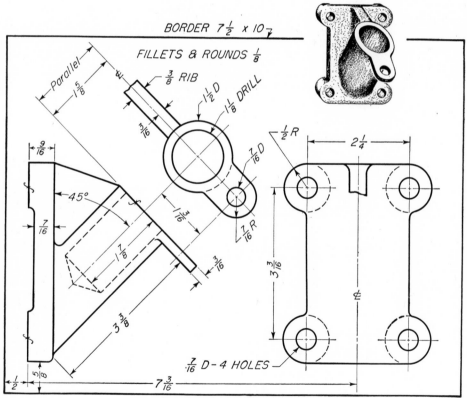

Prob. 10-14. Pole holder, cast iron.

10-15. Complete the given front and side views. Show only the inclined surface in the auxiliary view. Dimension completely, but omit dimensions that locate views on the drawing sheet. (Time: 3 hr.)

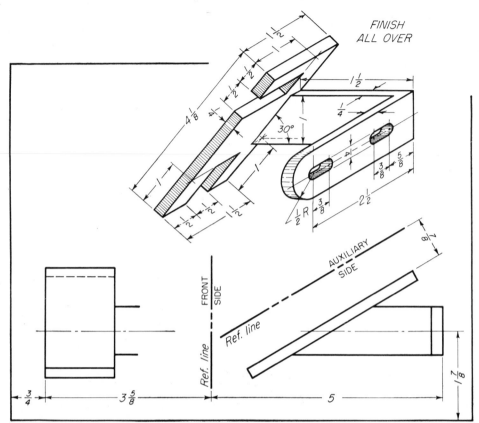

Prob. 10-15. Belt guide, aluminum.

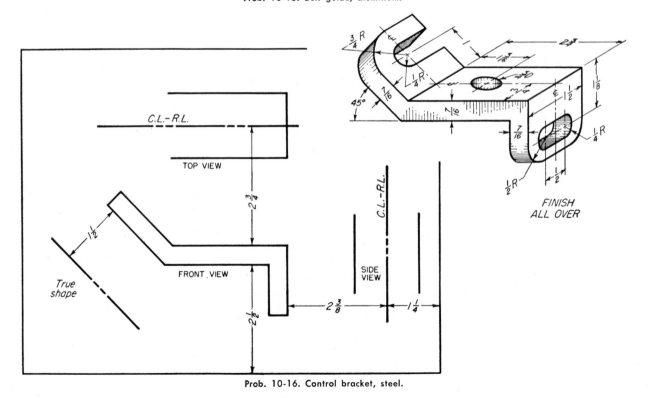

Prob. 10-16. Control bracket, steel.

10-16. Show complete front, top, and side views. Project only the inclined portion of the object to the auxiliary. Dimension completely, but omit dimensions that locate views on the drawing sheet. Use center line as reference line. (Time: 3½ hr.)

10-17. Show complete front and top views. Draw only the true shapes of the inclined surfaces in the auxiliaries. Dimension completely, but omit dimen-

sions that locate the views on the drawing sheet. Use center line as reference line. (Time: 4 hr.)

10-18. Draw object three-quarter size on an 8½- by 11-in. sheet. Show complete front and top views. Draw the true shape of the inclined surface in the auxiliary. Dimension the drawing completely. Use center line as reference line. (Time: 4 hr.)

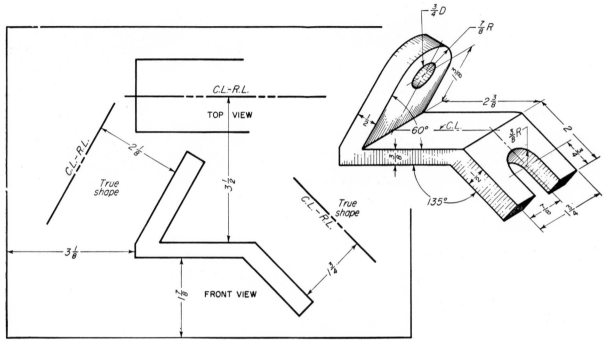

Prob. 10-17. Cable anchor, steel.

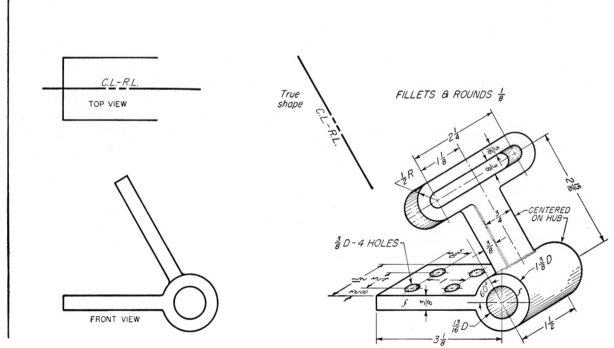

Prob. 10-18. Adjustable shaft support, cast iron.

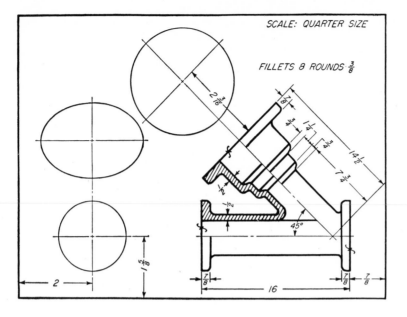

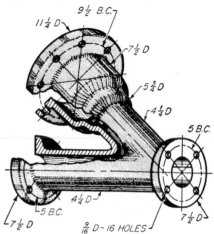

SCALE: QUARTER SIZE

FILLETS & ROUNDS $\frac{3}{8}$

(ALL HOLES EQUALLY SPACED IN FLANGES)

Prob. 10-19. Reducer lateral, cast iron.

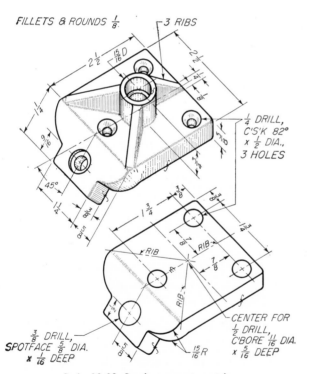

FILLETS & ROUNDS $\frac{1}{8}$.

3 RIBS

$\frac{1}{4}$ DRILL,
C'S'K 82°
x $\frac{1}{2}$ DIA.,
3 HOLES

$\frac{3}{8}$ DRILL,
SPOTFACE $\frac{5}{8}$ DIA.
x $\frac{1}{16}$ DEEP

CENTER FOR
$\frac{1}{2}$ DRILL,
C'BORE $\frac{11}{16}$ DIA.
x $\frac{5}{16}$ DEEP

Prob. 10-20. Bearing support, cast iron.

10-19. Complete the side view and the flange in the auxiliary. Draw the front view with a minimum of dotted lines showing behind the inclined flange surface. Dimension the drawing completely, omitting those that locate the views on the drawing sheet. Use center line as reference line. (Time: 5 hr.)

10-20. Draw a front view in full offset section, a top view in ordinary orthographic projection, and a true-shape auxiliary of the inclined surface. Dimension the drawing completely. (Time: 4 hr.)

Chapter 11

SECONDARY AUXILIARY VIEWS

There are times when it may be necessary to show the true-shape projection of a plane surface that does not appear as an edge in any of the principal views. In these circumstances, what is known as a *secondary auxiliary view* must be drawn. A secondary auxiliary view (also called a double auxiliary view) may be defined as a projection on a plane that lies oblique to *all* the principal planes or views. It is perpendicular to a primary auxiliary plane, from which the secondary auxiliary is *always* projected. In order to draw the true shape of an oblique surface, a line-projection view of the surface must be found. Since the secondary auxiliary plane lies oblique to the principal planes, the necessary line-projection view of the surface can be obtained only by first drawing a primary auxiliary view showing the desired surface as an edge.

Throughout engineering-drawing procedure, practically all drafting requisites can be satisfied by utilizing four, or possibly five, different types of planes of projection, namely, two adjacent principal planes (front and top or front and side), a primary auxiliary, and a secondary auxiliary; or three principal planes in combination with a primary auxiliary and secondary auxiliary. *A primary auxiliary is always projected from a principal view*

and a secondary auxiliary is always projected from a primary auxiliary.

Any plane of projection that is passed (or projected) from another plane is always perpendicular to the plane from which it is projected. A plane (flat) surface is seen in its true shape only when it lies parallel to the plane of projection. If the surface does not show as a line projection in a principal view, a primary auxiliary view must be taken to show it in this manner, after which a secondary auxiliary is passed parallel to the line projection to show the plane in its true shape.

11-1. To find the line projection, or edge view, of an oblique plane. Figure 11-1 shows the front and top views of a triangular solid that has a lower base parallel to the top view and an upper base *ABC* lying oblique to the three principal planes. By descriptive geometry, if we can draw a view in which a line lying in an oblique plane shows as a point, then this same view will show a line projection of the oblique plane. The point projection of a line can be secured only by projecting it from the view showing the true length of the line. It is also a fact that any line in one view that is parallel to its reference line for that projection plane will show in its true length in the adjacent view. Obviously, no line of the plane

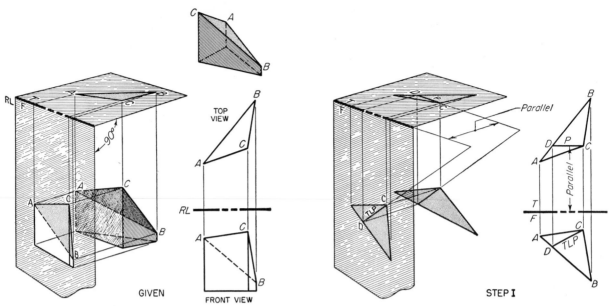

Fig. 11-1. Projections of an oblique plane in the principal views.

ABC shows in its true length in either the front or top views. Therefore, in the top view an arbitrary line *DC* is drawn parallel to the reference line between the front and top views so that the line may be projected and appear in its true length in the front view (as in Step I). (The procedure could have been reversed by drawing an arbitrary line in the front view parallel to the reference line and projecting it to the top view, where it would appear in its true length.)

Step II in Fig. 11-2 indicates the manner in

which the point projection of the line and the line projection of the plane are secured. Draw the reference line of the primary auxiliary perpendicular to the true-length projection of *DC* in the front view. Project points *D* and *C* of the line and points *A*, *B*, and *C* of the plane into the primary auxiliary, locating their positions on their projectors by taking their depth distances with a compass or dividers in the top view and transferring these to the auxiliary. If the draftsman has worked carefully the line *CD* will show as a point and the

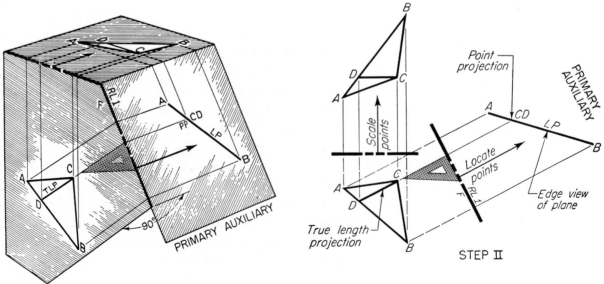

Fig. 11-2. Securing the edge view, or line projection, of an oblique plane.

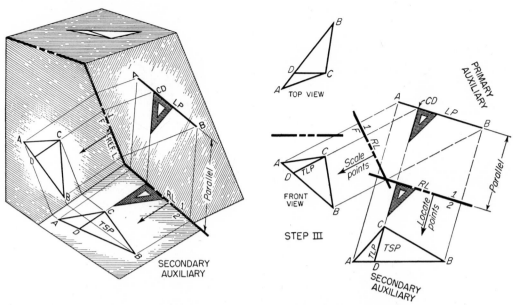

Fig. 11-3. Securing the true shape of a plane from its edge view.

plane *ABC* will show as an edge in the primary auxiliary view.

11-2. Finding the true shape from the edge view. The procedure for drawing the true shape of the plane after the edge view has been found is similar to that followed in the previous chapter where the edge view appeared in a principal view instead of the primary auxiliary (see Fig. 11-3, Step III). The reference line between the primary and secondary auxiliaries is passed parallel to the line projection, or edge view, of the plane *ABC* as seen in the primary auxiliary. The points of the plane are projected perpendicular to the reference line into the secondary auxiliary view, where they are located by scaling their distances from the reference line to their positions in the front view and transferring these distances to the point projectors in the secondary auxiliary view. The line *CD* may also be carried to this view where it will show as a true-length projection and may be used as a check on the accuracy of the work by comparing it with its true-length projection in the front view. Any details of construction appearing in the plane, such as holes or slots, may now be drawn and dimensioned in this view, and their shapes and contours brought back through the edge view

to the principal views by reversing the projection procedure.

11-3. Practical application and procedure. The pictorial of Fig. 11-4 shows an angle bracket that is to be represented orthographically and completely dimensioned. After studying the object, it has been decided that four views are required as indicated by the arrows: a front view parallel to the front surface of the base, a top view parallel to the top surface of the base, a primary auxiliary perpendicular to the line *AB* (which is common to both lugs), and a secondary auxiliary parallel to the curved lug.

In Step I only the triangular base and its hole can be shown in the top and front views. The oblique surface can be represented in the principal views only after its true shape is shown in a secondary auxiliary and projected back point by point through the primary auxiliary and then to the principal views.

Since the line *AB* in the front view is parallel to the reference line of the adjacent (top) view, it appears in its true length in the top view. (If a line already appears as a true-length projection in a view, there is no need to pass a parallel in one view to find its true length in the adjacent view.) Now

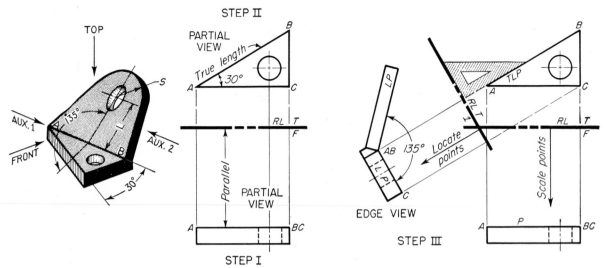

Fig. 11-4. Practical application of auxiliary views.

by setting up a primary auxiliary plane that will show the point projection of *AB* and the edge view of the base *ABC*, as in Step III, the angle which the oblique surface makes with the base can be shown in the auxiliary view (because a view that shows the point projection of the line of intersection of two planes shows the angle between the planes). In this primary auxiliary view the base has been projected to its position, and the angle, length, and thickness of the oblique surface are drawn from known dimensions.

In Fig. 11-5, Step IV, the reference line of the secondary auxiliary is passed parallel to the edge view of the oblique plane. In this view the points

A and *B* are located by taking their depth distances from the reference line to the top view and transferring these to their projectors in the secondary auxiliary. The remaining portion of the oblique surface and the representation of the hole on its center lines are accomplished by using the dimensions on the object.

The remainder of the task is now simply a matter of locating as many points as are necessary on the true shape in the secondary auxiliary and projecting these points back to both surfaces of the oblique plane shown as edge views in the primary auxiliary. From these two surfaces in the primary auxiliary the points are projected perpendicular to

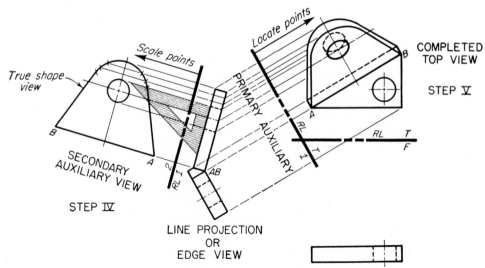

Fig. 11-5. Completing a principal view from the auxiliaries.

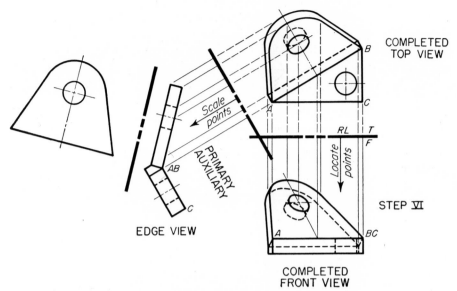

Fig. 11-6. Completing the principal views.

the reference line into the top view (Step V), where their positions on their projectors are located by scaling the distances of the points in the secondary auxiliary from its reference line. The representation of the oblique surface in the top view is completed by using a straightedge and a french curve. The ellipse for the hole may be drawn by the four-center method after the long and short diameters have been determined (the long diameter is the actual diameter of the hole; the short diameter is projected from the edge view). The points of the oblique surfaces in the top view are now projected into the front view, (Step VI, Fig. 11-6), where they are located on their projectors by scaling their distances from the primary auxiliary to its reference line.

11-4. Engineering-drawing representations. Good engineering-drawing practice requires that at least two adjacent views of a complex object be complete representations. These two views are

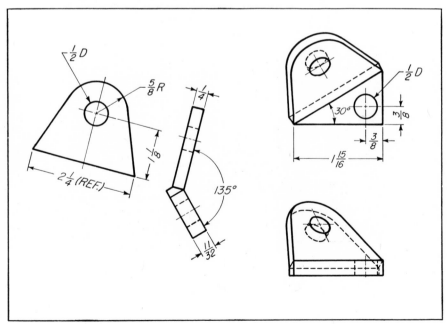

Fig. 11-7. Principal and auxiliary views properly placed and dimensioned.

generally principal views. Auxiliary views, therefore, need show only the true sizes and shapes of details drawn on their inclined or oblique planes. Good practice also requires that adjacent views be placed in their proper projected relationship to the other views on the drawing sheet to facilitate reading the drawing. For the same reason the rule that dimensions be given only on true-length and true-shape projections should not be violated.

Figure 11-7 shows the principal views and the required auxiliaries of the object shown in Fig. 11-4 properly dimensioned and arranged in their correct relationship to one another on the drawing sheet.

PROBLEMS

These problems have been selected to give the student an opportunity to apply the fundamental principles involved in projecting and dimensioning true-shape secondary auxiliary views. Although in practice, when a true-shape view of an oblique surface is required, it is customary to show in the primary auxiliary only the edge view of the oblique plane and in the secondary auxiliary to show only the shape and details of the oblique surface, it is suggested that the entire object be shown for at least one problem to permit the student to gain experience in auxiliary-view projection procedure. A small thumbnail sketch will aid in selecting and arranging the views on the sheet, and numbering the points of the planes will avoid confusion in projecting them between views.

In problems where dimensioning is required, the

projection and reference lines may be erased and the dimensions locating views and their reference lines on the sheet should be omitted. Problems 11-1 to 11-7 can be shown on 8½- by 11-in. sheets, while Probs. 11-8 to 11-12 should be drawn on 11- by 17-in. sheets. A simple detail title should be shown where convenient.

11-1. Truncated triangular pyramid, wood. Reproduce the front view and complete the top view. Show the top oblique surface as a line projection in the primary auxiliary and in its true shape in the secondary auxiliary. Do not dimension. (Time: 1 hr.)

11-2. Angle gage block, steel. Assuming the squares to be ¼ in., reproduce the two given views. Show the appearance of the block in the view that

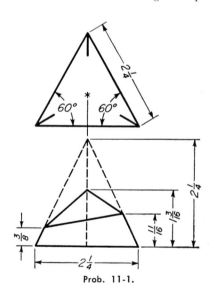

Prob. 11-1.

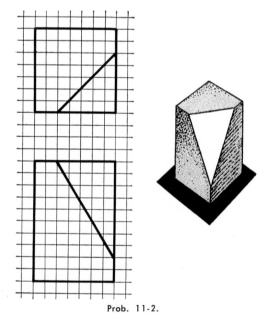

Prob. 11-2.

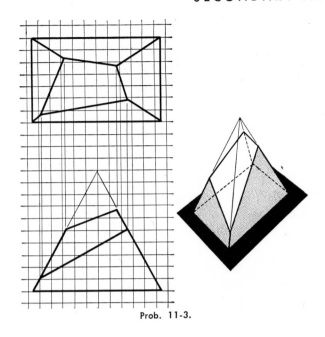

Prob. 11-3.

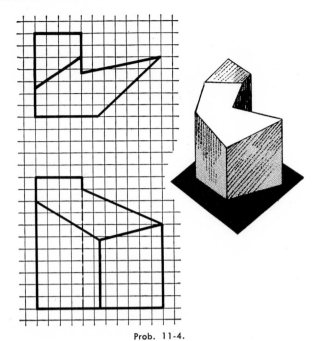

Prob. 11-4.

illustrates the oblique surface as an edge and in the view that shows the surface in its true shape. Do not dimension. (Time: 1½ hr.)

11-3. Truncated rectangular pyramid, wood. Using the ¼-in. squares, reproduce the top and front views and add auxiliary views that show the top oblique surface as an edge and in its true shape. Do not dimension. (Time: 1½ hr.)

11-4. Wedge block, cast iron. Using the ¼-in. squares, redraw the front and top views and show the auxiliaries that present the edge view and the true-shape view of the top oblique surface. (Whenever an

oblique plane is shown bounded by more than three sides, or edges, extreme accuracy in drawing is required or it may not project as an edge in the primary auxiliary view.) Do not dimension. (Time: 1½ hr.)

11-5 and 11-6. Angle blocks, steel. Using the ¼-in. divisions, reproduce the given front and top views. Draw the view that shows surface *A* as an edge and the view that shows it in its true shape. Do not dimension. (Time: 1 hr. for each problem.)

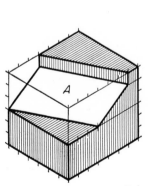

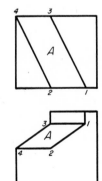

Prob. 11-5.

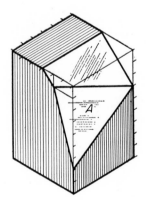

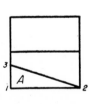

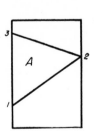

Prob. 11-6.

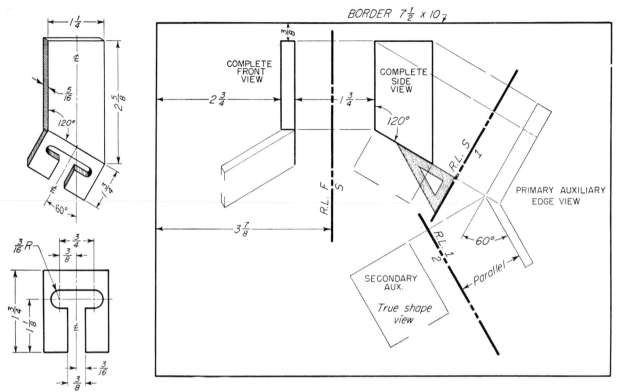

Prob. 11-7.

11-7. Angular corner bracket, steel. Using the layout shown and the pictorial and true-shape orthographic at the left, make a suitable completely dimensioned working drawing. The front, side, and primary auxiliary must be complete views. In the secondary auxiliary show only true shape of the oblique lug. Erase all projection and reference lines and omit dimensions that locate views and reference lines. (Time: 3 hr.)

11-8. Corner rod anchor and guide, cast iron. Show two complete principal views. Draw a primary auxiliary that shows only the oblique surface *A* as an edge and a secondary auxiliary that shows only the oblique surface with its hole. Dimension completely. (Time: 2½ hr.)

11-9. Corner brace guide, brass. Draw two complete principal views. Show only the oblique lug with its slot in the edge and true-shape auxiliary views. Dimension completely. (Time: 3 hr.)

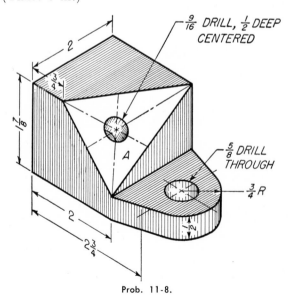

Prob. 11-8.

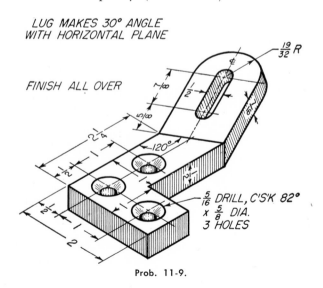

Prob. 11-9.

11-10. Strut anchor bracket, aluminum. Make a drawing showing two complete principal views and the necessary primary and secondary auxiliaries to permit proper dimensioning of the surfaces and the holes in the views where they are seen in their true shapes. Follow strictly the rules of projection. (Time: 3 hr.)

11-11. Cable anchor, cast iron. Using the pictorial at the left to obtain the dimensions of the object and the layout at the right for the location of the views and the reference lines on the sheet, complete the front and top views and show the true shapes of both lugs with the holes in the proper auxiliary views. Erase projection lines and reference lines. Omit dimensions locating views on the sheet and dimension the drawing completely. (Time: 5 hr.)

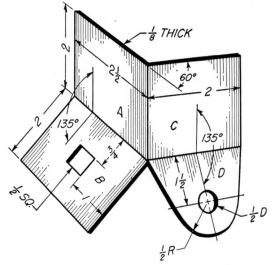

Prob. 11-10.

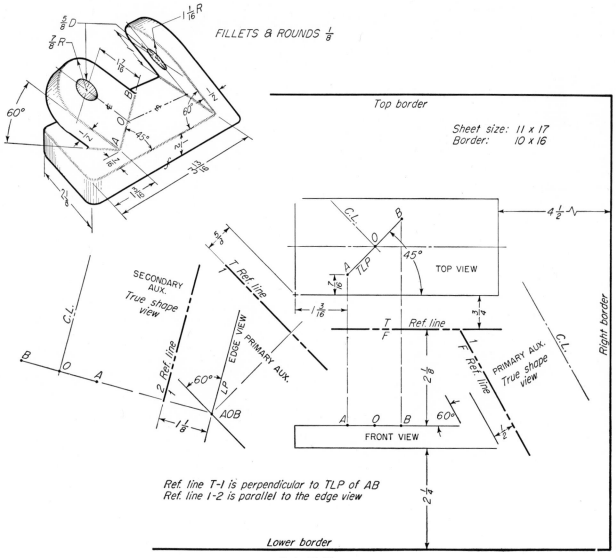

FILLETS & ROUNDS $\frac{1}{8}$

Ref. line T-1 is perpendicular to TLP of AB
Ref. line 1-2 is parallel to the edge view

Prob. 11-11.

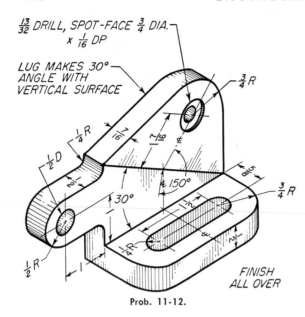

$\frac{13}{32}$ DRILL, SPOT-FACE $\frac{3}{4}$ DIA.
x $\frac{1}{16}$ DP

LUG MAKES 30°
ANGLE WITH
VERTICAL SURFACE

$\frac{3}{4}$R

$\frac{1}{4}$R

$\frac{1}{2}$D

$\frac{1}{16}$

150°

30°

$\frac{3}{4}$R

$\frac{1}{4}$R

$\frac{1}{2}$R

1

FINISH
ALL OVER

Prob. 11-12.

11-12. Adjustable angle bracket, cast iron. Draw two complete principal views. Show only the lug with the spot-faced hole in the primary and secondary auxiliaries. Dimension the drawing completely. (Time: 4 hr.)

Chapter 12

PICTORIAL DRAWING

In engineering drafting procedure it is often necessary to prepare drawings that can be read by individuals who lack the technical knowledge to enable them to read orthographic representations. In such cases, either *isometric* or *oblique* drawings are usually prepared. These are actually pictorial views drawn according to a number of well-defined principles that permit accurate size representation. The drawings may be scaled with a measuring stick and the novice can read them with comparative ease. As a general rule, the isometric and oblique drawings are suitable only for relatively simple objects, since accurately scaled drawings can be made only when the constructional details are not complex.

12-1. Theory of isometric projection. An isometric *projection* of a rectangular solid such as a cube is obtained by revolving the cube through 45° about a vertical axis and tilting it forward so that the receding surfaces may be seen on the picture plane (see Fig. 12-1). It should be imagined that a diagonal is passed through extreme corners of the cube, which is then tipped forward toward the picture plane until its receding edges appear to make angles of 30° with a horizontal line, while its vertical edges remain perpendicular. In Fig. 12-1, the three heavy lines intersecting at point

O are the *isometric axes*. The remaining lines outlining the isometric planes are parallel to these axes and are called *isometric lines*. The receding isometric axes make an angle of 120° with each other, an angle of 60° with the vertical axis, and angles of 30° with the horizontal. In the isometric-projection view the lines of the cube are foreshortened and do not show in their true lengths, as can be noted by comparison with the orthographic view.

12-2. Isometric drawings. In making an isometric drawing, the principle of isometric projection is employed, but one important modification is made: *The lines of the object are drawn in their actual length and the foreshortening effect is disregarded.* This means that an isometric drawing will be larger than an isometric projection, but it will still be in the same proportion (see Fig. 12-2). In commercial practice, isometric *drawings* (as opposed to isometric projections) are used almost exclusively because they can be prepared easily and the lengths of the lines may be scaled directly. It is important to keep in mind the difference between an isometric projection and an isometric drawing. In this chapter the isometric drawing is discussed exclusively.

The significant difference between an isometric

191

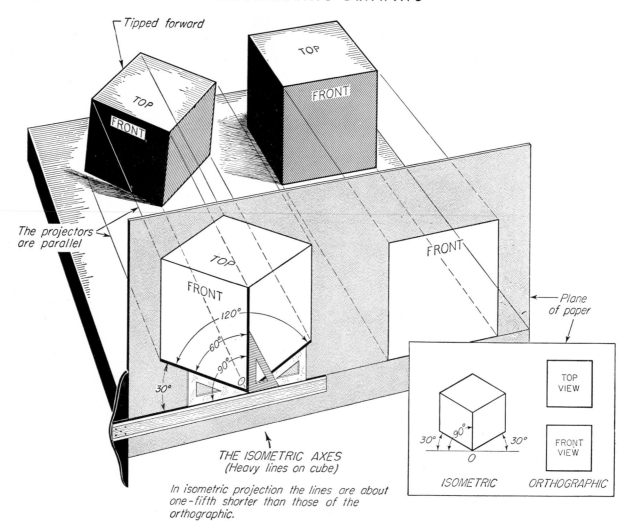

Tipped forward

The projectors
are parallel

TOP

FRONT

TOP

FRONT

120°

60°

90°

0

30°

THE ISOMETRIC AXES
(Heavy lines on cube)

In isometric projection the lines are about
one-fifth shorter than those of the
orthographic.

Plane
of paper

TOP
VIEW

FRONT
VIEW

30°   90°   30°

0

ISOMETRIC   ORTHOGRAPHIC

Fig. 12-1. Theory of isometric projection.

An isometric projection is almost one fifth smaller
than an isometric drawing. Isometric lines lie
parallel to the isometric axes

The receding lines of a perspective
shorten and converge to a
vanishing point.

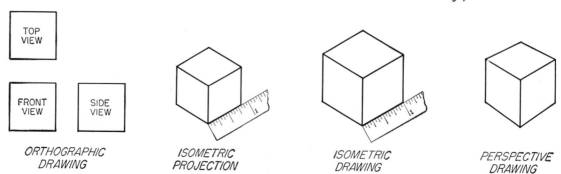

TOP
VIEW

FRONT
VIEW

SIDE
VIEW

ORTHOGRAPHIC
DRAWING

ISOMETRIC
PROJECTION

ISOMETRIC
DRAWING

PERSPECTIVE
DRAWING

Fig. 12-2. Comparison of isometric projection, isometric drawing, and perspective drawing.

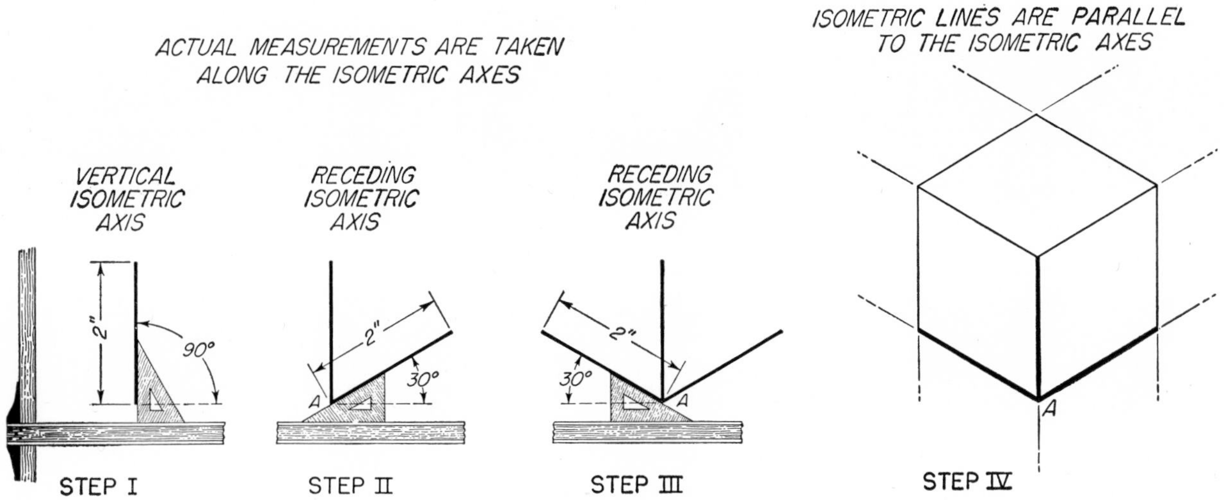

ACTUAL MEASUREMENTS ARE TAKEN
ALONG THE ISOMETRIC AXES

ISOMETRIC LINES ARE PARALLEL
TO THE ISOMETRIC AXES

VERTICAL
ISOMETRIC
AXIS

RECEDING
ISOMETRIC
AXIS

RECEDING
ISOMETRIC
AXIS

2"

90°

2"

30°

A

30°

2"

A

A

STEP I   STEP II   STEP III   STEP IV

Fig. 12-3. Isometric drawing of a cube.

and a perspective drawing is that receding lines in the perspective converge, while in the isometric they remain parallel. The principal difference between an isometric drawing and an orthographic view lies in the fact that the orthographic view generally shows only one surface in a given view, while the isometric usually shows three or more.

12-3. Isometric drawing of a cube. The step-by-step procedure in making an isometric drawing of a cube is shown in Fig. 12-3. The principal axes are drawn first and the actual lengths of the edges of the sides are scaled on them. The remaining edges are then drawn parallel to the principal axes.

12-4. Various positions of the isometric axes. The positions of the isometric axes may be varied to suit the needs of the draftsman or to present the usual appearance of the object to the observer. The angles between the axes should not be changed, however, even though their positions on the drawing sheet are varied (see Fig. 12-4).

12-5. Isometric drawing of a rectangular solid. The method employed in making an isometric drawing of a rectangular solid is similar to that used in drawing the cube (see Fig. 12-5).

To draw the isometric view, start with the vertical axis *OB* (Step I). Draw axis *AO* toward the left and axis *OC* toward the right to make an

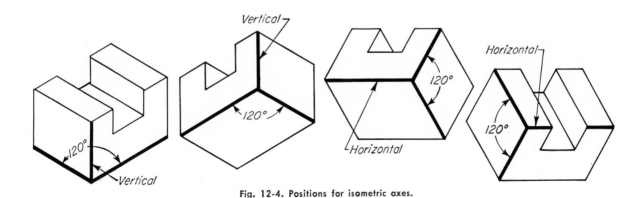

Fig. 12-4. Positions for isometric axes.

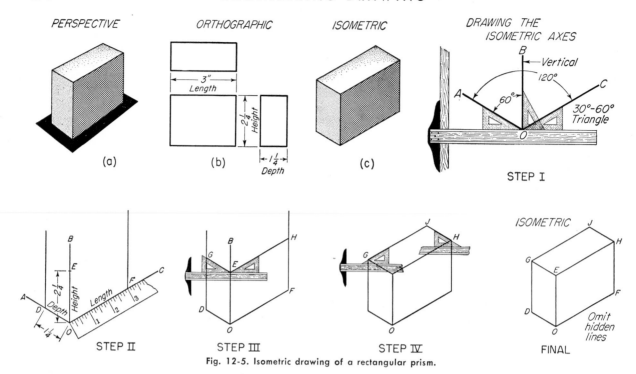

Fig. 12-5. Isometric drawing of a rectangular prism.

angle of 120° with each other and 30° angles with a horizontal line. In Step II the actual height OE of 2¼ in. is laid off on the vertical axis OB. The actual length OF of 3 in. is laid off on axis OC, and the depth OD of 1¼ in. is measured off on axis OA. In Step III, points G and H are found by drawing lines through E parallel to the receding axes. These lines establish the heights DG and FH which will be equal to the measured distance OE. In Step IV lines are drawn through points G and H, parallel to the receding axes, to intersect at J and to complete the visible outline of the solid as seen in the final drawing.

All the lines of the rectangular solid are isometric lines and direct measurements may be taken along any of them. The instruments used in making the drawing were the T square, the 30°-60° triangle, and the measuring stick.

Most engineering forms can be likened to rectangular solids appearing boxlike in construction, and the draftsman will usually find it helpful to construct an isometric drawing of an object in a boxlike framework, portions of which may be discarded if unnecessary (see the construction in Fig. 12-7, for example).

12-6. Hidden lines and center lines. Hidden lines are omitted in isometric views and in all forms of pictorial drawing unless they are absolutely necessary to show important hidden shapes and details. Center lines are also omitted unless required for the proper dimensioning of the object. In general, all unnecessary lines should be avoided for the sake of clarity and simplicity in the representation.

12-7. Nonisometric lines. All lines of an object that are not parallel to the isometric axes are called *nonisometric lines*. Figure 12-6 illustrates some typical nonisometric lines. Since nonisometric lines do not show in their true length in isometric views, measurements cannot be taken from them. In isometric drawings, isometric lines are the only ones from which measurements may be taken.

12-8. Isometric angles. The only angles that will appear in their true size in isometric drawings are those between lines shown on planes parallel to the surface of the drawing sheet. Referring again to Fig. 12-6, it can be noted that none of the angles on the different objects is on a surface parallel to the plane of the paper, and as a result they do not appear in their true size. To draw iso-

NONISOMETRIC LINES ARE LOCATED ON ISOMETRIC DRAWINGS
BY OFFSETS FROM ORTHOGRAPHICS WHICH LOCATE DESIRED
POINTS ON RECTANGULAR COORDINATES

(Fine lines are nonisometric lines)

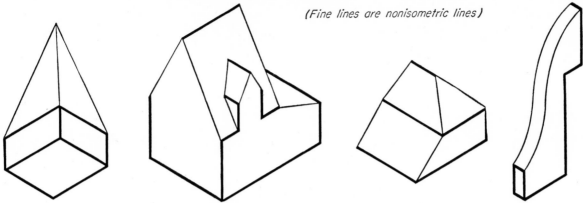

Fig. 12-6. Nonisometric lines.

metric angles formed by nonisometric lines, therefore, first construct an orthographic drawing of the object showing the true size of the angle and the true lengths of its sides. The true lengths of the sides of the angle are transferred from the orthographic by measuring them along the related isometric lines in the isometric drawing to produce the desired angle.

12-9. Locating nonisometric lines and angles in isometric drawings. Figure 12-7 illustrates the method used in laying out nonisometric lines and angles in an isometric drawing. These lines and

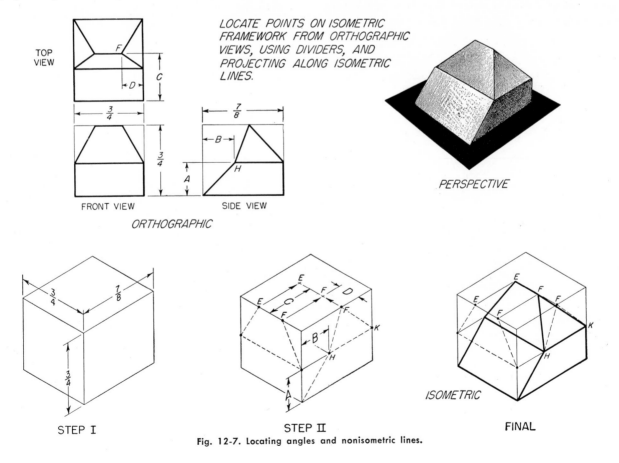

Fig. 12-7. Locating angles and nonisometric lines.

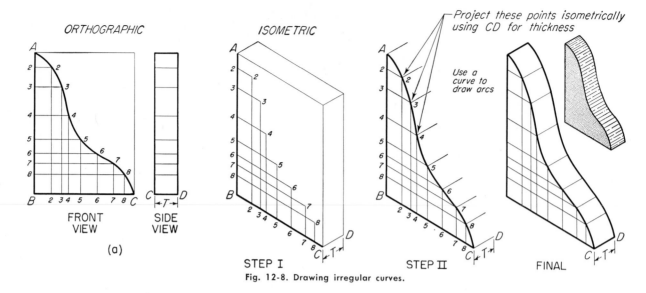

Fig. 12-8. Drawing irregular curves.

angles are first located on orthographic views drawn to the same scale as the isometric. They are then located on the isometric by projecting their significant intersections along isometric lines to their proper positions in the pictorial.

The drawing of irregular curves is handled in the same manner (see Fig. 12-8). The true shape of the curve is first drawn orthographically. Then mark off any convenient number of points on the curve, say eight, and draw lines vertically and hori-

zontally through these points. These lines are known as the *rectangular coordinates* of the points. The rectangular coordinates are then transferred to their proper positions on the isometric planes. For example, in Fig. 12-8 the distance A-2 along AB in the orthographic view is transferred to AB in the isometric drawing; B-2 along BC in the orthographic is transferred to BC in the isometric. The isometric lines drawn through these points will intersect at point 2 on the curve. All other points

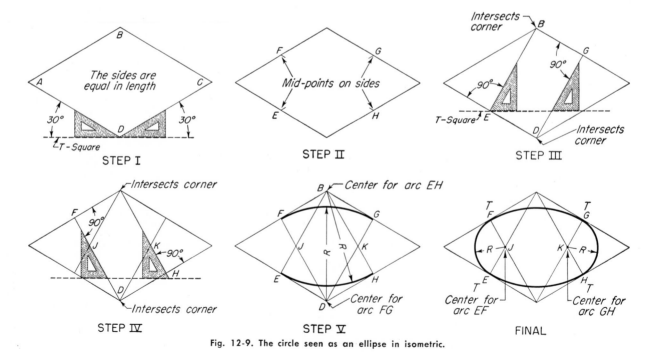

Fig. 12-9. The circle seen as an ellipse in isometric.

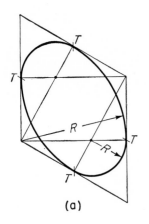
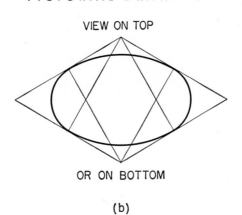
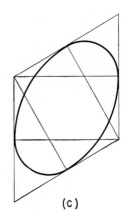

VIEW ON TOP

OR ON BOTTOM

(a)   (b)   (c)

Fig. 12-10. Common positions of the ellipse in isometric drawings.

on the curve are secured in the same manner, and the points are connected to form the finished curve.

12-10. Drawing the circle in isometric. The circle rarely appears in its true shape in isometric drawings. Usually a circle is located on one of the isometric planes where it takes the shape of an ellipse. The manner in which such circles are drawn is shown in Fig. 12-9. In Step I, lay out an isometric square in the required position, making the sides AB, BC, CD, and AD equal in length to the diameter of the circle. In Step II, locate the points E, F, G, and H at the mid-points of the sides. In Step III, erect perpendiculars to the sides through these points. If the work has been done accurately the perpendiculars will intersect the opposite corners B and D. Follow the remaining steps as shown to complete the drawing. Note particularly the manner in which the instruments are used in the sequence of operations illustrated.

Figure 12-10 shows the representation of circles as ellipses in isometric squares on the planes most often encountered in isometric drawing.

12-11. Concentric circles in isometric drawings. When concentric circles are to be shown on an isometric plane, a complete set of centers must be found for the construction of each ellipse, as shown in Fig. 12-11. This must be done regardless of whether the circles are produced in an isometric square or by the four-center method (see Secs. 6-25 and 6-28).

12-12. Shafts, holes, and tapers. A method of showing shafts and holes in isometric drawings is illustrated in Fig. 12-12. Note that the ellipse nearer the observer is first constructed. Then the centers for the arcs required to complete the construction of the farther ellipse are moved back parallel to the isometric axis of the cylinder a distance equal to the length of the shaft or the depth of the hole. These newly located centers are used to strike the visible portions of the arcs necessary to complete the drawing of the shaft or hole.

The manner in which tapers are constructed in isometric drawings is illustrated in Fig. 12-13. Note that the length is measured along the axis.

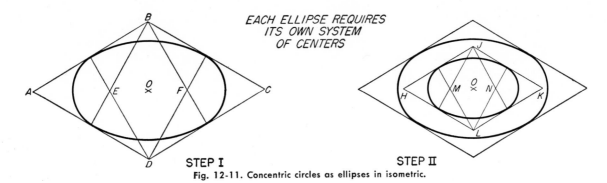

EACH ELLIPSE REQUIRES
ITS OWN SYSTEM
OF CENTERS

STEP I   STEP II

Fig. 12-11. Concentric circles as ellipses in isometric.

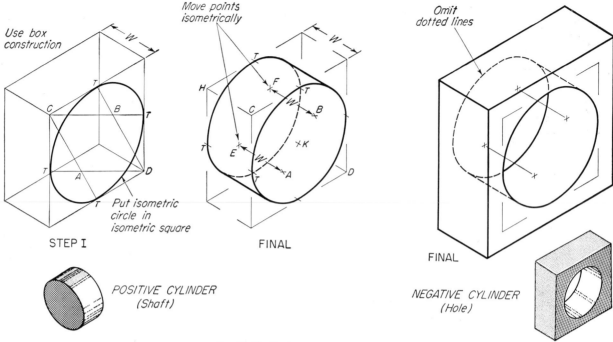

Fig. 12-12. Shafts and holes in isometric.

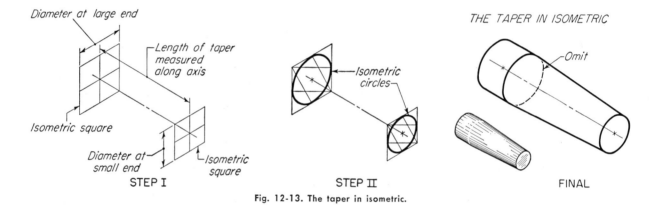

Fig. 12-13. The taper in isometric.

12-13. Circle arcs. The procedure followed in the construction of rounded forms and corners is shown in Fig. 12–14. Measure the radius of the arc along the sides of the angle from their point of intersection O. Erect perpendiculars to the sides at points A and B. The intersection X of the perpendiculars is the center for the arc that forms the round. If the material is $\frac{3}{8}$ in. thick, for example, move the center that distance isometrically to point Y, and use this point to strike the visible portion of the farther arc. Finish the contour with a straight line drawn tangent to the arcs. As shown at the right in the illustration, the procedure is the

same when the arc falls between lines that form an obtuse angle.

If a part ends in a complete round, follow the steps pictured in Fig. 12-15. Note that only the centers for the required small and large arcs need be found. The centers are then moved isometrically to draw the farthermost arcs.

The procedure for drawing a slot with rounded ends is shown in Fig. 12-16. Begin with an isometric rectangle, the length and width of whose sides are equal to the over-all dimensions of the slot. Construct half ellipses at each end of the rectangle. Then move the centers isometrically to

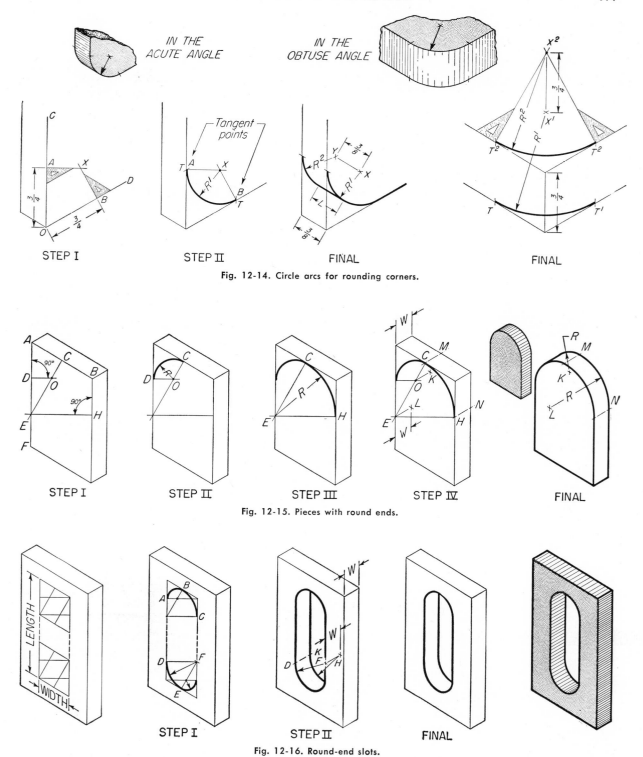

Fig. 12-14. Circle arcs for rounding corners.

Fig. 12-15. Pieces with round ends.

Fig. 12-16. Round-end slots.

draw the portions of the partially visible arcs. Complete the drawing of the slot by joining the arcs with straight lines.

12-14. The ellipse in a nonisometric plane.

To draw an ellipse in a nonisometric plane it is first necessary to draw a true-shape orthographic view of the ellipse, as shown in the auxiliary view of Fig. 12-17a. The rectangular coordinates intersecting at significant points on the ellipse are found (see method described in Sec. 12-9) and are projected back to the orthographic side view. These coordinates are then placed on the framework of the isometric to locate the ellipse on the inclined surface in the pictorial.

In Fig. 12-17b, the isometric framework is first drawn, after which the conjugate diameters of the ellipse are located. To find the long and short diameters of the four-center ellipse that was drawn on the inclined surface, use the method described

in Sec. 6-25. In Fig. 12-17c, the isometric framework with its inclined surface and the isometric circle in the base are first drawn, after which points on the circle are projected vertically, then isometrically from the circle to the side of the framework, next to the edge, and finally across the inclined surface. The intersections of the rectangular coordinates thus projected locate points that outline the ellipse on the inclined surface.

12-15. The sphere in isometric. The isometric representation of a sphere consists of the envelope of all its great circles. The drawing procedure as illustrated in Fig. 12-18 is as follows: Draw the

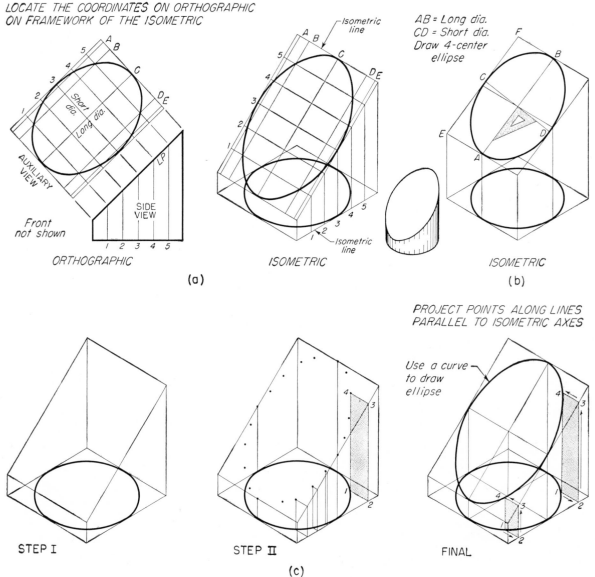

Fig. 12-17. Drawing the ellipse in a nonisometric plane.

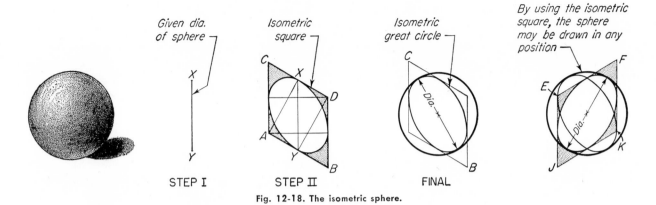

Given dia. of sphere

Isometric square

Isometric great circle

By using the isometric square, the sphere may be drawn in any position

STEP I   STEP II   FINAL

Fig. 12-18. The isometric sphere.

given diameter of the sphere located within an isometric square. Construct an isometric circle within this square. The long diameter of the ellipse thus formed is the diameter of the desired isometric sphere.

12-16. Isometric full section. Isometric section views may be drawn to show unusual details of interior construction (see Fig. 12-19). The imaginary cutting plane for a full section is passed through the center of the object parallel to one of the receding isometric axes. The revealed interior features are completed according to the principles of isometric drawing. The section lining for the cut portion may be drawn at any appropriate angle, but care should be taken to make sure that it does not run parallel with the principal lines of the cut

contours of the object. As a general rule a 60° slope for the section lining will be found satisfactory on most isometric section drawings.

12-17. Isometric half section. The imaginary cutting planes for the isometric half section are passed parallel to the receding isometric axes and intersect the center line (see Fig. 12-20).

12-18. Broken-out sections. The imaginary cutting planes for showing broken-out sections may be passed at any desired position parallel to the isometric axes (see Fig. 12-21). The cutting planes should pass through the axis of holes, shafts, and similar features if a true cross section of their cut contours is desired.

12-19. Isometric dimensioning. Basically, isometric drawings are dimensioned according to the

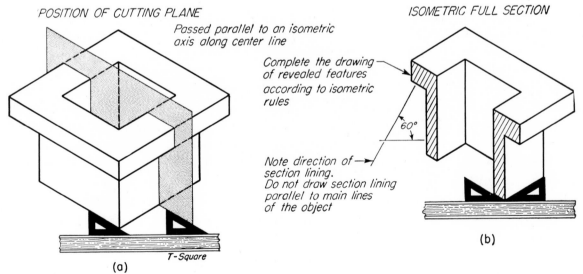

POSITION OF CUTTING PLANE

Passed parallel to an isometric axis along center line

ISOMETRIC FULL SECTION

Complete the drawing of revealed features according to isometric rules

60°

Note direction of section lining.
Do not draw section lining parallel to main lines of the object

T-Square

(a)

(b)

Fig. 12-19. The isometric full section.

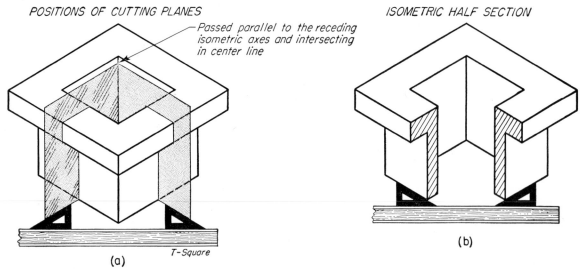

Fig. 12-20. The isometric half section.

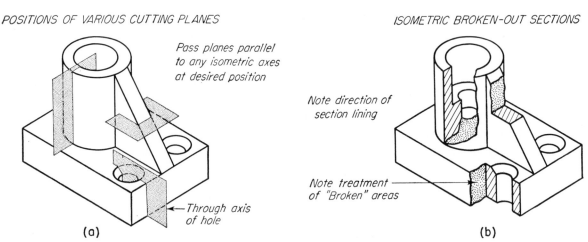

Fig. 12-21. Isometric broken-out sections.

same general rules followed in orthographic dimensioning. The dimensions given should be clear and should provide all the information necessary for the fabrication of the part. As shown in Fig. 12-22, in isometric drawings the dimension and extension lines, the slope and guide lines, and the dimension figures are all drawn parallel to the isometric axes. Notes, on the other hand, should lie in the plane of the paper. Whenever possible, dimensions should be placed to read horizontally or from the right. This rule may be violated, however, if it leads to inverted, or nearly inverted, lettering.

12-20. Theory of oblique projection. The simplest type of pictorial to make is the oblique

drawing. Figure 12-23 compares an orthographic representation of a cube whose nearest face is parallel to the picture plane, or surface of the paper, with an oblique projection appearing on the same surface. While only one surface may be seen in a given orthographic view, an oblique view shows the front and two receding planes in one projection. The front face of the cube is seen in its true size and shape in both drawings. The projectors of the orthographic image are parallel to each other and are perpendicular to the picture plane. The projectors of the oblique view are also parallel to each other, but are not perpendicular to the picture plane. In this case, they make an angle of

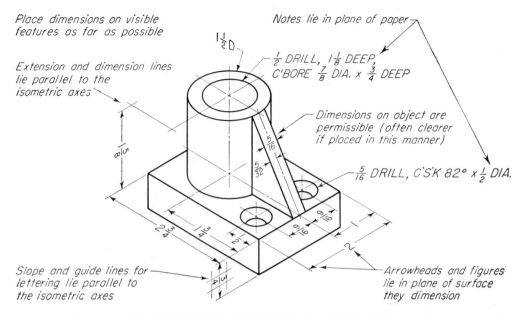

Place dimensions on visible features as far as possible

Notes lie in plane of paper

$1\frac{1}{2}$ D

$\frac{1}{2}$ DRILL, $1\frac{1}{8}$ DEEP, C'BORE $\frac{7}{8}$ DIA. x $\frac{3}{4}$ DEEP

Extension and dimension lines lie parallel to the isometric axes

Dimensions on object are permissible (often clearer if placed in this manner)

$\frac{5}{16}$ DRILL, C'SK 82° x $\frac{1}{2}$ DIA.

Slope and guide lines for lettering lie parallel to the isometric axes

Arrowheads and figures lie in plane of surface they dimension

Fig. 12-22. Rules for dimensioning an isometric drawing.

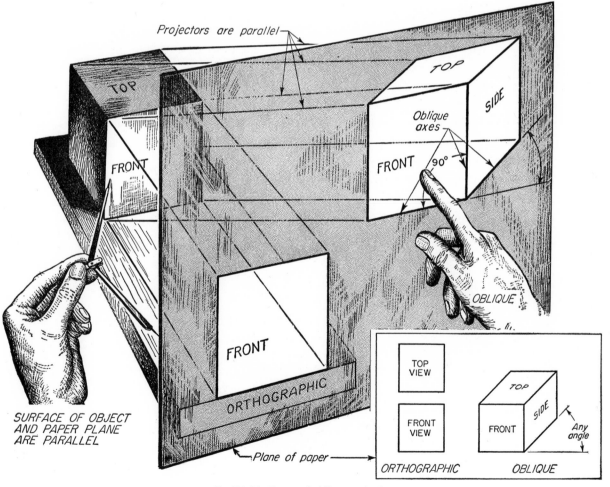

Projectors are parallel

SURFACE OF OBJECT AND PAPER PLANE ARE PARALLEL

Plane of paper

Fig. 12-23. Theory of oblique projection.

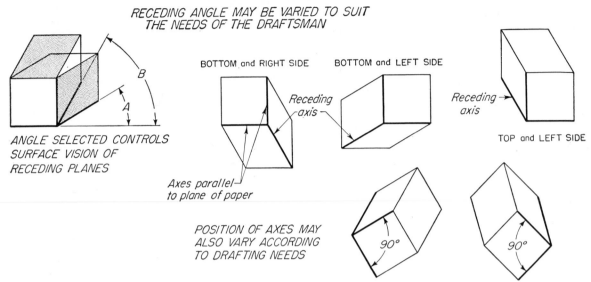

RECEDING ANGLE MAY BE VARIED TO SUIT THE NEEDS OF THE DRAFTSMAN

Fig. 12-24. Varying positions for oblique axes.

less than 90° with the drawing surface, thus indicating that the observer is looking toward and down at the cube. Since the projectors are parallel, the nonreceding horizontal lines of the cube will appear horizontal and parallel in the oblique view, the verticals will appear vertical and parallel, and the receding lines will appear parallel and make the same angles with any horizontal line or any vertical line. An immediate advantage over isometric projection is noticeable in that one face of an object—the one parallel to the surface of the drawing sheet—may always be represented in its true size and shape.

12-21. The oblique axes. The oblique axes are three lines, two of which are always perpendicular to each other and rest in the plane of the paper, while the third is a receding line that may make any convenient angle with a horizontal line. The angle selected should be one that permits showing the details of the desired receding surface as clearly as necessary (see Fig. 12-24). The positions of the axes on the drawing sheet are not fixed except for the fact that the two axes resting on or parallel to the plane of the paper must make angles of 90° with each other.

12-22. Drawing a cube in oblique. Figure 12-25 illustrates the steps followed in making a simple oblique drawing. As in isometric drawing,

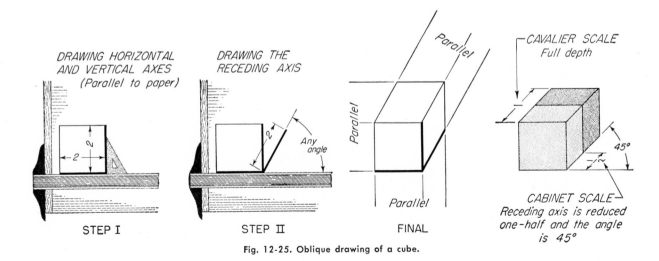

Fig. 12-25. Oblique drawing of a cube.

the actual dimensions (or scaled dimensions) of a given object are measured along the main axes and any lines parallel to them. In the first step, the two mutually perpendicular axes lying on the drawing sheet are scaled to 2 in. In the next step, the receding axis is drawn at any angle with the horizontal and is also scaled to 2 in. In the third step, the remaining edges of the object are drawn parallel to the oblique axes to complete the drawing. Dotted lines indicating hidden edges are omitted. For convenience the receding angle is usually made 30°, 45°, or 60°.

To avoid the distortion that is often apparent in the final drawing, the receding axis may be foreshortened to satisfy the expectations of the human eye. If the angle is 45° and the receding axis is full scale, the drawing is in *cavalier style*. If the angle is 45° and the depth scale is reduced one-half, the result is known as a *cabinet drawing* (see Fig. 12-26). As a general rule, a more pleasing effect is obtained by reducing the scale of the receding axis.

12-23. Positions for rectangular forms. In making an oblique drawing, the usual procedure is to draw an object with the surface showing its most characteristic appearance parallel to the surface of the paper. In order to avoid undue distortion in the case of some forms, however, it is good practice to place them so that their long dimension lies parallel to the drawing surface (Fig. 12-27).

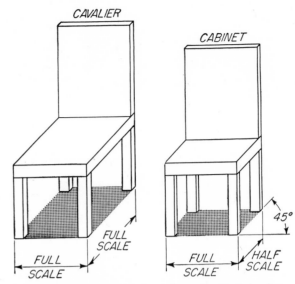

Fig. 12-26. Comparison of cavalier and cabinet drawing.

When drawing angles that appear on the receding or on the nonoblique planes, apply the methods of construction used in isometric (see Sec. 12-9).

12-24. Positions for circular and irregular curved forms. If objects whose contours are formed by circular arcs or irregular curves are to be drawn, the outlines of these surfaces should be placed parallel to the plane of the paper. This saves both time and labor, because the circular curves can be drawn with a compass and the irregular curves can be produced in their true size and shape as they would appear in an ortho-

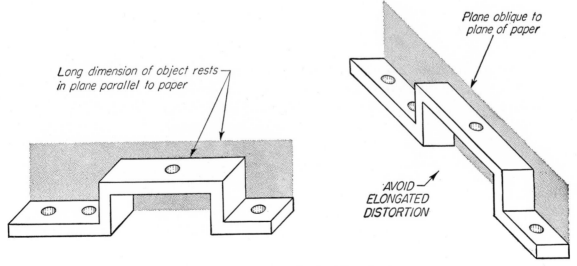

Fig. 12-27. Avoiding distortion in oblique drawings.

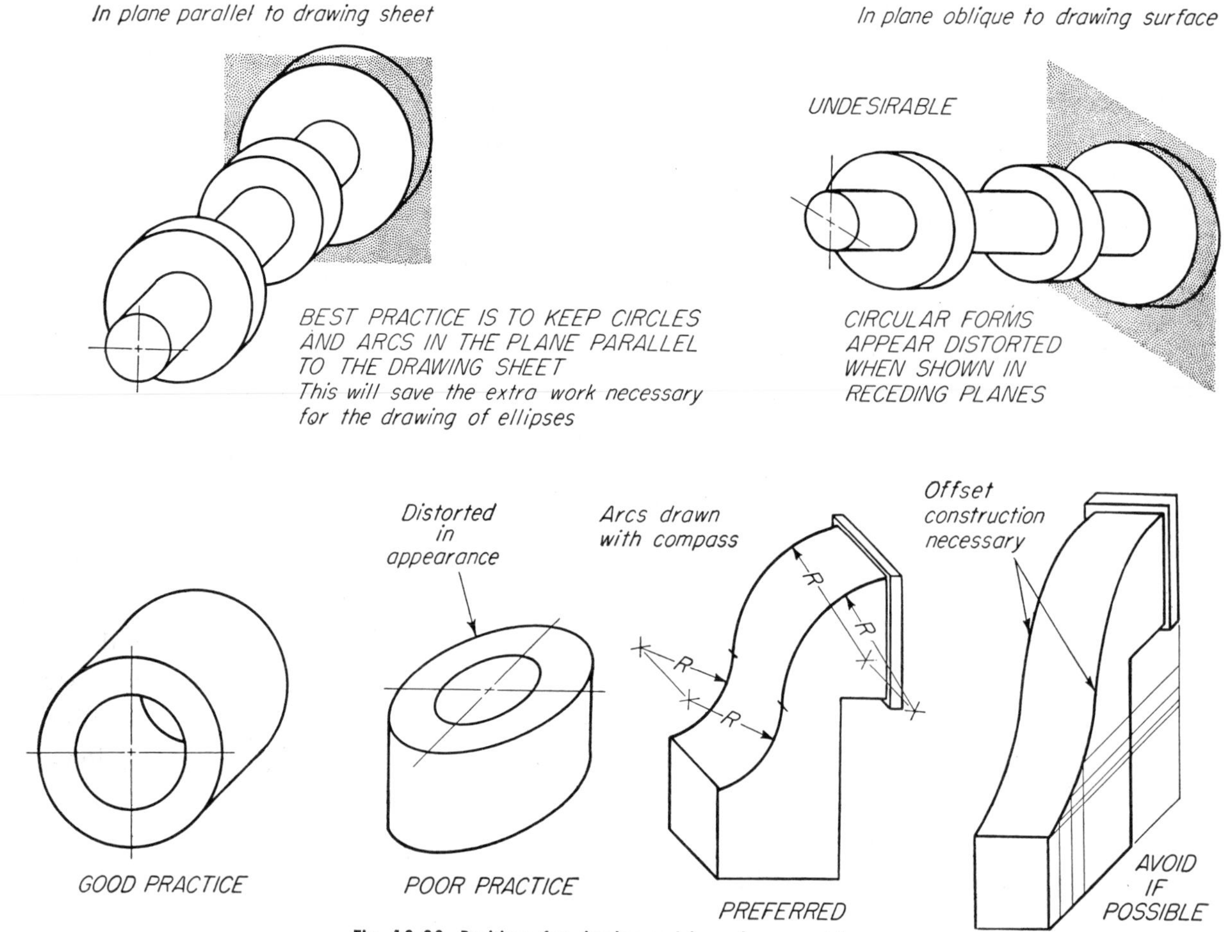

In plane parallel to drawing sheet

In plane oblique to drawing surface

UNDESIRABLE

BEST PRACTICE IS TO KEEP CIRCLES
AND ARCS IN THE PLANE PARALLEL
TO THE DRAWING SHEET
*This will save the extra work necessary
for the drawing of ellipses*

CIRCULAR FORMS
APPEAR DISTORTED
WHEN SHOWN IN
RECEDING PLANES

*Distorted
in
appearance*

*Arcs drawn
with compass*

*Offset
construction
necessary*

GOOD PRACTICE

POOR PRACTICE

PREFERRED

AVOID
IF
POSSIBLE

Fig. 12-28. Positions for circular and irregular curved forms.

graphic view (see Fig. 12-28). Therefore, in the case of curved forms, it is usually best to place the circular or irregularly curved surface of an object, rather than its long dimension, parallel to the plane of the paper. In any case, try to select axes that will present the most pleasing and realistic drawing possible.

12-25. Construction of the circle as an ellipse. At times it is necessary to show the circles on the receding planes, where they will appear as ellipses (see Fig. 12-29). If the receding axis is full scale, the ellipse may be drawn in the suitable oblique square by the four-center method. The method of construction is similar to that used for the iso-

metric ellipse (see Sec. 12-10). However, note that only when the angles of the oblique square are similar to those of the isometric square will the construction of the resulting ellipse be like the isometric. In other cases the centers for the large arcs may fall either inside or outside the parallelogram of the oblique square. The four-center method of constructing the oblique ellipse can be used only when the receding axis is full scale. When reduced scale is used, the ellipse must be located by rectangular coordinates.

Partial ellipses are drawn by locating the centers for the required portions of the arcs (see Fig. 12-30a). Circle arcs and irregular curves on a reced-

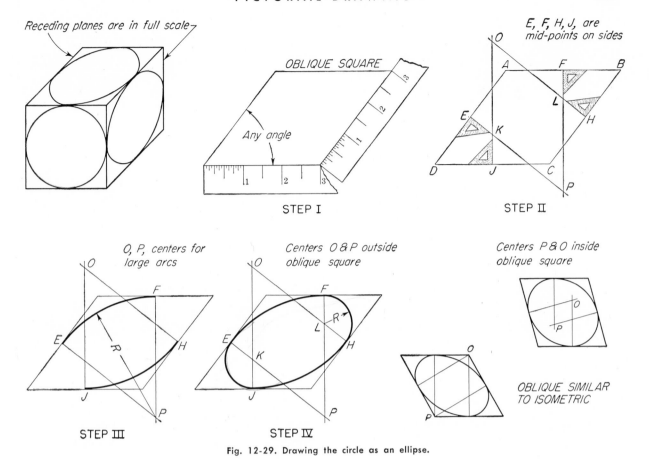

Receding planes are in full scale
OBLIQUE SQUARE
Any angle
1 2 3
STEP I
E, F, H, J, are mid-points on sides
O A F B L E H K D J C P
STEP II
O, P, centers for large arcs
O F E H R J P
STEP III
Centers O & P outside oblique square
O F L R E H K J P
STEP IV
Centers P & O inside oblique square
O P
OBLIQUE SIMILAR TO ISOMETRIC

Fig. 12-29. Drawing the circle as an ellipse.

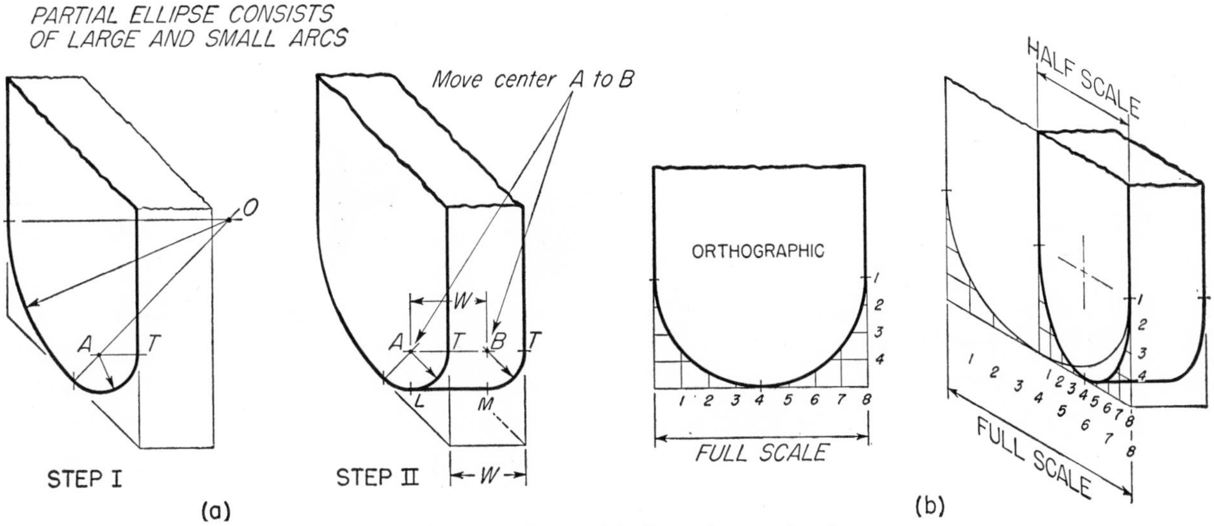

PARTIAL ELLIPSE CONSISTS OF LARGE AND SMALL ARCS
O A T
STEP I
Move center A to B
W A T B T L M
STEP II
W
(a)
ORTHOGRAPHIC
1 2 3 4
1 2 3 4 5 6 7 8
FULL SCALE
HALF SCALE
1 2 3 4
1 2 3 4 5 6 7 8
FULL SCALE
(b)

Fig. 12-30. Drawing partial ellipses for curved ends.

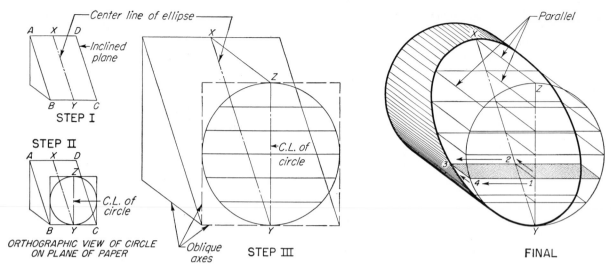

STEP I

STEP II

ORTHOGRAPHIC VIEW OF CIRCLE
ON PLANE OF PAPER

STEP III

FINAL

Fig. 12-31. Drawing the ellipse on an inclined surface.

ing plane can also be drawn by transferring the intersecting points of rectangular coordinates with points on the curve appearing on the full size orthographic (see Fig. 12-30b). Note in the illustration that the vertical axis resting in the plane of the drawing sheet is in full scale regardless of whether the receding axis is in full or half scale. Circular forms that must appear as ellipses on receding oblique planes always make a better appearance if the receding dimension is shortened.

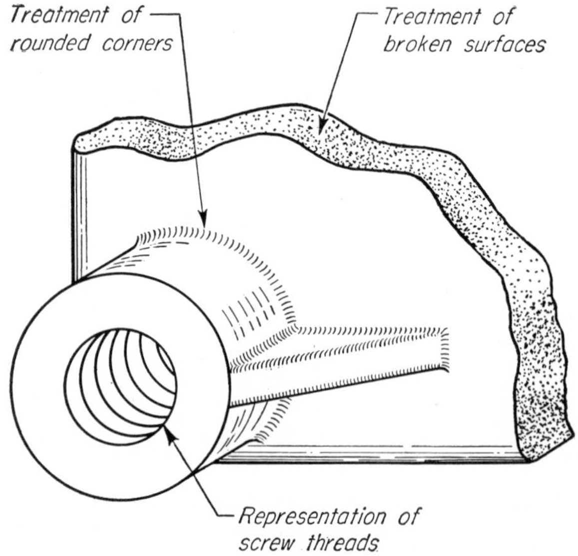

12-26. Constructing the circle as an ellipse on any inclined plane. A method of projecting a circle to an inclined surface is shown in Fig. 12-31. An ellipse with a long diameter XY is to appear on the inclined surface $ABCD$ shown in the top left corner of the illustration. The true shape of the circle is drawn on a plane lying parallel to the surface of the paper as shown. The vertical center line YZ for the circle and the inclined center line XY for the ellipse intersect at Y. The points that form the path of the ellipse are found by using a system of rectangular coordinates in the manner explained in Sec. 12-9. The points on the circle are projected to the coordinates on the inclined plane of the ellipse in a direction parallel to the receding axis. This construction is useful not only for the drawing of ellipses in oblique projections, it also may be used to construct an ellipse on any inclined surface, including constructions in ordinary orthographic drawing.

Fig. 12-32. Conventional treatment of rounded corners, screw threads, and broken edges.

12-27. Rounded edges. The conventional manner of treating the rounded intersections on parts, especially on castings, is illustrated in Fig. 12-32. Note also the manner of showing screw threads. The full radius of the nearest circle of the cylinder has been struck off at regular intervals along the receding oblique axis of the hole, allowing only the portions of the arcs within the circle to remain on the finished drawing.

12-28. Oblique section views. In general, the procedures employed in drawing isometric sections are used in the preparation of oblique section views. Oblique full sections (Fig. 12-33) are rarely used because the cutting plane, passing completely through the object along its center line, often makes it impossible to show important external features. The half section (Fig. 12-34) and the broken-out section are more frequently employed because these enable the draftsman to show external as well as internal details.

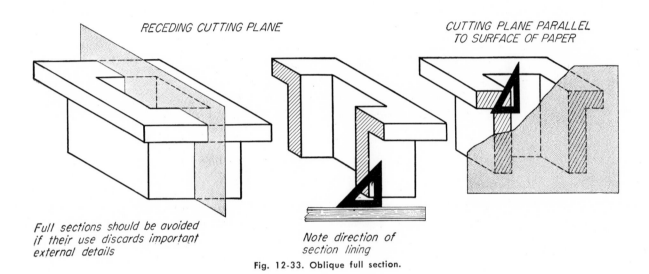

RECEDING CUTTING PLANE

CUTTING PLANE PARALLEL TO SURFACE OF PAPER

Full sections should be avoided if their use discards important external details

Note direction of section lining

Fig. 12-33. Oblique full section.

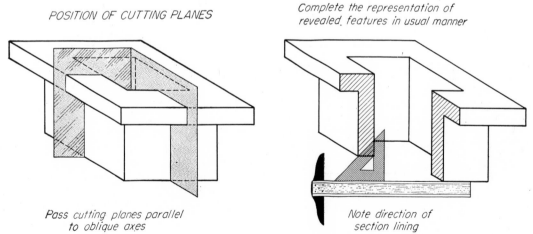

POSITION OF CUTTING PLANES

Complete the representation of revealed features in usual manner

Pass cutting planes parallel to oblique axes

Note direction of section lining

Fig. 12-34. Oblique half section.

12-29. Oblique drawing and dimensioning.

In preparing an oblique drawing it is important to keep in mind that all lines, angles, circles, circle arcs, and irregular curves project in their true size and shape when drawn parallel to the drawing surface no matter how far into the background they may appear to recede. This fact was deemed most important in selecting the position of the object shown in Fig. 12-35, and the long axis of the object accordingly was placed on a receding plane rather than parallel to the surface of the drawing paper. In Step I, the center lines and the boxlike framework are first drawn, after which the proper locations of the centers for the required arcs and circles are marked off. Step II shows the semicircles of the large arcs terminating at the tangent points of the arcs and the straight-line edges. The circles for the holes are then drawn in, and the portions of the circles located on the further planes are shown. When important details are obscured, parts of the object may be sectioned away to reveal them. Center lines are added to facilitate the dimensioning procedure illustrated in the final drawing. Note that, as in isometric drawing, the dimension figures, dimension lines, etc., are drawn so that they lie in the plane of the surface they dimension.

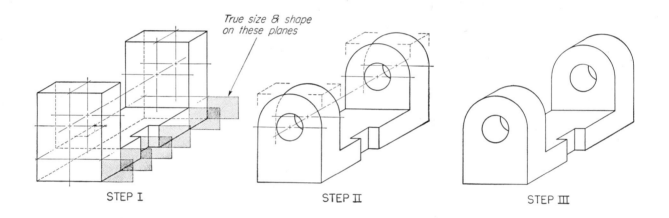

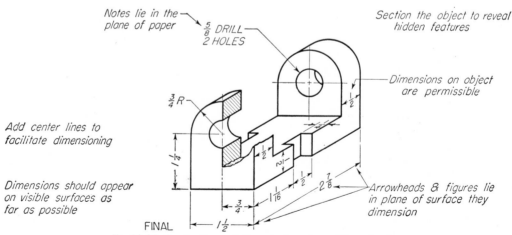

Fig. 12-35. Construction and dimensioning of an oblique drawing.

PROBLEMS

These problems may be sketched freehand on ordinary sketch paper at a suitable scale to fit the drawing sheet. Instrument drawings to scale may also be made by scaling the objects with dividers or by following the measurements of the dimensioned drawings. Each problem can be produced on a standard 8½- by 11-in. sheet, although they may be enlarged to fit an 11- by 17-in. sheet if desired.

Problems 12-1 to 12-10. The given figures are oblique drawings. Make a freehand thumbnail sketch of each problem as it appears in oblique; then make a full-size sketch or instrument drawing in isometric. Dimensioning and sectioning may be required at the suggestion of the instructor.

Problems 12-11 to 12-18. The illustrations are isometric drawings. Make a thumbnail sketch of each problem as an isometric; then prepare a large-scale freehand sketch or an instrument drawing of the object in oblique. Dimensioning and sectioning may be required at the suggestion of the instructor.

Problems 12-19 to 12-33. The orthographic views of various objects are given. They may be assigned as either isometric or oblique problems in which the student may be required to make a pictorial thumbnail sketch before working with instruments. Sectioning practices should be used where desirable, and some of the drawings should be dimensioned in order to give the student practice in this phase of the work.

The instructor may assign additional problems for pictorial drawing by selecting suitable objects from other problem sections elsewhere in the text.

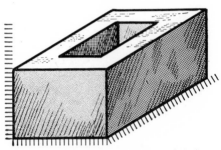

Prob. 12-1. Steel base. (Time: 1 hr.)

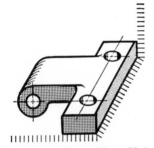

Prob. 12-4. Hinge. (Time: 1½ hr.)

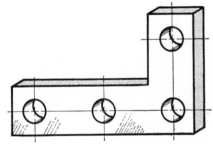

Prob. 12-5. Corner brace. (Time: 1½ hr.)

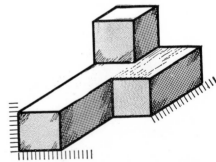

Prob. 12-2. Corner block. (Time: 2 hr.)

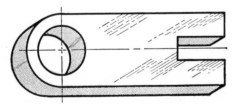

Prob. 12-6. Clevis. (Time: 1½ hr.)

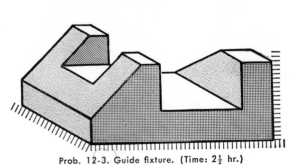

Prob. 12-3. Guide fixture. (Time: 2½ hr.)

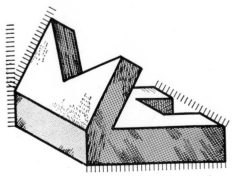

Prob. 12-7. Tool support. (Time: 1½ hr.)

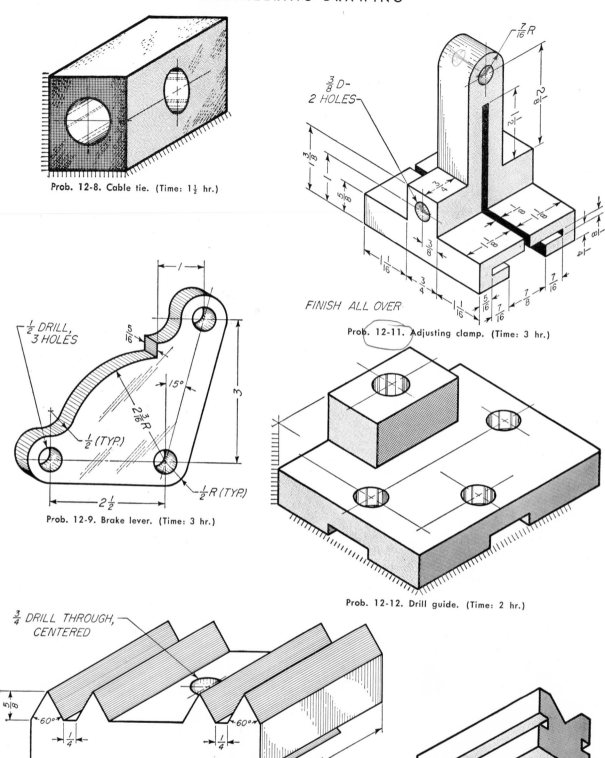

Prob. 12-8. Cable tie. (Time: 1½ hr.)

$\frac{3}{8}$ D—
2 HOLES

$\frac{7}{16}$ R

FINISH ALL OVER

Prob. 12-11. Adjusting clamp. (Time: 3 hr.)

$\frac{1}{2}$ DRILL,
3 HOLES

$\frac{5}{16}$

15°

$2\frac{3}{16}$ R

$\frac{1}{2}$ (TYP.)

$\frac{1}{2}$ R (TYP.)

$2\frac{1}{2}$

Prob. 12-9. Brake lever. (Time: 3 hr.)

Prob. 12-12. Drill guide. (Time: 2 hr.)

$\frac{3}{4}$ DRILL THROUGH,
CENTERED

$\frac{5}{8}$
60°
$\frac{1}{4}$
60°
$2\frac{1}{4}$
$\frac{5}{8}$
45°　45°
45°　45°
$\frac{7}{8}$
$3\frac{1}{4}$
3
5

FINISH
ALL SURFACES

Prob. 12-10. Sliding clip. (Time: 2 hr.)

Prob. 12-13. Clamp base. (Time: 1½ hr.)

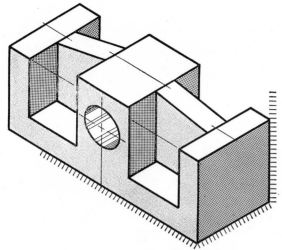

Prob. 12-14. Rod guide. (Time: 2½ hr.)

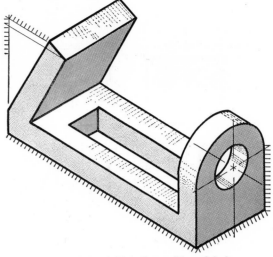

Prob. 12-15. Cable adjuster (Time: 3 hr.)

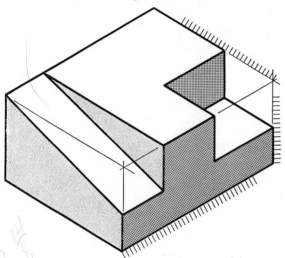

Prob. 12-16. Stop block. (Time: 2 hr.)

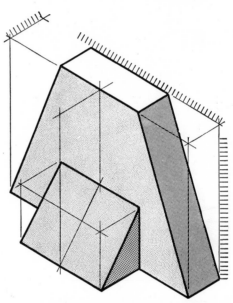

Prob. 12-17. Base anchor. (Time: 2 hr.)

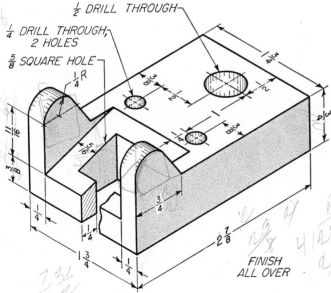

½ DRILL THROUGH

¼ DRILL THROUGH, 2 HOLES

⅝ SQUARE HOLE

¼ R

1¾

2

¾

11/16

3/8

½

⅝

¼

¼

1¾

¼

2 7/8

¾

FINISH ALL OVER

Prob. 12-18. Sliding block. (Time: 3 hr.)

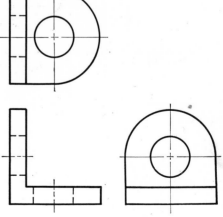

Prob. 12-19. Rod anchor. (Time: 2 hr.)

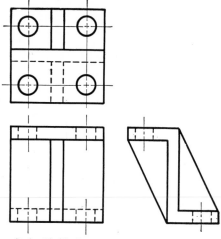

Prob. 12-20. Beam support. (Time: 2½ hr.)

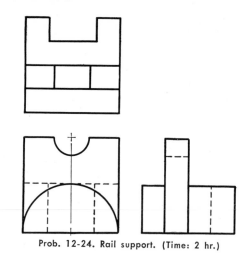

Prob. 12-24. Rail support. (Time: 2 hr.)

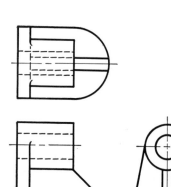

Prob. 21. Shaft support. (Time: 2½ hr.)

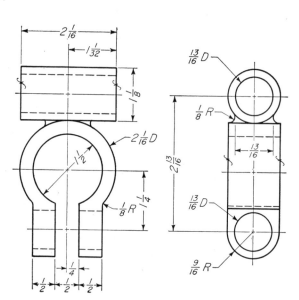

Prob. 12-25. Cable clamp. (Time: 3 hr.)

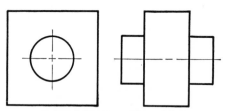

Prob. 12-22. Plug. (Time: 1 hr.)

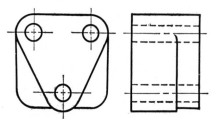

Prob. 12-23. Cover plate. (Time: 2½ hr.)

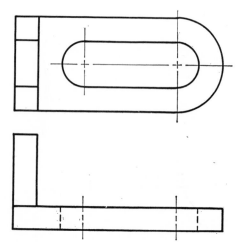

Prob. 12-26. Sliding adjuster. (Time: 2 hr.)

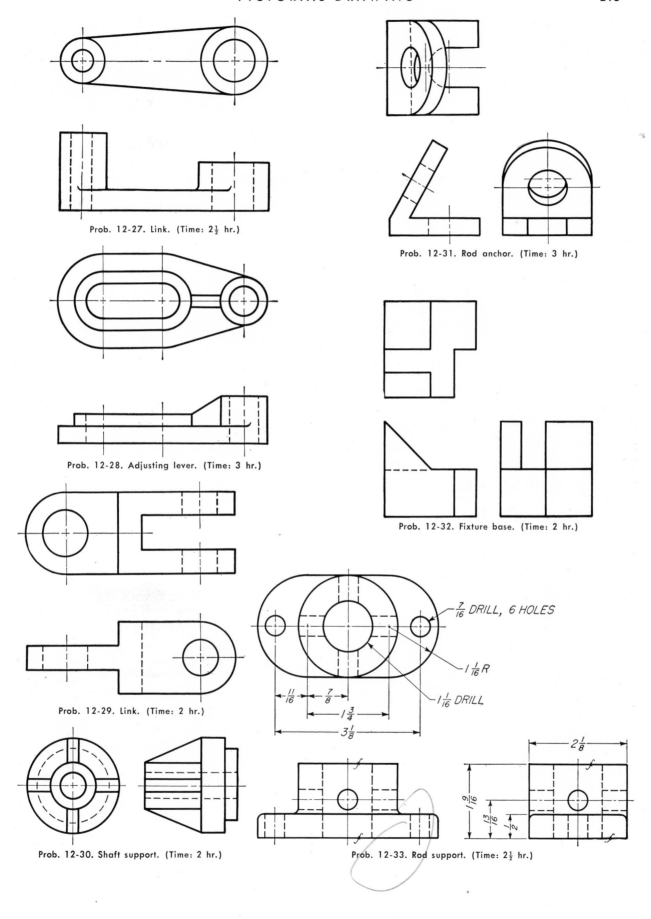

Prob. 12-27. Link. (Time: 2½ hr.)

Prob. 12-31. Rod anchor. (Time: 3 hr.)

Prob. 12-28. Adjusting lever. (Time: 3 hr.)

Prob. 12-32. Fixture base. (Time: 2 hr.)

Prob. 12-29. Link. (Time: 2 hr.)

$\frac{7}{16}$ DRILL, 6 HOLES

$1\frac{1}{16}R$

$1\frac{1}{16}$ DRILL

$\frac{11}{16}$ $\frac{7}{8}$

$1\frac{3}{4}$

$3\frac{1}{8}$

Prob. 12-30. Shaft support. (Time: 2 hr.)

Prob. 12-33. Rod support. (Time: 2½ hr.)

$2\frac{1}{8}$

$1\frac{9}{16}$

$\frac{13}{16}$ $\frac{1}{2}$

Chapter 13

COMMON FASTENERS

The engineering draftsman should become familiar with the design and representation of the common fasteners, for they appear frequently in the drawing of machine assemblies. A number of the more common fasteners are shown in Fig. 13-1. Rivets and welds are permanent fasteners. Bolts, screws, keys, pins, etc., are removable fasteners.

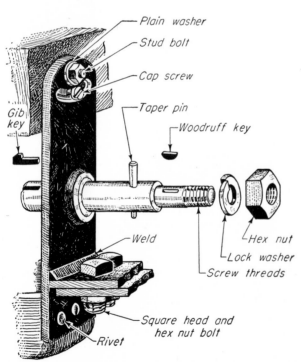

Fig. 13-1. Common fastening devices.

Plain washer
Stud bolt
Cap screw
Taper pin
Woodruff key
Gib key
Weld
Hex nut
Lock washer
Screw threads
Square head and hex nut bolt
Rivet

13-1. Screw threads. Basic screw-thread terminology is given in Fig. 13-2. Screw threads have three primary functions: to hold parts together, to adjust parts in relation to each other, or to transmit power. Various types of threads in common use are illustrated in Fig. 13-3. The sharp V (which is fast falling into disuse) and the unified or American (National) Standard are used for holding parts together. The square, the Acme, and the Browne & Sharpe worm threads are used to transmit power. The buttress thread transmits power in one direction only. The Whitworth and British Association Standard are British threads, the former being the British Standard. The knuckle thread is a rolled thread used for light sockets, etc., while the standard pipe thread may be either tapered or straight and is used to join pipe sections. In general, any standard thread may be shown symbolically on the drawing sheet if its proper specifications and complete dimensions are given by note (see Secs. 13-4 to 13-8).

13-2. Right-hand and left-hand threads. A right-hand thread advances when turned clockwise; a left-hand thread advances when turned counterclockwise; (see Fig. 13-4). All threads are considered right-hand unless otherwise specified. A left-hand thread is always indicated with the letters "LH" in the thread specification.

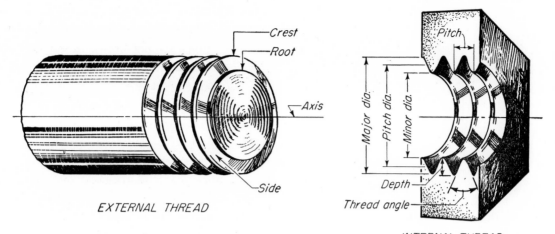

EXTERNAL THREAD

INTERNAL THREAD

Fig. 13-2. Screw-thread terminology.

13-3. Single and multiple threads. If a thread consists of a single continuous ridge, it is a single thread and its lead is equal to its pitch. The *pitch* (*P*) of a thread is the distance measured parallel to the axis between two succeeding points on the thread. The *lead* (*L*) is the distance the thread travels in one complete turn. On a single thread, the lead and the pitch are equal; on multiple threads, the lead is always greater than the pitch (see Fig. 13-5). Multiple threads are found on many

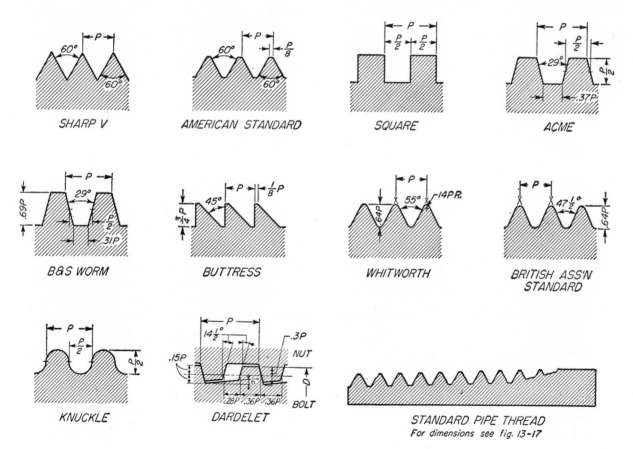

SHARP V

AMERICAN STANDARD

SQUARE

ACME

B&S WORM

BUTTRESS

WHITWORTH

BRITISH ASS'N STANDARD

KNUCKLE

DARDELET

STANDARD PIPE THREAD
For dimensions see fig. 13-17

ALL THREADS (EXCEPT SPECIAL DESIGNS) MAY BE SHOWN SYMBOLICALLY ON ENGINEERING DRAWINGS

Fig. 13-3. Screw threads (sections).

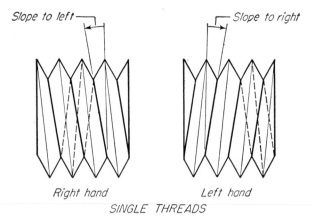

Slope to left

Slope to right

Right hand   Left hand

SINGLE THREADS

Fig. 13-4. Right-hand and left-hand threads.

types of locking devices and are often used where travel instead of power is desired. Two or more ridges cut side by side produce this type of thread. The lead of the double thread is twice its pitch, and a nut would travel twice as far as on a single thread in one complete turn of the screw. The lead of a triple thread is three times its pitch, and the screw travels three times the distance a single-thread screw of the same design would travel in one turn. If the screw is drawn in profile, as in Fig. 13-5, study of the thread will indicate whether it is single, double, triple, etc.

13-4. Semiconventional screw-thread representation. The true projection of a screw thread would take the form of a series of helices. However,

the representation of helical curves is a time-consuming and tedious procedure, and in practice the helical curves are not drawn except for very large diameter threads. Instead a so-called *semiconventional treatment* is often employed, in which the helices are represented by straight lines. Actually, even this semiconventional procedure has been further simplified so that in commercial drafting practice only special threads and those over 1 in. in diameter are represented semiconventionally. Threads of smaller diameter are shown symbolically, as discussed in Secs. 13-6 to 13-8.

Figure 13-6 illustrates the semiconventional representation of the sharp V, the unified, and the American Standard thread. Start by laying out the axis, the outside diameter, and the length of the screw thread. Find the number of threads to the inch for the given diameter by referring to Table 5 in the Appendix. The pitch distance, which is found by dividing 1 in. by the number of threads per inch, is then set off along the full length of the thread on the upper line representing the major diameter. This procedure is repeated along the lower line of the diameter except that a distance equal to one-half the pitch is marked off first. Draw straight lines connecting the pitch points to indicate the crest lines. Next draw 60° lines through the pitch points to intersect as shown in the illustration. Join these

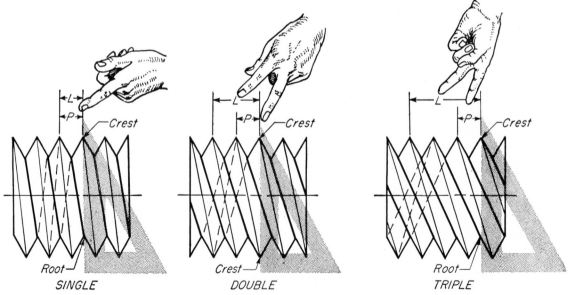

Fig. 13-5. Single and multiple threads.

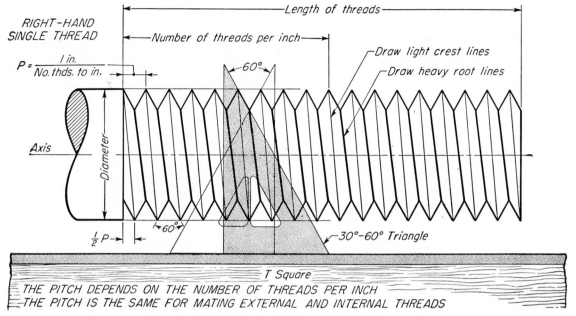

Fig. 13-6. Semiconventional single screw-thread representation.

intersections to produce the root lines. Note that root and crest lines are not parallel.

In drawing single threads and all odd-numbered multiple threads, a root is always opposite a crest; in drawing even-numbered multiple threads, a root is opposite a root and a crest is opposite a crest (see Fig. 13-5). For right-hand external threads, the slope lines lean toward the left; for right-hand internal threads (shown in section), the slope lines lean toward the right. Left-hand external and internal threads are drawn with the same general procedure, except that the slope is different, of

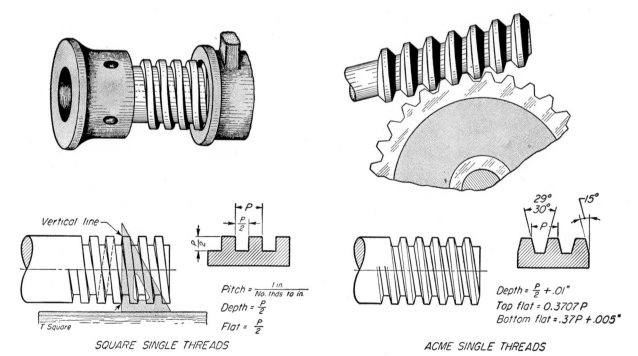

Fig. 13-7. Semiconventional representation of square and Acme threads.

course, and the distance equal to one-half the pitch is laid off along the top line rather than along the bottom.

13-5. Semiconventional representation of square and Acme threads (Fig. 13-7). Lay out the axis and the major diameter. The number of threads per inch for the given diameter (for internal as well as external threads) may be found in the Appendix. Lay out the pitch distances along the upper major diameter line. Then lay out these pitch distances along the lower line by starting one-half pitch away from a vertical drawn through the top starting pitch point. Locate the flat crests and valleys as shown in the sectioned views. The final steps require care in order to make certain that the proper points are joined to form the sides of the threads.

13-6. Conventional representation of threads. When threads are less than 1 in. in diameter, it is customary to show the threads symbolically. The ASA has approved two types of conventional thread symbols: the *regular* symbolic thread and the *simplified* symbolic thread (see Figs. 13-8 and 13-9). The simplified form saves drafting time but is not as pleasing or as effective as the regular symbolic representation.

13-7. Drawing regular symbolic threads. The steps in drawing the regular symbolic thread are shown in Fig. 13-10. The alternate long thin lines represent the crests and the shorter heavier lines the roots. The crest and root lines are spaced by eye, since no attempt is made to show the actual pitch. However, when a number of different sizes of screw threads are shown on a drawing, the spacing should

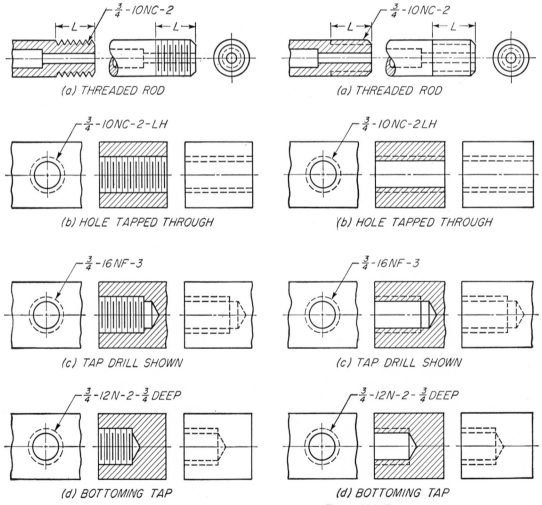

(a) THREADED ROD   (a) THREADED ROD

(b) HOLE TAPPED THROUGH   (b) HOLE TAPPED THROUGH

(c) TAP DRILL SHOWN   (c) TAP DRILL SHOWN

(d) BOTTOMING TAP   (d) BOTTOMING TAP

Fig. 13-8. Conventional representation of threads. (*From ASA* Z14.1—1946.)

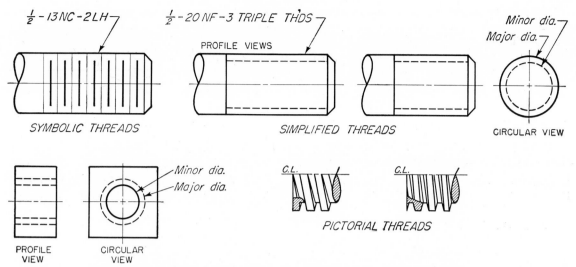

Fig. 13-9. Conventional representation of internal and external threads (all types).

vary sufficiently to give the worker an idea of the difference in the number of threads on one part compared to those on another.

13-8. Drawing the simplified threads. Figure 13-11 shows the steps to be followed in the drawing of simplified threads.

13-9. Threads in section views. Figure 13-12 illustrates the semiconventional representation of a thread in section when the diameter is 1 in. or over. Note that the slope lines of an internal thread lean in a direction opposite to the slope lines for its mating external thread.

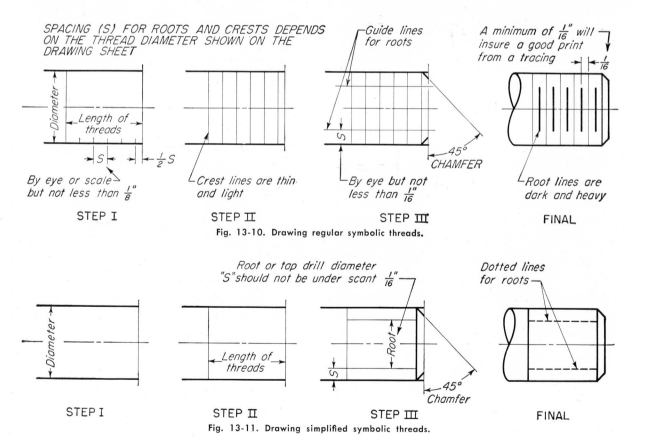

Fig. 13-10. Drawing regular symbolic threads.

Fig. 13-11. Drawing simplified symbolic threads.

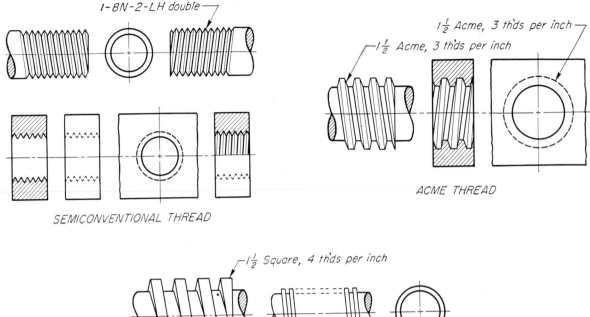

1-8N-2-LH double

SEMICONVENTIONAL THREAD

1½ Acme, 3 th'ds per inch

1½ Acme, 3 th'ds per inch

ACME THREAD

1½ Square, 4 th'ds per inch

1½ Square, 4 th'ds per inch

MODIFIED SQUARE THREAD

Fig. 13-12. Representation of threads in section. (*From ASA Z14.1—1946.*)

The conventional internal-thread symbols recommended by the ASA for threads under 1 in. in diameter are seen in Fig. 13-8. If two or more mating threaded pieces are drawn in section, a combination of the semiconventional and the symbolic representations may be used as shown in Fig. 13-13.

13-10. American Standard threads. The American Standard threads (same as United States Standard) consist of five series of threads having the same shape or form, but a different pitch (number of threads to the inch) for a given diameter. The basic angle between the sides of the thread measured parallel to the axis is 60°. The difference between the V form and the American Standard is seen in the flattening of the crests and roots (see Fig. 13-3). The width of the flat roots and crests in

the American Standard thread should be about one-eighth the pitch.

The five American Standard thread series are the coarse thread series, the fine thread series, the 8-pitch, the 12-pitch, and the 16-pitch thread series (see Table 5 in the Appendix). The *coarse thread series* is widely used in industry and is suitable for ordinary holding purposes. It is designated by the abbreviation NC, which stands for National (or American) coarse. The *fine thread series* has more threads per inch and is better adapted to requirements demanding ease of assembly, great strength, and resistance to vibration. It is designated by the abbreviation NF. The *8-pitch series* (8 threads to the inch, diameters 1 to 6 in.) is used primarily on bolts to give high tension to sealing surfaces such as a cylinder or a boiler head. It is designated by the symbols 8N, where the numeral represents the number of threads per inch and N stands for National. The *12-pitch series* (12 threads to the inch, diameters ½ to 6 in.) is mainly used for thin parts in machine construction. It is designated by the symbols 12N. The *16-pitch series* (16 threads to the inch, diameters ¾ to 4 in.) is used on forms such as bearing retainers and collars. It is designated by the symbols 16N.

13-11. SAE extra-fine thread series. The Society of Automotive Engineers has adopted a thread that has the same form as the American thread yet seems to be better adapted to the needs of the automobile industry for very close adjustments and vibrationless adherence. This series, designated by the abbreviation EF, provides for a greater number of threads than the American Standard for any of the given diameters (see the table in the Appendix).

13-12. Unified screw-thread series. The International Organization for Standardization has selected six basic thread series, together with several special types of foreign and American threads, as unified standards to facilitate international manufacturing procedures. The threads that make up the unified screw-thread series are similar to the American Standard threads but have rounded roots and flat or rounded crests on the external threads and flat crests and roots on the internal threads (see Fig. 13-14). A unified thread may be drawn semiconventionally or conventionally by using the symbolic representations employed to show the American Standard types (see Fig. 13-16).

The various threads of the unified series differ from each other in the number of threads per inch for a given diameter. The unified threads are described completely in ASA B1.1—1949. The unified coarse thread series is recommended for general industrial use and is designated by the abbreviation UNC. The fine thread series employed in the aircraft and automotive fields is indicated by the abbreviation UNF. A few of the extra-fine threads, characterized by a greater number of threads per inch for a given diameter, have also been selected

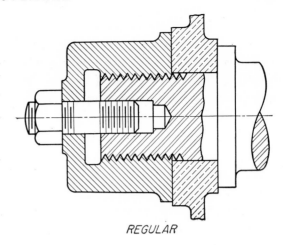

REGULAR

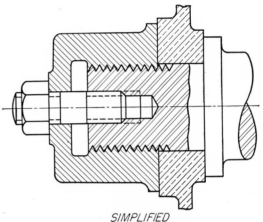

SIMPLIFIED

Fig. 13-13. Threads in section in assemblies. (*From ASA Z14.1—1946.*)

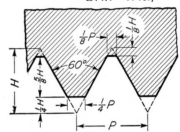

UNIFIED INTERNAL THREAD

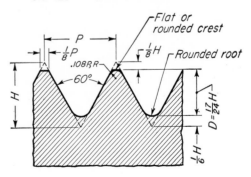

UNIFIED EXTERNAL THREAD
Fig. 13-14. Unified thread.

for unification and are designated by the letters UNEF. The unified threads corresponding to the American Standard 8, 12, and 16 series are designated 8UN, 12UN, and 16UN. (Although the U may be dropped when designating any thread of the unified system, it is not recommended by the author until widespread usage overcomes the likelihood of errors.) Unified threads range between ¼ and 6 in. in diameter (see Table 5 in the Appendix).

13-13. American Standard screw-thread fits. Four types of screw-thread fits have been standardized by the ASA. A "fit" refers to the manner in which two mating threads, such as those on a nut and bolt, are brought together into assembly. The following descriptions are taken from the ASA Standards (ASA B1.1—1935).

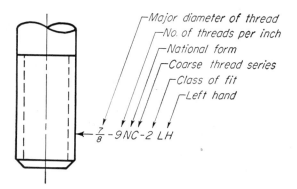

Fig. 13-15. Explanation of a thread note.

Class 1 Fit. Recommended only for screw-thread work where clearance between mating parts is essential for rapid assembly and where shake or play is not objectionable.

Class 2 Fit. Represents a high quality of commercial thread product and is recommended for the great bulk of interchangeable screw-thread work.

Class 3 Fit. Represents an exceptionally high quality of commercially threaded product and is recommended only in cases where the high cost of precision tools and continual checking is warranted.

Class 4 Fit. Intended to meet very unusual requirements more exacting than those for which Class 3 is intended. It is a selective fit if initial assembly by hand is required. It is not, as yet, adaptable to quantity production.

13-14. Unified screw-thread fits. The fits for external threads in the unified thread system are classified as 1A, 2A, and 3A. Fits for the internal threads are classified as 1B, 2B, and 3B. The fits for classes 1A and 1B are similar to the class 1 fit of the American Standard. Classes 2A and 2B are the fits recommended for external and internal threads, screws, bolts, and nuts. Classes 3A and 3B represent slight changes in the relationship of the allowances and tolerances as indicated in the American Standard fits in the same class. (For adapting unified fits to designs of unified screw threads refer to ASA B1.1—1949.)

13-15. Specifications and notes for American Standard threads. The approved method for giving a thread note for an American Standard

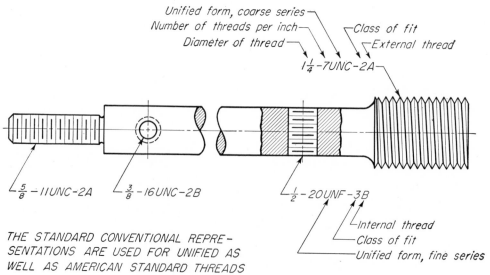

THE STANDARD CONVENTIONAL REPRE-
SENTATIONS ARE USED FOR UNIFIED AS
WELL AS AMERICAN STANDARD THREADS

Fig. 13-16. Representing and specifying unified threads.

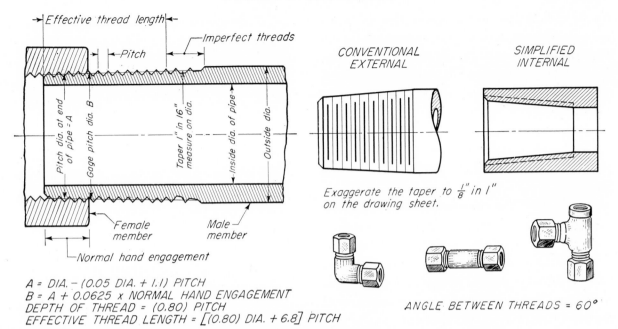

$A = DIA. - (0.05\ DIA. + 1.1)\ PITCH$
$B = A + 0.0625 \times NORMAL\ HAND\ ENGAGEMENT$
$DEPTH\ OF\ THREAD = (0.80)\ PITCH$
$EFFECTIVE\ THREAD\ LENGTH = \left[(0.80)\ DIA. + 6.8\right]\ PITCH$

Fig. 13-17. Pipe-thread information.

thread is shown in Fig. 13-8. The tap-drill size must be given, as well as the depth if the hole does not go entirely through. If a left-hand thread is called for it must be indicated by the abbreviation LH. Multiple threads are specified by adding the words "double," "triple," etc. All threads are understood to be single and right-hand unless otherwise noted in the specification. Figure 13-15 explains the terms used in a specification.

13-16. Identification and specification for a unified thread. A thread of the unified system is represented like any American Standard thread, and its specification is the same except that the U is added to the thread series and the letter A is added to indicate an external thread and the letter B to indicate an internal thread (see Fig. 13-16).

13-17. American Standard pipe-thread specifications and notes. The American Standard pipe threads are of two forms, the tapered threads and the straight threads. The number of threads per inch, the angle between threads (60°), and the depth of the threads is the same in both forms, their only difference being that the threads on the straight form are cut parallel to the axis of the pipe. The threads are shown on the drawing in the same manner as for the regular American Standard threads, that is, either semiconventionally or by use

of the regular or simplified symbolic representations (see Fig. 13-17). The taper is drawn only when this feature is to be emphasized, since the taper is indicated in the thread note. If the taper is shown, it should be exaggerated on the drawing sheet. As shown in Fig. 13-18, the thread note always gives the nominal diameter of the thread and is followed by the letters NPT (National pipe taper) or NPS (National pipe straight). As a general rule, pipe

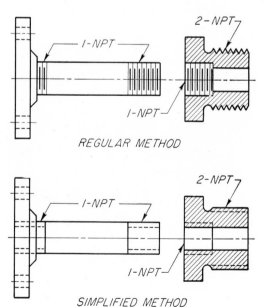

Fig. 13-18. Conventional pipe-thread representation and specifications. (*From ASA Z14.1—1946.*)

threads should be shown in the regular or simplified conventional style; the semiconventional treatment is used only when threads are larger than 1 in. in diameter or are to be shown in assembly with other parts. For data on pipe threads of various diameters, see Table 24 in the Appendix.

13-18. Helical springs. The windings of torsion extension, and compression springs follow the same helical path as that of the single screw thread. In a detail representation, springs are shown semiconventionally in their free length and with the type of ends required. When sectioned, the cut portion is filled in solid black for a small spring and sectionlined for a large one. The procedure for drawing a spring is the same as that for drawing a single right-hand screw thread. The pitch distances are set off along the line of the outer diameter and the coils are sloped leaning toward the left at an angle equal to one-half the pitch. Small springs are represented conventionally in assembly drawings, as shown in Fig. 13-19.

The specifications required for a spring are its free length, size and shape (round or square) of the wire, inside diameter (if working on a shaft), outside diameter (if working free or in a hole), number of coils (or pitch), material from which the spring is to be made, and style of ends. Figure 13-19 gives the information that satisfies the requirements of commercial practice (see also Fig. 8-28).

13-19. American Standard bolts and nuts. Three series of bolts and nuts have been approved by the ASA, as follows:

1. *Regular series boltheads and nuts.* This series is recommended for most uses.

2. *Heavy series boltheads and nuts.* This series is designed to give a greater bearing surface for a wrench and greater clearance between bolthead and hole.

3. *Light series nuts.* The nuts in this series are smaller across flats than the nuts in the regular series. They are usually fine-threaded and are designed to save material and weight.

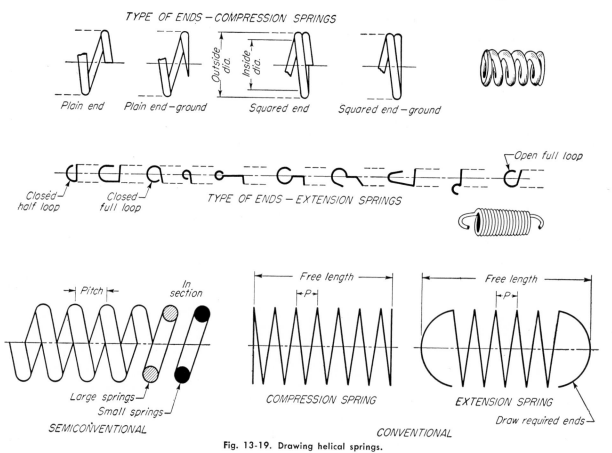

Fig. 13-19. Drawing helical springs.

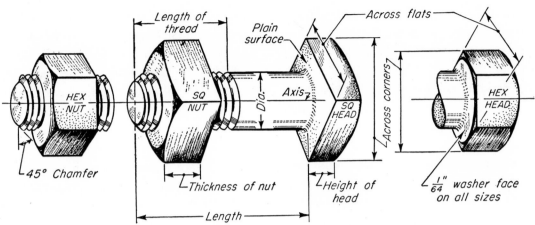

Fig. 13-20. American Standard bolts and nuts.

Nuts and bolts are also classified as *unfinished*, *semifinished* (finish on bearing surface only), or *finished* (finished all over). Semifinished or finished nuts and bolts may have a washerface machined on the bearing surface side of the bolthead or nut to lessen the stress at the corners (see Fig. 13-20). A washerface is $\frac{1}{64}$ in. thick and its diameter is equal to the distance across the flats of the head or nut.

This $\frac{1}{64}$ in. is always included in the height of the head or thickness of the nut. The thickness of finished, semifinished, and unfinished nuts is the same for the same thread diameters and finish (except for the United States Standard bolt). However, the heights of the unfinished hexagonal head, the finished hexagonal head, and the square head vary in size for the same thread diameter and finish (see

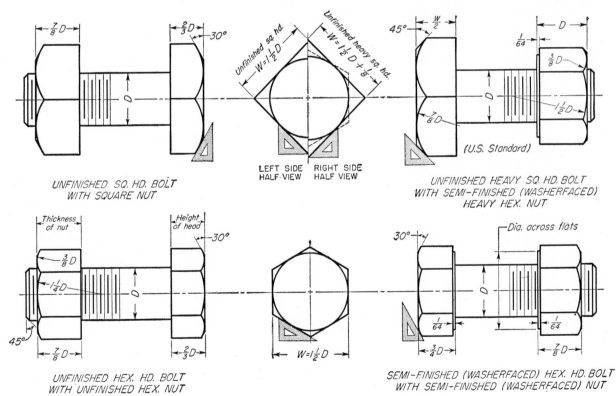

STANDARD LENGTH OF THREAD FOR BOLTS IS $1\frac{1}{2}D + \frac{1}{8}$
Never show finish marks (f, $\vee$) on nuts and bolts

Fig. 13-21. Formulas for drawing bolts and nuts.

Fig. 13-21). To avoid confusion, all nuts and bolt-heads, both square and hexagonal, are presented as drawn across corners in all views on the drawing sheet (see Fig. 9-29).

13-20. Formulas for drawing bolts and nuts.

In commercial practice, standard bolts and nuts need not be shown on the detail sheet. However, they are shown on assembly drawings, where they are encountered very frequently. To save time, the draftsman follows a procedure that enables him to scale all significant dimensions of a bolt and nut in proportion to the given diameter of the bolt. The dimensions of the features of the American Standard bolts and nuts shown in Fig. 13-21 are given in terms of the bolt diameters. Note that the chamfer angle at the top of the heavy series (old U.S. Standard) bolthead is 45° and the chamfer on the lighter square and hex heads and nuts is 30°. If the bolt diameter is less than 1 in., the head and nut chamfers may be omitted. The lengths of bolts are not standardized. Square-head bolts may range in length from ½ to 24 in. Hex-head bolts range from ½ to 12 in. in length. Most manufacturers thread their bolts a distance of 1½ times the diameter plus ⅛ in. When precise measurements are required, the actual dimensions in inches of the various features of bolts and nuts, such as the distance across flats, the distance across corners, the length of the bolt, the length of the thread, the chamfers, etc., for any

given diameter of thread may be found in manufacturers' catalogues. See the Appendix for a table of typical dimensions.

13-21. Drawing a bolt and nut.

For purposes of completeness in demonstration, the bolt in Fig. 13-22 has a square head and a hex nut. Start by laying out the major diameter, axis, and length of the bolt (bolt length is measured from the under surface of the head to the end of the shaft). Draw the adjacent views (contours) of the hex nut and square head, as shown in Step II. Note that they are drawn on vertical corners and that the circles representing the distances across flats are inscribed. Complete the representation as suggested in Steps III, IV, and V. If only the profile view of the bolt is desired, the adjacent hex-nut and square-head views may be drawn as half views, as seen in Step IV, and the required construction lines projected to the profile. The half views may be erased after they have served their purpose.

13-22. Dimensioning and specifying a bolt.

The manner in which a bolt is dimensioned is shown in Fig. 13-23. The specification requires the diameter, length, number of threads to the inch, series, class of fit, finish, type of head, and type of nut. The dimensions are shown on the detail drawing. In assembly drawings, the dimensioning is omitted and the specification is given in the bill of materials.

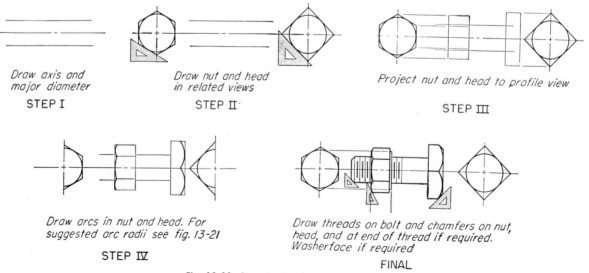

Draw axis and
major diameter
STEP I

Draw nut and head
in related views
STEP II

Project nut and head to profile view
STEP III

Draw arcs in nut and head. For
suggested arc radii see fig. 13-21
STEP IV

Draw threads on bolt and chamfers on nut,
head, and at end of thread if required.
Washer face if required
FINAL

Fig. 13-22. Steps in drawing a bolt and nut.

The specification shown in Fig. 13-23 can be abbreviated to read

½ × 1¾ UNC SEMI-FIN

HEX HD BOLT & NUT

13-23. Stud bolts. Stud bolts, or studs, are cylindrical pieces that are threaded at both ends (see Fig. 13-24). One end, the stud end, is for insertion in a tapped hole that is slightly longer than the thread on the stud. The other end receives one or two nuts—the second, if used, locking the first in place. Studs are used for holding cylinder heads, covers, etc., in place. In the automotive industry, studs vary from $\frac{5}{16}$ to $\frac{3}{4}$ in. in diameter, and the lengths beyond the stud-end threading range from $\frac{5}{8}$ to $4\frac{3}{4}$ in. The stud ends (tapped-hole ends) have American Standard (or unified) coarse threads; American Standard (or unified) fine threads are cut on the outside, or nut, ends. The end chamfers are 45° and are $\frac{1}{32}$ to $\frac{3}{32}$ in. in length. Study the illustration for further information on drawing procedure.

Figure 13-25 illustrates the manner in which a stud with unified thread is dimensioned when shown as a detail (not in assembly). The specification serves in place of dimensioning when the stud

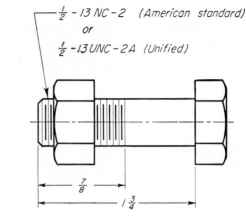

DIMENSIONING A BOLT ON THE DRAWING SHEET

$\frac{1}{2}$ - 13 NC - 2 (American standard)

or

$\frac{1}{2}$ - 13 UNC - 2A (Unified)

SPECIFIED IN PARTS LIST AS:

$\frac{1}{2}$ x 1$\frac{3}{4}$ - 13 NC - 2 SEMI-FIN HEX HD BOLT & NUT
(American standard)

or

$\frac{1}{2}$ x 1$\frac{3}{4}$ - 13 UNC - 2A SEMI-FIN HEX HD BOLT & NUT
(Unified)

Fig. 13-23. Dimensioning and specifying a bolt.

is shown in an assembly drawing. (For American Standard studs make the thread specification read like the sample shown in Fig. 13-23.) The specification in Fig. 13-25 can be abbreviated by giving only the diameter and length of the stud

$\frac{5}{8}$ × 2$\frac{3}{8}$ STUD

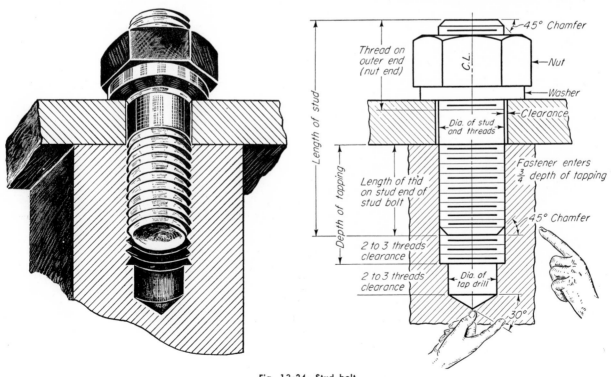

Fig. 13-24. Stud bolt.

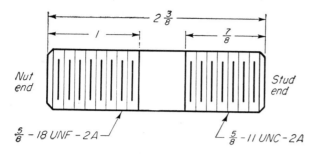

Specified in parts list as:

$$\frac{5}{8} \times 2\frac{3}{8} - 11 \, UNC - 2A \quad STUD \; END$$
$$18 \, UNF - 2A \quad NUT \; END$$

Fig. 13-25. Dimensions and specification for stud with unified threads.

13-24. Cap screws. Cap screws are fasteners that hold together two pieces by passing through a nonthreaded hole in one piece and screwing into a tapped hole in the other. There are five basic types of cap screws: the hex head, the flat head, the round head (formerly button head), the fillister head, and the socket head (see Fig. 13-26). Cap screws are used when accurate fits and a fine appearance are desired. The hex-head cap screws are usually finished all over and are provided with a washerface $\frac{1}{64}$ in. thick that has a diameter equal to the distance across flats. The other types of cap screws are usually semifinished, although they are also available finished all over. Cap screws may be had with either unified or National coarse or fine threads. In the unified series the fit is usually class 2; in the National series they are customarily class 3.

Finished cap screws are produced to conform with ASA-approved proportions and are made in body diameters ranging from $\frac{1}{4}$ to $1\frac{1}{4}$ in. (except socket-head cap screws, which are made in diameters of 0.0860 in. to $1\frac{1}{2}$ in.) Table 6 in the Appendix lists the body, head, and slot dimensions for cap screws. The lengths for cap screws have not been standardized.

When the length of a cap screw is 1 in. or less, the threads extend to the neck under the cap. If the length is greater than 1 in., the length of thread for coarse thread screws is equal to twice the diameter plus $\frac{1}{4}$ in. For the fine-thread series, the length of the threads is equal to $1\frac{1}{2}$ times the diameter plus $\frac{1}{4}$ in.

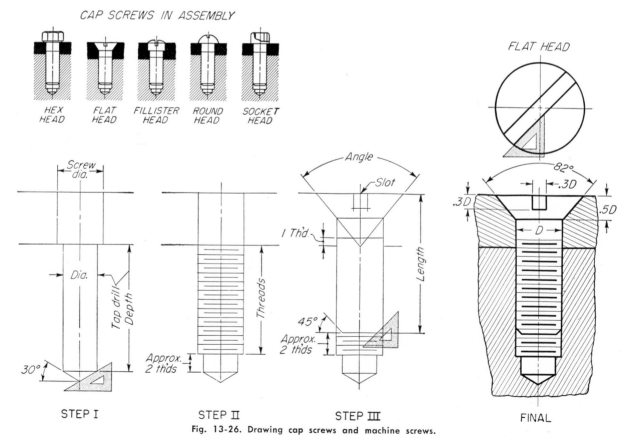

Fig. 13-26. Drawing cap screws and machine screws.

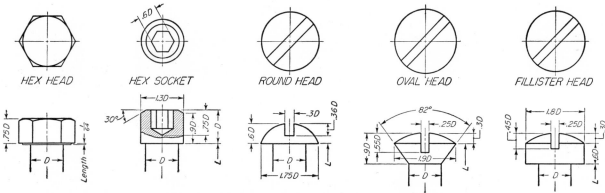

HEX HEAD   HEX SOCKET   ROUND HEAD   OVAL HEAD   FILLISTER HEAD

Fig. 13-27. Formulas for drawing cap screws and machine screws.

A cap screw is specified by giving its diameter, length, number of threads per inch, thread series, fit, type of head, and designation, such as the following example:

⁹⁄₁₆ × 3¼-12 UNC-2A FLAT HD CAP SCR

which can be abbreviated to read

⁹⁄₁₆ × 3¼ UNC FLAT HD CAP SCR

The formulas for drawing cap screws are shown in Figs. 13-26 and 13-27. Note in particular that the slots of the flat-head, round-head, and fillister-head cap screws are shown at a 45° angle in the circular views regardless of true projection.

13-25. Machine screws. Machine screws are similar to cap screws, but they are generally smaller in diameter (0.060 to 0.750 in.). They are available with eight different types of heads, including all those found on cap screws. Unlike the cap screws, however, machine screws are rarely manufactured with the hex or socket heads. Machine screws are used primarily for light-duty work. They are available in either the unified or National coarse thread or fine thread series, and are usually class 2 fit. Machine screws may be drawn with the same formulas used for cap screws (see Figs. 13-26 and 13-27). Exact dimensions, types of heads, and other information about machine screws may be found in Table 9 in the Appendix.

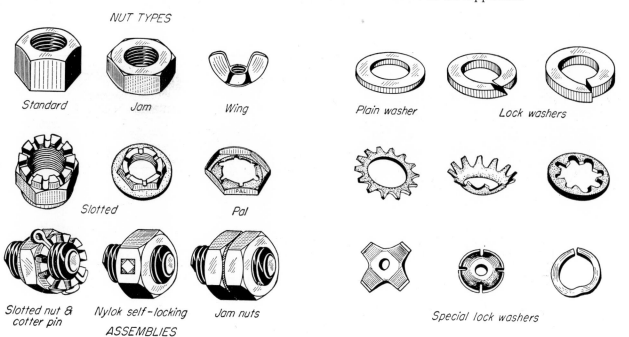

NUT TYPES

Standard   Jam   Wing   Plain washer   Lock washers

Slotted   Pal

Slotted nut & cotter pin   Nylok self-locking   Jam nuts   Special lock washers

ASSEMBLIES

Fig. 13-28. Nut types and washers.

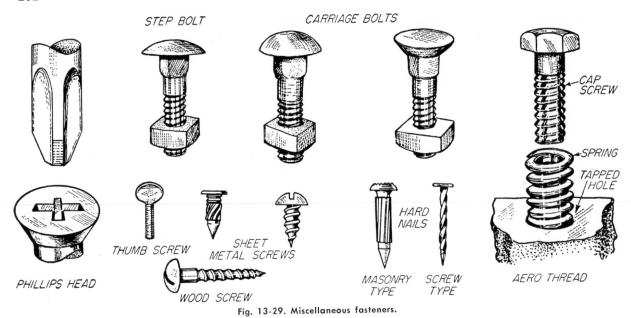

Fig. 13-29. Miscellaneous fasteners.

A machine screw is specified by giving its diameter, the length, thread specification, fit, type of head, and designation. The following is an example:

No. 8 × ¾-32 UNC-2A OVAL HD MACH SCR

which may be abbreviated to read

No. 8 × ¾ UNC OVAL HD MACH SCR

Although the lengths of both the cap screws and machine screws have not been standardized, various manufacturers stock cap screws varying between ¼

and 6 in. long and machine screws ranging between ⅛ and 3 in. Nearly four-fifths of all machine screws are manufactured with coarse threads.

13-26. Locking devices. There are many types of locking nuts and other such devices available that are intended to prevent fastened parts from working loose under vibration (see Fig. 13-28). The commonest form of locking nut is the jam nut. It is hexagonal in shape with a flat top chamfered at 30°. Its thickness is half its diameter. It is sup-

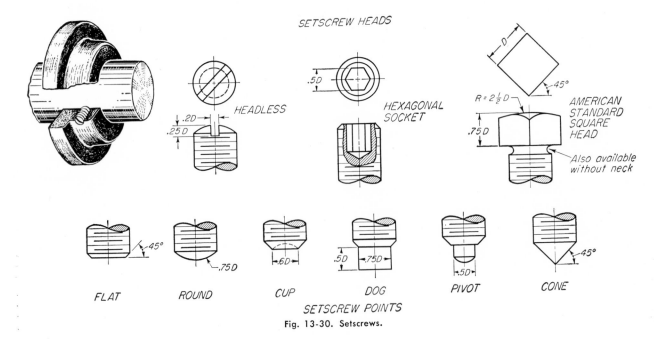

Fig. 13-30. Setscrews.

plied semifinished and washerfaced, or unfinished with a plain bearing surface. The slotted type of nut is assembled with a cotter pin. All slotted nuts are semifinished and are available in the regular, heavy, and light series. The tops are flat and chamfered. The castle nut is higher than the standard slotted nut. A wire or cotter pin is passed through the slot and through a hole in the shaft in order to prevent the nut from working loose on its mounting.

Standard plain and lock washers (Fig. 13-28) are used with regular standard nuts. These and special washers are used with cap screws and machine screws. Standard washers are specified by giving the type, inside diameter, outside diameter, and thickness (see Appendix for dimensions).

Several types of stop nuts are also available. These are manufactured with a semiplastic insert that acts as the locking device when the nut is tightened firmly in position.

The aero thread used in the airplane industry consists of a bronze or steel spring insert conforming to a standard thread which is placed in the tapped hole before the insertion of a cap screw or stud (see Fig. 13-29). The use of the spring insert affords a secure hold for the screw or stud in the soft aluminum alloys used in the airplane industry.

For information on the many other types of locking nuts and special screws, washers, etc., the draftsman may avail himself of the manufacturers' catalogues, which usually give the basic dimensions and specifications of their products.

13-27. Setscrews. Setscrews are mainly used to prevent rotary motion between two assembled parts, such as a pulley or collar mounted on a shaft. The setscrew is placed in a hole tapped in the hub of the pulley or collar and is then turned tight against the shaft. Setscrews are also used to make slight adjustments in the fit between mating parts and to permit changing locations of tools and other moving parts. In general, they are not used where the fixed parts may be subjected to heavy stresses or loads. The dangerous projecting-head types are being used less and less frequently, while the hollow or safety type has become more popular. The so-called "safety types" are either slotted or have square or hexagonal holes for receiving tightening wrenches. The American Standard setscrews range between ¼ and 1½ in. in diameter. The lengths are not standardized. They are available in a variety of points, and commonly have threads of the unified or American Standard coarse series. They are also available with fine threads. Formulas for representing setscrews are shown in Fig. 13-30.

A setscrew is specified by giving its diameter, length, number of threads per inch, thread series, fit, type of head, type of point, and designation, as shown in the following example:

$\frac{7}{16} \times 1\frac{1}{4}$-14 UNC-2A

H'DLESS OVAL PT SET SCR

and is abbreviated to read

$\frac{7}{16} \times 1\frac{1}{4}$ UNC H'DLESS OVAL PT SET SCR

13-28. Keys and taper pins. Generally speaking, a key is a square, rectangular, or semicircular piece of steel that is inserted in a keyway or keyseat cut in a shaft and pulley, or gear, and when in position, prevents relative rotary motion between the mating parts. In some cases keys may prevent axial motion in the two parts. Typical keys are shown in assembly in Fig. 13-31. The width of a sunk key is about one-fourth the diameter of the shaft. The thickness of a flat key is equal to about one-sixth the diameter of the shaft. For light duty and small parts, smaller keys may be used. American Standard square and flat keys have a taper ranging from ⅛ to 3/16 in. per ft.

A key that engages a slot formed in both the pulley and shaft is known as a sunk key. The Woodruff key is an almost semicircular sunk key with either a round or flat bottom (see Fig. 13-32). It is always specified by a number, the last two digits of which indicate the nominal diameter in eighths of an inch, while the one or two digits preceding the last two give the nominal width in thirty-seconds of an inch. Note from the illustration that the round key is not a complete semicircle, since the center for the circular arc of the key is located above the top edge. Keyways and keyseats are cut by special cutters used on milling machines, on special key-slotting machines, or in some spe-

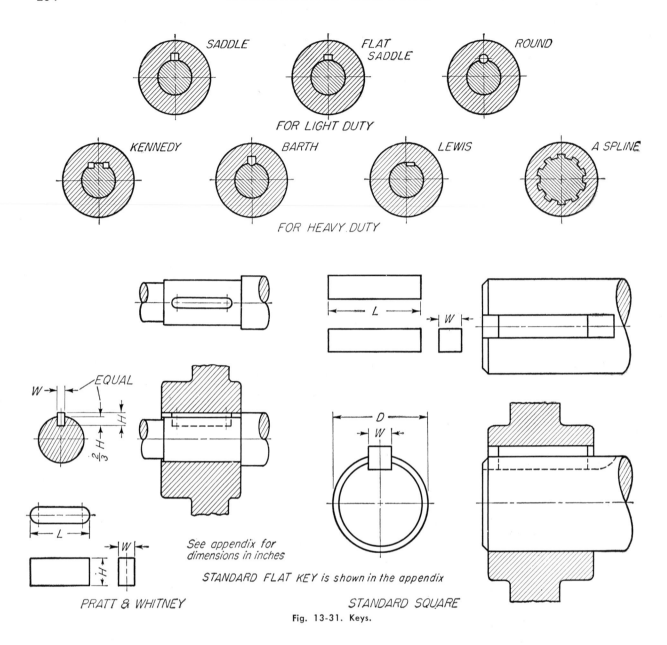

Fig. 13-31. Keys.

cial cases, on broaching machines or planers and shapers.

The gib-head key (Fig. 13-32) is a sunk key which is placed in assembly with its head protruding far enough from the hub to permit the insertion of a tool for removal. The slot for the gib key must have an open end to permit assembly; for this reason it is usually placed at the end of a shaft. A feather or spline key is fixed to either the shaft or the hub. It permits axial motion while preventing

rotary motion between the parts. Gib-head keys may be either saddle-shaped or flat. The saddle key is slightly curved on the under side and slightly tapered on top. The slot is cut into the hub and when the key is forced into position it grips the shaft through friction on that member. The flat key fits into a slot cut into the hub and rests on a slight flat surface machined on the shaft.

Keys and keyways should be shown to scale in assembly drawings. Only special designs or changes

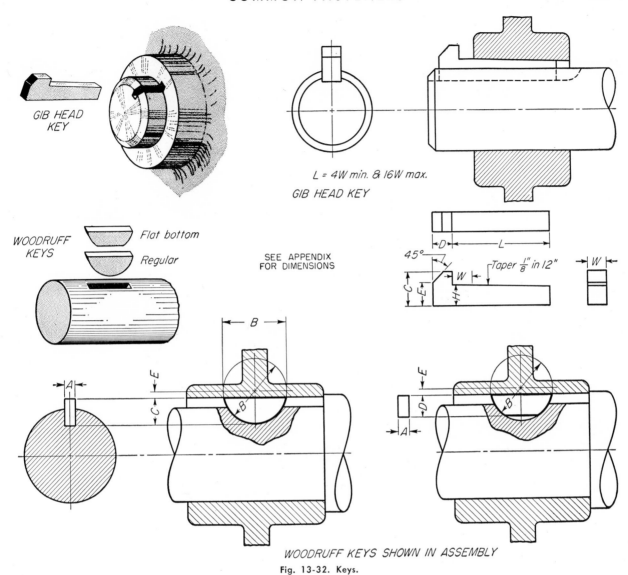

Fig. 13-32. Keys.

need be drawn on the detail sheets. Keys are specified in the manner illustrated by the following samples (see Appendix for dimensions):

No. 14 PRATT & WHITNEY KEY
No. 608 WOODRUFF KEY
⅜ SQ × 1¾ KEY
⅜ × ¼ × 1¾ FLAT KEY

Taper pins are driven into mating holes drilled in the hub and shaft (see Fig. 13-33). They are sometimes referred to as round tapered keys. Taper pins are available in various sizes ranging from 0.078 to 0.706 in. in diameter (at the large end) and from

⅜ to 6 in. in length. They are specified by code number, as follows:

No. 4 ST'D TAPER PIN

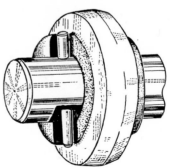

Fig. 13-33. The taper pin in assembly.

Table 12 in the Appendix lists the standard taper pins, their diameters, and their minimum and maximum lengths, together with specifications indicating the proper taper pin to use for a given diameter of shaft. When taper pins are shown in assembly, the smaller end may be cut off at the required length.

13-29. Rivets. Rivets are permanent fasteners used to join metal parts. They may be made of mild steel, wrought iron, copper, or other metals or alloys. A rivet has a cylindrical body and a head that may be flat, spherical, or conical. When in assembly, the head at the other end may be formed in the same shape. There is always a clearance between the body of the rivet and the hole it enters. To fill this clearance after insertion and while the second head is being formed, the length beyond the plate should be equal to three-fourths the diameter for forming a flat or countersunk head, and 1.3 to 1.7 times the diameter for forming the other types of heads. American Standard rivets are classified into two general sizes—large and small. Figure

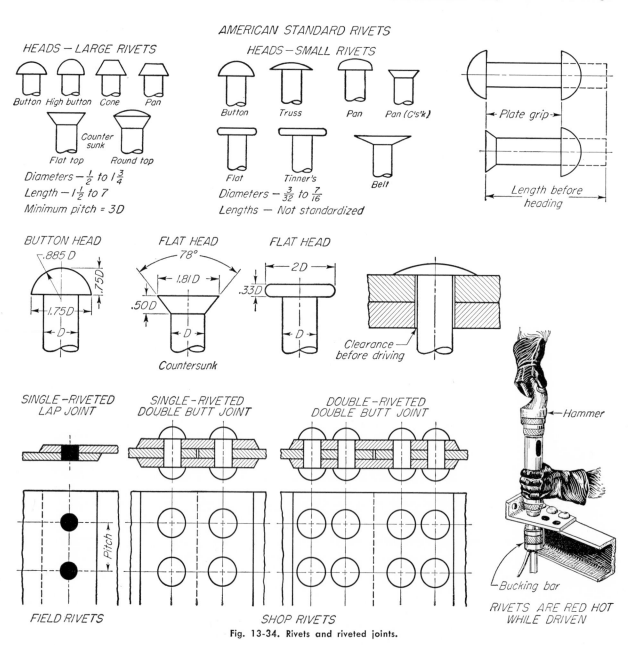

Fig. 13-34. Rivets and riveted joints.

13-34 illustrates the types of heads and shows the formulas used in drawing several of them. See Table 18 in the Appendix for formulas for small rivets.

13-30. Riveted joints. A lap joint is formed when one plate is placed over another and the two plates are riveted together by one or more rows of rivets. When the plates are held together by a cover plate or strap they form a butt joint (see Fig. 13-34). If a lap joint is held together by a single row of rivets, or a butt joint is held together by a single row of rivets on either side of the joint, they are said to be single-riveted. Two rows of rivets on a lap joint, or two rows of rivets on both sides of a butt joint, form a double-riveted joint. Joints may be triple or quadruple riveted also. For large rivets the clearance between the shank and the hole is $\frac{1}{16}$ in. The distance from the edge of the plate to the rim of the hole should never be less than the diameter of the rivet. On large construction work, rivets that are to be driven on the job (as opposed to those driven in the shop) are called "field rivets" and are indicated as black circles on the drawing (see Fig. 13-34).

13-31. Welding. Welding is a method of making a permanent joint between two metal parts. It is used extensively in the fabrication of cylindrical forms, such as ducts and containers, and it is also used frequently in the manufacture of complicated parts in order to simplify casting procedures.

Practically all ferrous and nonferrous metals can be welded. Cast iron, steel and iron alloys, brass, copper, aluminum, etc., are used in the welding in-dustry. The elimination of sand-casting patterns and savings in labor and material have made it possible to produce many machine parts, and in some cases whole units, at greatly reduced expense as compared with other methods of construction or fabrication.

There are many different welding processes, but the ones most often used are forging, gas welding, and electric welding. In forging welds, the parts are heated until the metal is in a plastic state, and they are then joined by pressure or heavy blows from a hammer. When preparing joints for pressure welding, the metal is high or crowned near the center of the weld so that in the hammering procedure the joining of the metal will occur at that point and work outward toward the extremities. To avoid burning the metal and to assure a clean weld, a flux of fine sand or borax is commonly used.

Gas welding is a method whereby a gas flame is used to heat the pieces to the fusion point. The parts form a weld without the use of pressure or a flux, although a filler material is often employed in the process.

Electric welding includes the two processes known as resistance welding and arc welding. Spot welding, seam welding, projection welding, and flash welding are forms of resistance welding. In electric welding the electric current is passed through the metals to be joined. Their resistance builds enough heat within them so that when pressure is applied to the plates the fusion or welding takes place. In the arc-welding process, fusion is brought about

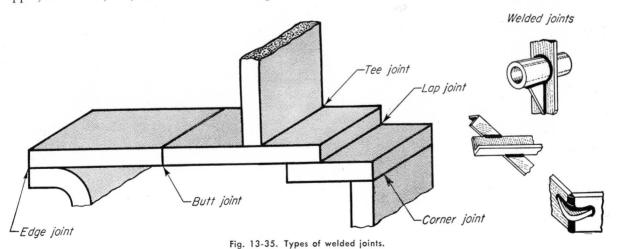

Fig. 13-35. Types of welded joints.

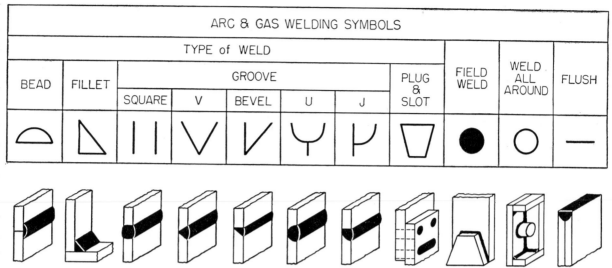

Fig. 13-36. Welding symbols and their graphic meanings.

without the use of pressure. However, the heating electrode used serves not only to bring the plates to a fusion heat but also supplies a filler material if the base metal is not of a sufficient quantity to insure a safe weld.

13-32. Types of welded joints. Figure 13-35 illustrates the five types of welded joints: the *butt joint*, the *lap joint*, the *tee joint*, the *corner joint*, and the *edge joint*.

13-33. Types of welds. There are four basic types of welds used to join together two metal pieces. These are called *bead, fillet, groove,* and *plug and slot* welds and are illustrated in Fig. 13-36. The groove welds are further classified as square, V, bevel, U, or J welds, where the shape of the symbol indicates the shape of the weld or the shape of the preparation needed on the pieces forming the joint.

13-34. Welding symbols. The American Standard symbol for indicating welds on drawings is shown in Fig. 13-37. The complete symbol consists of an arrowhead and leader joined to a reference line, on one or both sides of which are placed a basic symbol or symbols with figures that refer to the type of weld and its size. The tail is added to the reference line only when it is necessary to specify the type of filler material to be used. The side of a welded joint to which the arrow points is called the "arrow side" (formerly it was called the "near side") and the opposite side is called the "other side" (formerly termed the "far side"). If both

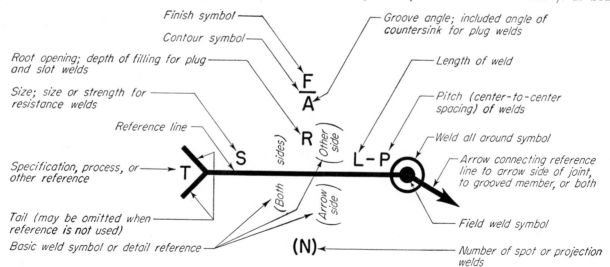

Fig. 13-37. Standard location of elements of a welding symbol. (*From ASA Z 32.2.1—1949.*)

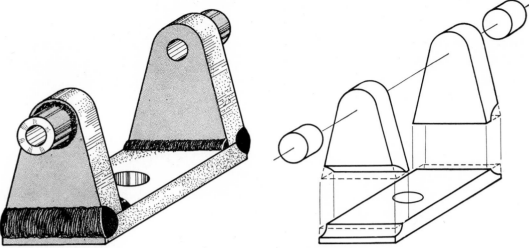

Fig. 13-38. A welded coaster frame.

members are to be grooved, the arrow touches the corner formed by the two plates. When only one member is to be grooved, the arrow touches that member alone just beyond the intersection. The symbol indicating the type of weld (Fig. 13-36) is always placed at the middle and above or below the reference line, with the perpendicular leg of the symbol (if any) to the left. The size of the weld (length of the side of the weld) is given at the left of the symbol indicating the type of weld; the length of the weld is given at the right. The symbol and size and length specifications for the arrow-side weld are placed below the reference line; the symbol and specifications for the other-side weld are placed

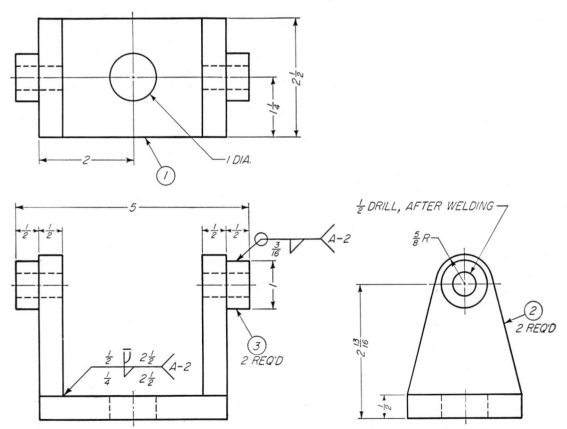

Fig. 13-39. A shop welding drawing (orthographics of coaster frame shown in Fig. 13-38).

above the reference line. For objects that are to be manufactured or fabricated principally by welding procedures, the draftsman should represent the different welds by using the complete welding symbol with all the required specifications as recommended and illustrated in Fig. 13-37. When only one or two welding operations need be shown on the drawing sheet, it is permissible to represent the accurate cross-sectional shape and the size and length of the weld, while omitting the basic weld symbol on the reference line.

The ASA has published a complete treatise on welding symbols titled "American Standard Graphical Symbols for Welding" (ASA Z32.2.1—1949), which should be in the hands of all draftsmen concerned with the preparation of welding drawings. The material in this Standard was originally prepared by the American Welding Society.

13-35. A welding drawing. Figure 13-38 shows the pictorial of a coaster frame made of welded pieces that have been cut from bar and plate-metal stock readily available in the ordinary machine shop. At the right the single pieces have been shown before welding. Note that preparation of a piece to be welded is always required for groove welds, while fillet welds need no preparation other than cleaning of the surfaces.

Figure 13-39 shows a welding working drawing made for the shop. This drawing is similar to one that might be prepared for a casting of the bracket, with the exception that the pieces are numbered and symbols completely describing the welding procedure are employed. All fillets and rounds are eliminated. Note in particular that only one symbol and specification is used to identify the two identical welds joining the sides to the base, as is the case for the welds joining the bar pieces to the sides. In all welding representations, the line between the joints at the point of welding is always shown. All other necessary dimensions, notes, and information relating to fabrication, assembly, or finish are also included on the drawing or in the title block.

PROBLEMS

The following problems have been selected to give the student practice in drawing some of the simpler fasteners before proceeding to the problems on assembly drawing, where a great variety of the various types of common fasteners will be encountered. Drawings of dimensioned objects may be shown in increased or reduced scale to allow a pleasing representation on the drawing sheet. If no dimensions are shown, a pair of dividers may be used to transfer the proportions to the drawing sheet. Each fastener should be identified with a specification similar to that required on a detail drawing. The instructor may cover most of the common fasteners and save time by assigning only Prob. 13-16, the pulley-bracket assembly. The text and the tables in the Appendix should be referred to where necessary for detailed information. The drawings should be prepared on 8½- by 11-in. sheets unless otherwise noted.

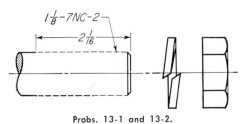

Probs. 13-1 and 13-2.

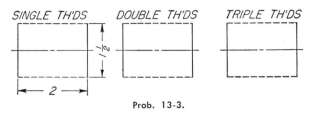

Prob. 13-3.

13-1. Draw semiconventional threads, lock washer, and hex nut for the thread shown in the figure. Show parts in assembly in the side view. (Time: 2½ hr.)

13-2. Redraw the screw and nut given in Prob. 13-1 with left-hand threads. Show the proper specifications on your drawing sheet. (Time: 2½ hr.)

13-3. Make three separate semiconventional representations on one sheet showing (a) a single thread, (b) a double thread, and (c) a triple thread for standard screw threads on a 1½-in.-diameter shaft 2 in. long. (Time: 2 hr.)

13-4. On center line *AA* construct a semiconventional representation of a section of square threads 1¾ in. in diameter and 3 in. long. On *BB* show a semiconventional representation of Acme threads of the same length and diameter using four threads to the inch in each case. (Time: 2 hr.)

13-5. Make a drawing (four times actual size) of the valve body. At each end show regular symbolic representations of the required pipe threads. Do not dimension the drawing. (Time: 2 hr.)

13-6. Reproduce a figure similar to the one shown in the illustration and draw an ordinary top and a section front view of the following fasteners: At *AA* show a square-head bolt ⅞ in. in diameter and 1⅝ in. long with a square nut. At *BB* show a semifinished hex-head bolt ½ in. in diameter and 1¾ in. long with a standard plain washer and a standard semifinished hex-head nut. At *CC* show a stud bolt ½ in. in diameter and 2⅛ in. long, thread at nut end 1 in., at the stud end ⅞ in., with a standard lock washer and a hex nut. The threads for all the bolts should be indicated with unified specifications and shown in the *regular* symbolic form. (Time: 3 hr.)

13.7. With the specifications given in Prob. 13-6, show the threads in the *simplified* symbolic form. (Time: 3 hr.)

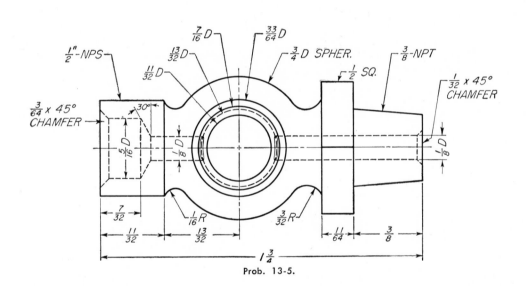

Prob. 13-4.

Prob. 13-5.

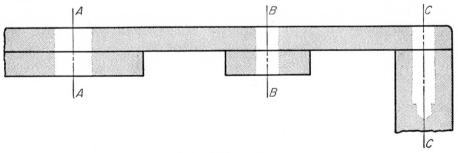

Probs. 13-6 and 13-7.

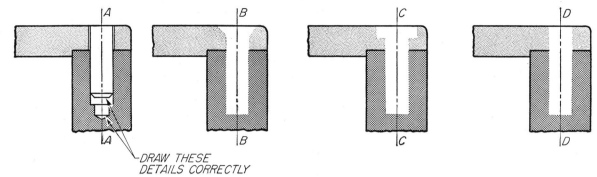

DRAW THESE
DETAILS CORRECTLY

Prob. 13-8.

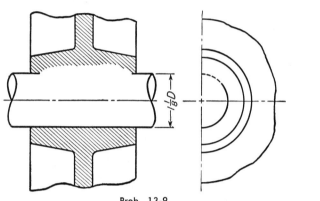

Prob. 13-9.

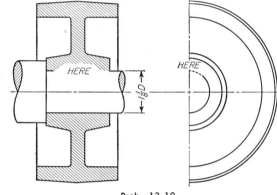

HERE   HERE

Prob. 13-10.

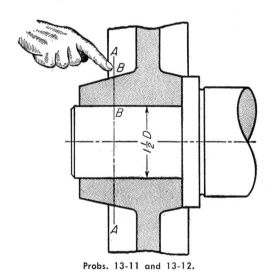

Probs. 13-11 and 13-12.

$\frac{1}{2} \times 1\frac{1}{2}$-13 UNC-2A. At *BB* show a flat-head cap screw with the following specification: $\frac{7}{16} \times 1\frac{3}{8}$-14 UNC-2A. At *CC* show a fillister-head machine screw with the following specification: $\frac{3}{8} \times 1\frac{1}{4}$-16 UNC-2A. At *DD* show a round-head cap screw with the following specification: $\frac{5}{8} \times 1\frac{3}{4}$-11 UNC-2A. (Time: 4 hr.)

13-9. Scale off the two views with dividers to twice the size shown. Draw in its proper position a square key with the dimensions $\frac{1}{4} \times \frac{1}{4} \times 2$. Be sure to represent the slot properly in both hub and shaft. (Time: 2 hr.)

13-10. Scale off the two views with dividers to the shaft size shown. Draw a No. 404 flat Woodruff key in the keyseat. (Time: 2 hr.)

13-11. Scale off the view with dividers to twice the size shown. On center line *AA* draw a standard No. 6 taper pin. (Time: 1½ hr.)

13-12. Reproduce the drawing for Prob. 13-11, omitting the line *AA*. Use dividers to scale the drawing twice the size shown. At *BB* draw a standard headless setscrew ¼ in. in diameter and ⁹⁄₁₆ in. long with a cone point. (Time: 1½ hr.)

13-8. Reproduce the joints about twice the size shown on an 11- by 17-in. sheet. Draw an ordinary top view and a front view in section. At *AA* show a hex-head cap screw with the following specification:

DRAW BOTH FRONT AND SIDE VIEWS

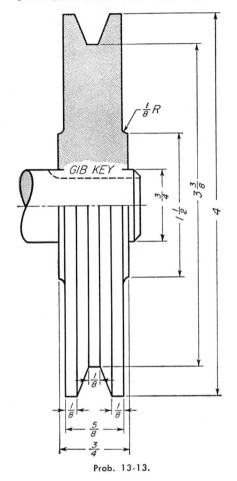

Prob. 13-13.

13-13. Redraw the given view and show the circular view of the pulley on an 11- by 17-in. sheet. Draw a standard square-type gib-head key with dimensions $\frac{3}{16}$ in. square by $1\frac{7}{16}$ in. long. Dimension the drawing completely. (Time: $4\frac{1}{2}$ hr.)

13-14. Redraw the cap screw and the body of the drill chuck as separate details. Dimension the drawing completely. (Time: 4 hr.)

13-15. On an 11- by 17-in. sheet draw the nut, tapered bushing, and shaft of the milling arbor as separate details. Break the shaft to permit placing it on the sheet. Draw the threads semiconventionally showing only several thread outlines and using ditto lines to indicate the others. Dimension the drawing completely. (Time: 5 hr.)

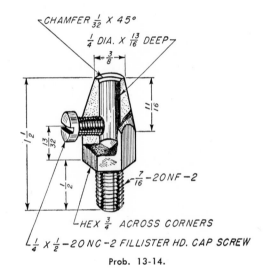

Prob. 13-14.

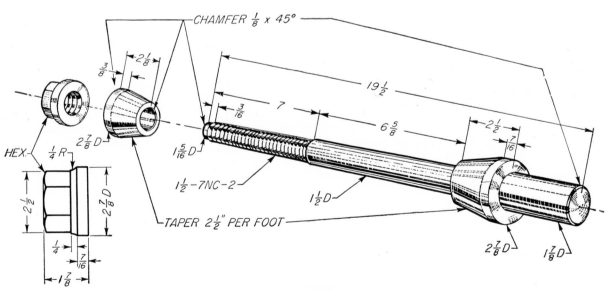

Prob. 13-15.

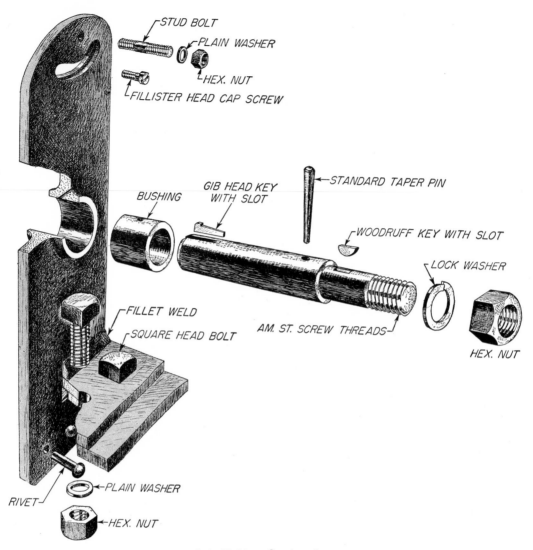

STUD BOLT
PLAIN WASHER
HEX. NUT
FILLISTER HEAD CAP SCREW
GIB HEAD KEY WITH SLOT
STANDARD TAPER PIN
BUSHING
WOODRUFF KEY WITH SLOT
LOCK WASHER
FILLET WELD
SQUARE HEAD BOLT
AM. ST. SCREW THREADS
HEX. NUT
PLAIN WASHER
RIVET
HEX. NUT

Prob. 13-16. (*Continued.*)

13-16. The assembly has been designed to fit an 11-by 17-in. sheet with ample room for a title block and bill of materials at the right of the two views when drawn to a scale of half size. However, the instructor may assign the problem omitting the representation of the pulleys if he desires, or he may assign only such parts as will fit a selected sheet size. Both the front and side views should be drawn.

At *AA* draw a ¾ × 2-10 NC-2 square-head bolt with a hex nut and standard lock washer, two required.

At *BB*, ⅜ × 1-16 NC-2 fillister-head cap screw.

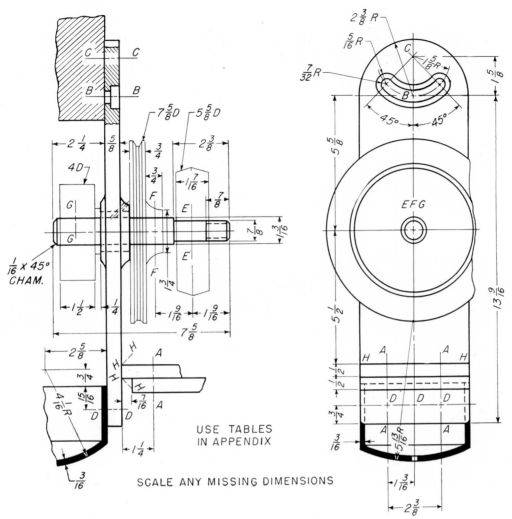

USE TABLES
IN APPENDIX

SCALE ANY MISSING DIMENSIONS

Prob. 13-16. (*Continued.*)

At *CC*, ⅝ × 2¼-11 NC-2 stud bolt, 1-in. threads on both ends, with plain washer and hex nut.

At *DD*, ⅜ × 1½ button-head rivet, three required.

At *EE*, No. 304 round-bottom Woodruff key.

At *FF*, No. 4 standard taper pin.

At *GG*, flat gib-head key 1¼ in. long for a 1³⁄₁₆-in.-diameter shaft.

At *HH*, ¼-in. double fillet weld.

The threads at the right end of the shaft are ⅞ in. long and are ⅞-14 NC-2 for a standard hex nut and matching standard lock washer.

Use sectioning where the fasteners may be shown advantageously in this manner. Specify each fastener properly but do not dimension the structural forms. (Time: 9 hr.)

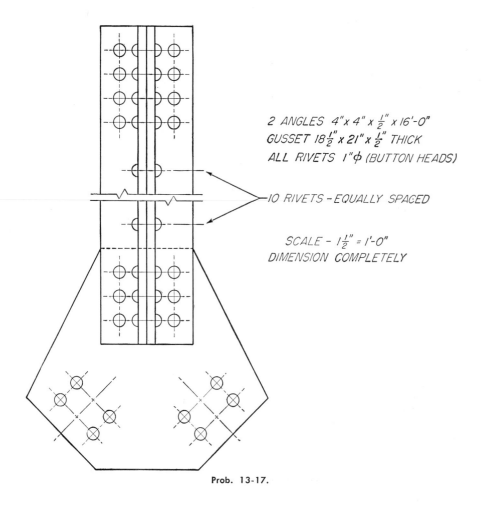

2 ANGLES 4"x 4" x $\frac{1}{2}$" x 16'-0"
GUSSET 18$\frac{1}{2}$" x 21" x $\frac{1}{2}$" THICK
ALL RIVETS 1"ϕ (BUTTON HEADS)

10 RIVETS - EQUALLY SPACED

SCALE - 1$\frac{1}{2}$" = 1'-0"
DIMENSION COMPLETELY

Prob. 13-17.

13-17. Transfer accurately to your drawing sheet the plate connection shown (leaving the break as illustrated). Using this as the front view, draw a side view employing the given data as necessary. At the given scale (1½" = 1'), dimension the views completely. Indicate by an added note how many shop rivets and how many field rivets are required. (Time: 4 hr.)

13-18. Make a suitable working drawing of the eccentric. Select the type of welds you feel are required and show the correct symbols in the proper places on your drawing. (Time: 2 hr.)

13-19. Make a suitable working drawing of the yoke. Select the type of welds you feel are required and show the correct symbols in the proper places on your drawing. (Time: 3 hr.)

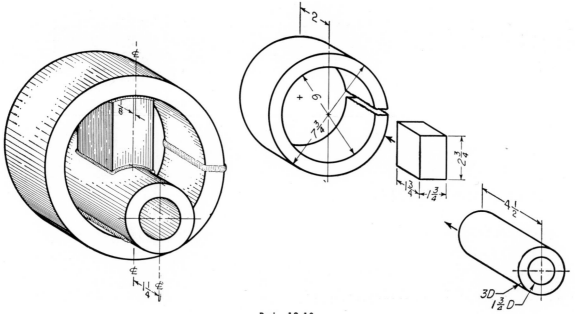

Prob. 13-18.

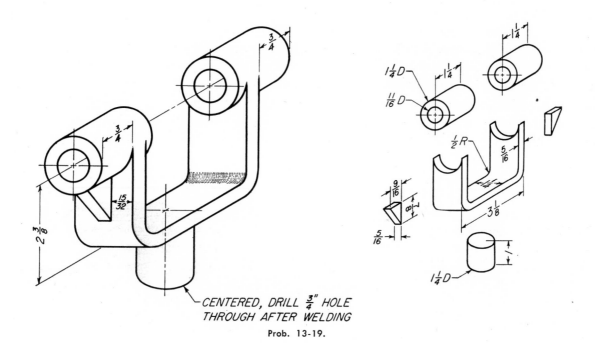

CENTERED, DRILL $\frac{3}{4}$" HOLE
THROUGH AFTER WELDING

Prob. 13-19.

Chapter 14

ASSEMBLY DRAWING

Most mechanisms and structures are made up of a various number of different parts. In order to show these parts in their proper working relationship, it is necessary to prepare an assembly drawing. The assembly drawing may show either the external features of a group of parts or it may be a section view that shows internal as well as external features. Since the creation of a mechanism involves many steps from the inception of the idea in the designer's mind to the final assembly of the component parts, it is obvious that a number of different types of assembly drawings may be required for use in the plant.

14-1. Design assembly. This type of assembly drawing is made with instruments, full size if possible, from the original freehand sketches and engineering calculations for the individual parts. Emphasis is placed on the way the parts go together or function in unison, and thus the drawing is usually left undimensioned. Section views, hidden lines, and partial or complete auxiliaries are used freely where necessary for clarity (see Fig. 14-1). Detail draw-

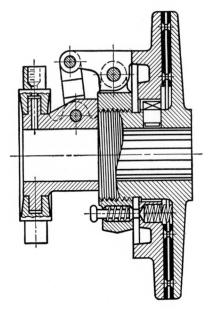
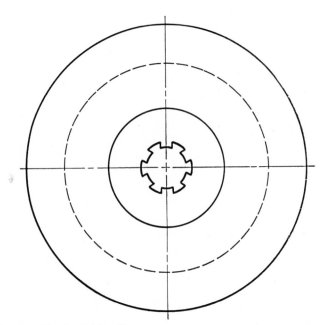

Fig. 14-1. A design assembly of a clutch unit.

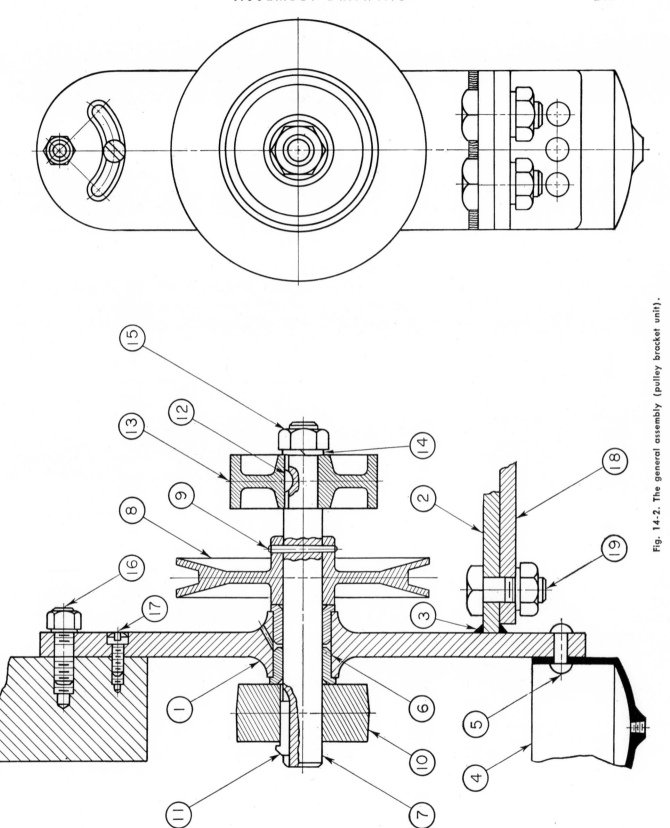

Fig. 14-2. The general assembly (pulley bracket unit).

ings and general assembly drawings are made from design assemblies.

14-2. General assembly. A general-assembly drawing shows the details (individual parts) of a mechanism or structure in their proper working relationship. The general assembly may be traced from the design assembly or prepared directly from the drawings of the details. If the assembly is simple, individual parts, fully dimensioned, may also be shown on the same sheet, and separate detail drawings are not necessary. Usually only two views of the assembly are shown: a main view and a view in section (see Fig. 14-2). Sometimes, however, when an assembly is not complicated, a single section view suffices.

The section view should show all significant parts and how they fit together. Adjacent parts should be sectioned in opposite directions, using the conventional section lining (see Sec. 9-9) to indicate the different materials. As explained in Chap. 9, ribs, webs, bolts, nuts, shafts, keys, pins, etc., should not be shown sectioned. Hidden lines are omitted in both views whenever feasible because they tend to overload the drawing and confuse the shop man. They may be used sparingly, however, where they aid in identifying or clarifying the position of unusual details or special parts. The individual parts appearing in a general-assembly drawing are not dimensioned, but over-all dimensions to show clearances, distances between important centers, and

alternate positions of details that might change the working size of the mechanism are usually indicated.

If the unit is symmetrical, a half section can frequently be used advantageously, for it shows the external appearance as well as the internal relationship of the parts of the mechanism. Indeed, it is often possible to describe a symmetrical assembly completely with a single half-section view. Sectioning should be used freely in all types of assembly drawings. When standard parts such as bearings, cables, chains, pipes, and fasteners, are drawn in assemblies they are represented symbolically (see Fig. 14-3).

14-3. Title block and bill of materials. In assembly drawings, the title box is accompanied by a bill of materials and often by a record strip. The *bill of materials* is a parts list that indicates the number or symbol used to identify each part, the name of the part, the material of which it is made, and the number required in making the assembly shown in the drawing. Figure 14-4 gives complete information on the drawing of the title block and bill of materials. The bill of materials is usually placed just above the title block, and the parts are numbered from below upward to allow for omissions or last-minute additions. If the assembly consists of only a few parts, notes are used to identify each part (see Fig. 14-5), and the bill of materials is omitted.

If changes in design or other alterations are nec-

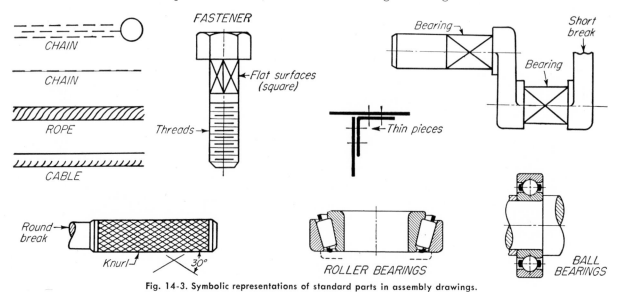

Fig. 14-3. Symbolic representations of standard parts in assembly drawings.

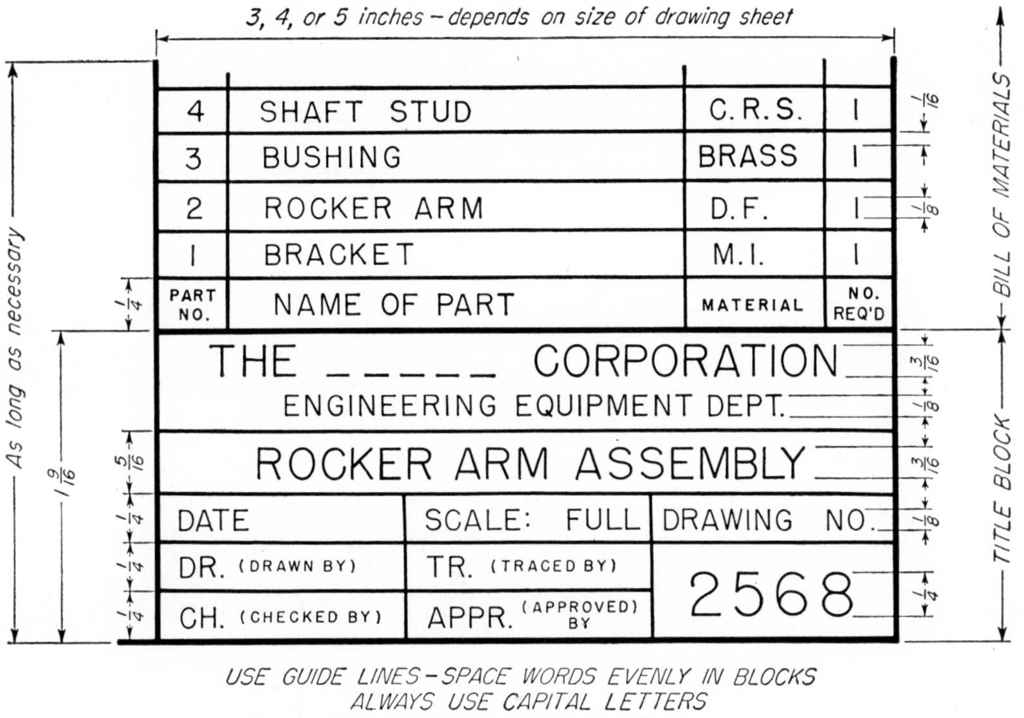

3, 4, or 5 inches – depends on size of drawing sheet

4	SHAFT STUD	C.R.S.	I
3	BUSHING	BRASS	I
2	ROCKER ARM	D.F.	I
I	BRACKET	M.I.	I
PART NO.	NAME OF PART	MATERIAL	NO. REQ'D

THE _ _ _ _ _ CORPORATION
ENGINEERING EQUIPMENT DEPT.

ROCKER ARM ASSEMBLY

DATE	SCALE: FULL	DRAWING NO.
DR. (DRAWN BY)	TR. (TRACED BY)	
CH. (CHECKED BY)	APPR. (APPROVED BY)	2568

BILL OF MATERIALS

TITLE BLOCK

As long as necessary

USE GUIDE LINES – SPACE WORDS EVENLY IN BLOCKS
ALWAYS USE CAPITAL LETTERS

Fig. 14-4. The title block and bill of materials, or parts list.

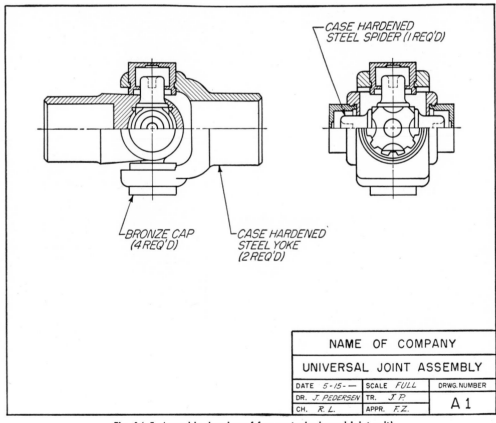

CASE HARDENED STEEL SPIDER (I REQ'D)

BRONZE CAP (4 REQ'D)

CASE HARDENED STEEL YOKE (2 REQ'D)

NAME OF COMPANY		
UNIVERSAL JOINT ASSEMBLY		
DATE 5-15-—	SCALE FULL	DRWG. NUMBER
DR. J. PEDERSEN	TR. J.P.	
CH. R.L.	APPR. F.Z.	A 1

Fig. 14-5. Assembly drawing of few parts (universal joint unit).

Title block ⌐

CONTINENTAL DIAMOND FIBRE CO.			
NEWARK, DEL.			

Revision record strip ⌐

FRACTIONAL DIM. ±1/64 - DECIMALS ±.005 UNLESS OTHERWISE SPECIFIED

				MATERIAL		DRAWN BY	DATE
						CHECKED BY	SCALE
						ORIGINATED BY	
		-		FINISH	f_1 ROUGH FIN. f_2 MACH. FIN.	APPROVED BY	
MARK	REVISION	BY	DATE		f_3 FINE FIN. f_4 POLISH	DWG. No.	

Fig. 14-6. Title block with record strip.

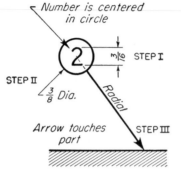

Number is centered in circle

STEP I $\frac{3}{16}$

STEP II $\frac{3}{8}$ Dia.

Radial

STEP III

Arrow touches part

Fig. 14-7. Identification number and arrow.

essary, they are indicated in a *record strip* placed above the lower border and to the left of the title block. Other information such as weight, stock sizes, special finishes, machining procedures, methods of assembly, etc., may also be shown in this strip (see Fig. 14-6).

14-4. Identification of parts. For ease of reference, each part in an assembly consisting of numerous pieces is identified by number. On the drawing proper the number is centered in a circle to

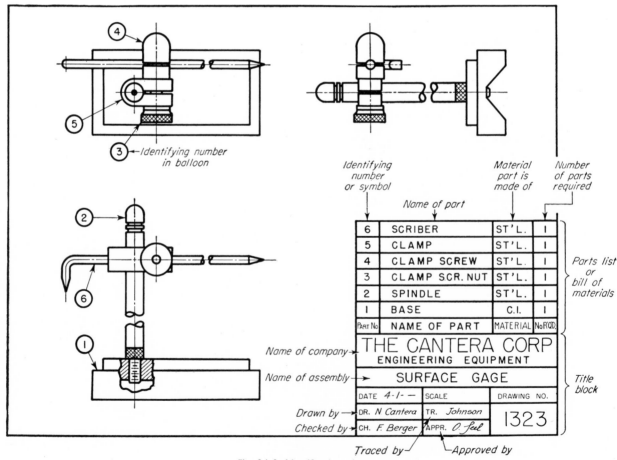

Identifying number in balloon

Identifying number or symbol

Name of part

Material part is made of

Number of parts required

Part No	NAME OF PART	MATERIAL	NoR'QD.
6	SCRIBER	ST'L.	I
5	CLAMP	ST'L.	I
4	CLAMP SCREW	ST'L.	I
3	CLAMP SCR. NUT	ST'L.	I
2	SPINDLE	ST'L.	I
I	BASE	C.I.	I

Parts list or bill of materials

Name of company →

THE CANTERA CORP
ENGINEERING EQUIPMENT

Name of assembly →

SURFACE GAGE

DATE 4-/- —	SCALE	DRAWING NO.
DR. N Cantera	TR. Johnson	1323
CH. F. Berger	APPR. O. feel	

Title block

Drawn by →
Checked by →

Traced by ⌐
Approved by

Fig. 14-8. Identification of parts.

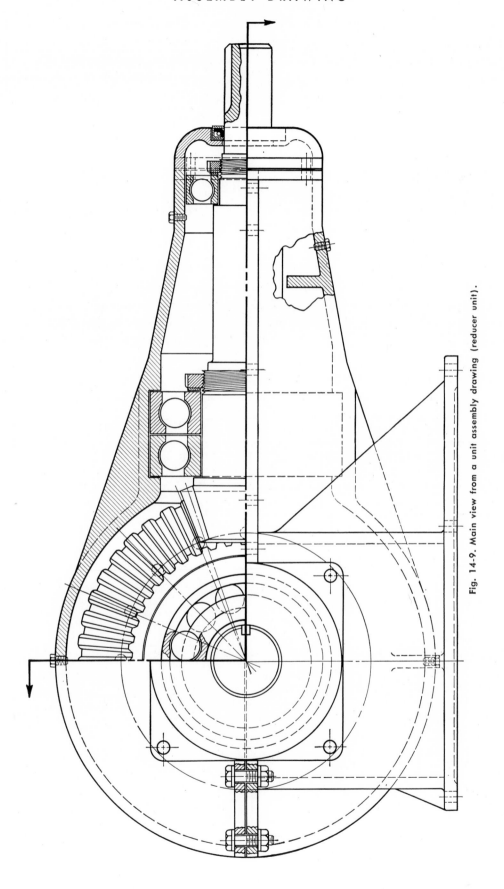

Fig. 14-9. Main view from a unit assembly drawing (reducer unit).

which is attached a leader extending radially and terminating in an arrow that touches a boundary line of the part it identifies (see Fig. 14-7). The circles should be grouped about the assembly in an orderly manner, arranged horizontally, vertically, or staggered, and should not be crowded or placed so that the leaders cross. The parts should not be numbered haphazardly, but should be identified according to a logical system. They may be numbered according to size, starting with the largest piece as number 1 and continuing progressively to the smaller ones with the higher numbers, or they may be numbered according to the material (cast iron, steel, copper, brass, aluminum, etc.) of which they are made. A better method, however, which has been widely adopted, is to number the parts according to the sequence in which they will be handled by the worker who is to assemble them (Fig. 14-8).

14-5. Unit assembly. It is usually impractical or impossible to show on the drawing sheet a clear and useful complete assembly of a large or very complicated mechanism. To present a more comprehensive picture of the many details of, let us say, an internal-combustion engine, the draftsman must prepare a series of drawings of the smaller units that make up the entire engine. The preparation of a detailed assembly of a portion of the whole, such as the fuel pump, the distributor, the fan mechanism, or a connecting rod coupled to the piston with its wrist pin, is known as a unit assembly, or subassembly (see Fig. 14-9). The unit assembly should provide by means of notes any information necessary for assembly to the larger mechanism, such as drilling operations, or finishing, pressing, crimping, or welding procedures required for the attachment. The individual parts themselves are not dimen-

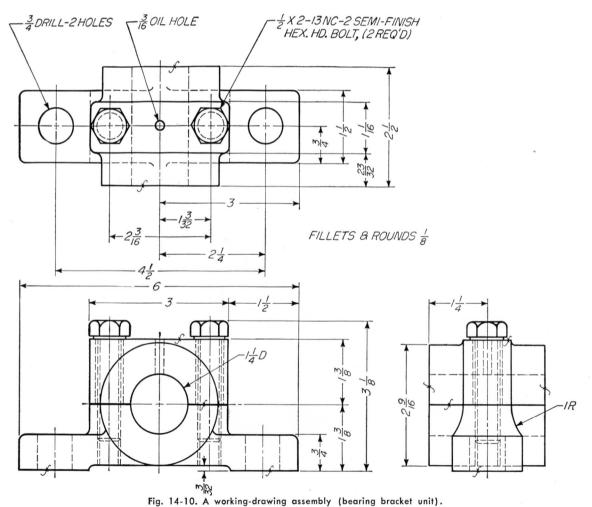

Fig. 14-10. A working-drawing assembly (bearing bracket unit).

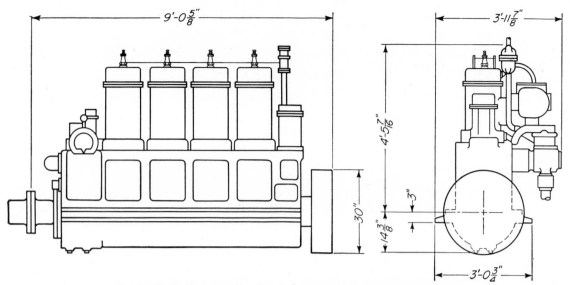

Fig. 14-11. Outline assembly (installation assembly) of a marine engine.

sioned. However, over-all dimensions to show the clearance space necessary, and center to center, or finished surface to center or finished surface dimensions, may be required along with other informative notes as aids in assembly procedure.

14-6. Group assembly. When a number of unit assemblies are shown combined in their working relationship, the drawing is known as a group assembly. No dimensioning is required, although the parts should be identified by complete notes or by numbers referring to a parts list.

14-7. Working-drawing assembly. If a complete mechanism consists of only a few parts, or of a number of parts of simple design and construction, a working-drawing assembly may be prepared. In this type of assembly, all details are completely dimensioned and identified by notes giving the necessary manufacturing and assembly procedures,

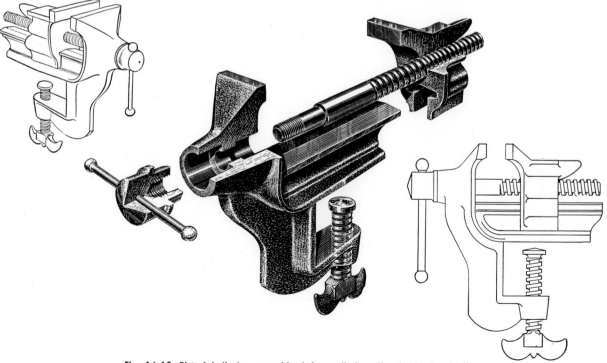

Fig. 14-12. Pictorial display assembly (often called an "exploded drawing").

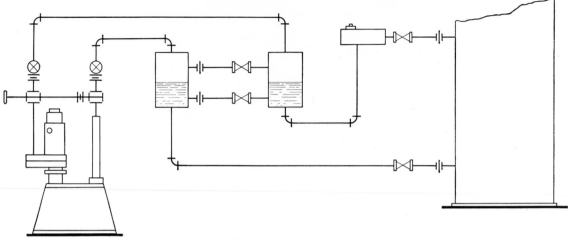

Fig. 14-13. Plumbing diagram drawing.

and separate detail drawings are not made (see Fig. 14-10). The views shown should be adequate and should not require additional detail drawings for further dimensioning. Unit and subassemblies of mechanisms that are to be produced in limited quantities are often shown in this manner because the drawings are needed by only a few people. A title block with parts list and record strip should be shown on the same sheet.

14-8. Outline assembly (installation assembly). An outline assembly drawing shows only the external contours and shape-describing lines of a structure or mechanism. Because it is often employed as a guide for erection or installation, it is

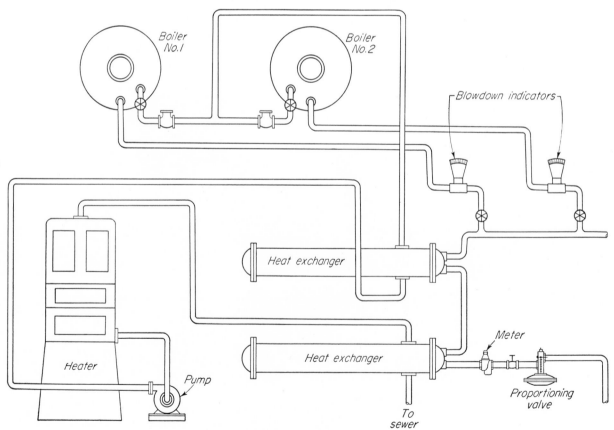

Fig. 14-14. Plumbing semipictorial drawing.

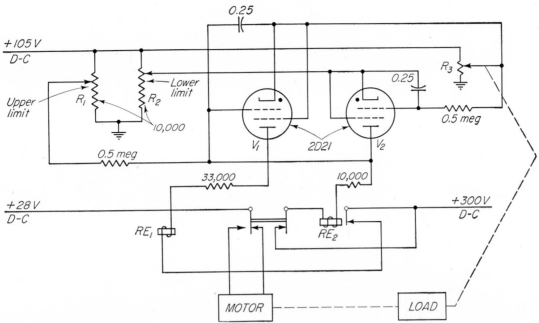

14-15. Electrical diagram drawing. (From Henney and Fahnestock, Electron Tubes in Industry, McGraw-Hill.)

also known as an installation assembly. Only the dimensions that show the over-all size of the external surfaces are given on the drawing (see Fig. 14-11).

14-9. Check assembly. In order to make sure that details designed for an assembly are of the proper size and material and will fit together correctly, a check assembly is sometimes prepared. All the parts are drawn accurately with instruments to their exact size and in their true relationship to other parts in the assembly. The details are scaled carefully but are not dimensioned. Once the check assembly has fulfilled its purpose, it may be used as a general assembly.

14-10. Display assembly. If an assembly drawing is to be used for display or catalogue purposes, a display assembly is usually prepared (see Fig. 14-12). This is an attractive pictorial with line or halftone shading to give the effect of depth and perspective, employing color if cost is not an important consideration. Descriptive text material in addition to identifying notes may accompany the drawing. A pictorial display assembly is more easily understood and far more convincing to a person not trained in the reading of orthographic presentations.

14-11. Diagram drawing. A type of drawing

that is very useful in the plumbing, electrical, and building industries is the diagram drawing (see Figs. 14-13 to 14-15). The diagram drawing is

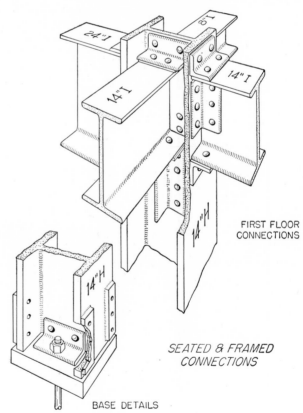

FIRST FLOOR CONNECTIONS

SEATED & FRAMED CONNECTIONS

BASE DETAILS

Fig. 14-16. Pictorial construction drawing (architectural engineering).

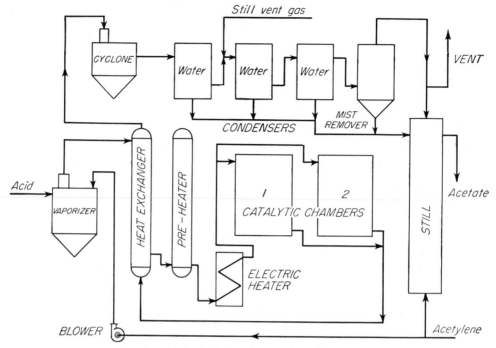

Fig. 14-17. Chemical-engineering flow diagram.

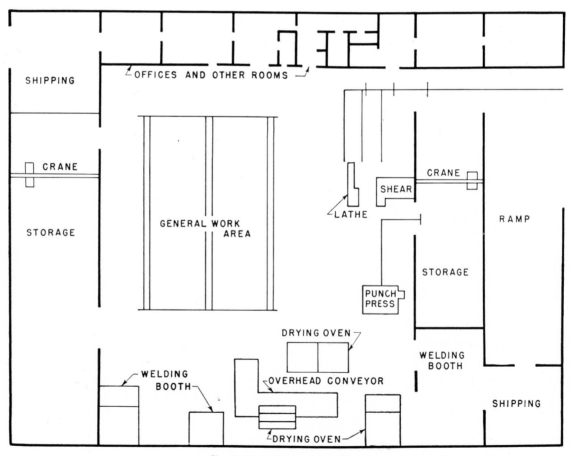

Fig. 14-18. Plant-layout drawing.

prepared either pictorially or orthographically and need not necessarily be drawn to scale. The draftsman should use the standard conventional symbols to represent details of piping, circuits, etc. (see the Appendix, Tables 25 to 28). If dimensions are to be given, the figures must indicate the true distances between the points measured. Any notes necessary for the assembly of the details or construction of the unit, together with the kind and sizes of the parts required, are included in the drawing. Diagram drawings are employed frequently in architectural engineering and in construction work (see Fig. 14-16).

The chemical engineer frequently has to construct flow diagrams similar to the one shown in Fig. 14-17. In such diagrammatic representations, the engineer is primarily concerned with the operational cycle and the placement of the necessary equipment for various processes such as mixing, grinding, dying, distillation, sedimentation, and evaporation. Simple outlines of forms similar in shape to the object may be used to indicate the various pieces of equipment, and the drawing need not be made to scale.

14-12. Plant-layout drawing. Because the plant engineer is often better acquainted with the particular needs of his organization than the architect, to him may fall the task of preparing the layout for a new factory or processing plant. If existing facilities are to be added to or revised, he will also be called upon to offer his advice. A successful plant layout is the result of careful analysis of process and flow sheets, manufacturing procedures, machine information, materials handling, work areas, and aisle and storage space. The building plans must be carefully scrutinized before decisions can be made concerning the arrangement and allotment of the available floor space. A layout drawing is prepared to scale and should show the outline of the building, the locations of aisles, work areas, and rooms, and the positions occupied by the various machines, conveyors, etc. (see Fig. 14-18). The scales employed range from $\frac{1}{32}$ to $\frac{1}{4}$ in. to the foot, depending upon the size of the drawing. The accepted conventional symbols for materials of construction are used, and doors, windows, walls, etc., are shown as the architect would draw them (see Table 29 in the Appendix).

PROBLEMS

The following problems have been especially selected to give the student practice in applying the principles of assembly drawing set forth in this chapter. The student need have no previous knowledge or training in the principles of mechanical design, nor will he find it necessary to refer to handbooks or to other texts in order to be able to produce the drawings required. The pictorial views and the orthographic details are to be used in conjunction to produce the assembly. In the pictorial views, it should be noted that a missing dimension on one part may be satisfied by a dimension appearing on its mating part. For instance, when the thread specification on one part has been shown it may have been omitted from the hole it fits into. The case may be the same with the mating slot forms, etc.

The parts should be numbered in the order in which they will be handled by the workman who will make the assembly. If more information than that appearing in the problem is required to produce standard parts and forms, such as screw threads, screws, bolts, nuts, washers, rivets, weldings, springs, etc., the student should refer to the Appendix or to the chapters where the particular features are discussed in detail. All the problems have been designed to fit 8½- by 11-in. or 11- by 17-in. sheets if drawn at actual size or reduced or enlarged as suggested in the problem assignments. A title block and bill of materials should be drawn and filled in completely for each problem. Screw threads conforming to the unified series should be indicated by their unified specifications.

Wherever a pictorial alone is shown as a problem, the instructor may assign it either as an assembly problem or as a detail-drawing exercise.

14-1. Redraw the two given orthographic views shown in the upper right of the assembly of the drill-auger arbor. Show one of the special washers (2) in full section. Refer to the orthographic details for dimensions. Make the drawing double size on an 11- by 17-in. sheet. Complete the title block and bill of materials. The parts are (1) shaft, cold-rolled steel; (2) special washer, steel, two required; (3) standard hex nut, steel. (Time: 4 hr.)

14-2. Redraw the two given orthographic assembly views (shown with the pictorial of the C clamp) on an 11- by 17-in. sheet. Refer to the details for the dimensions. The assembly consists of (1) cast-iron clamp jaw, (2) steel adjusting screw, (3) cast-iron swivel ring, and (4) cast-iron wing nut. (Time: 5 hr.)

14-3. Make a two-view general-assembly drawing of the sliding bolt lock. Show the assembly double size on an 8½- by 11-in. sheet. Use sectioning where desirable. Include over-all dimensions but do not dimension the individual details. The parts are all brass and consist of (1) bed, (2) bolt, (3) nob, and (4) end piece. Show a title block and bill of materials. (Time: 4 hr.)

14-4. Make a set of detail drawings of the tool post, completely dimensioned, on an 11- by 17-in. sheet. (Time: 7 hr.)

14-5. Make a two-view general-assembly drawing of the tool post on an 8½- by 11-in. sheet. Include a title block and bill of materials. Refer to the pictorial for the names of the parts, all of which are made of steel. Number the parts in order of their assembly. Section parts as desirable. Include only over-all dimensions. (Time: 5 hr.)

14-6. Make a set of completely dimensioned details of the Dilecto union on an 8½- by 11-in sheet. (Time: 5 hr.)

14-7. Make a two-view working-assembly drawing of the Dilecto union on an 8½- by 11-in. sheet. Dimension all details and include a title block and bill of materials. Employ sectioning where desirable. See tables in the appendix for information on pipe threads. Draw the threads semiconventionally, symbolically, or simplified according to the principles outlined in Chap. 13. The parts are made of fiber and consist of (1) connector nipple, (2) sealing ferrule, and (3) compression ring. (Time: 4 hr.)

14-8. Make a two-view working-assembly drawing of the wheel puller on an 11- by 17-in. sheet. Dimension completely and include a title block and bill of materials. Use sectioning where desirable. The parts in the assembly, all made of steel, are (1) yoke, (2) jaws, (3) pin, (4) pulling screw, and (5) loose-pin handle. (Time: 5 hr.)

14-9. Make a two-view working-assembly drawing of the tool holder on an 8½- by 11-in. sheet. Dimension all details and include a title block and bill of materials. Section where desirable. The parts are (1) body, cast iron; (2) flange, cast iron; (3) plain washer, steel; (4) standard hex-head cap screw, steel; (5) bushing, cold-rolled steel. (Time: 6 hr.)

14-10. Make a set of completely dimensioned details of the antenna support on an 11- by 17-in. sheet. (Time: 7 hr.)

14-11. Make a two-view general-assembly drawing of the antenna support at a suitable enlarged scale on an 11- by 17-in. sheet. Show over-all dimensions and include a title block and bill of materials. Employ sectioning where advantageous. All parts are made of aluminum with the exception of the standard steel machine screw and hex nut. (Time: 5 hr.)

14-12. Make a two-view general-assembly drawing of the adjustable wrench on an 11- by 17-in. sheet. Employ any standard conventional or sectioning procedures that you feel will help convey the best impression of the parts in assembly. The parts, all made of steel, are (1) handle jaw, (2) movable jaw, (3) setting screw, and (4) pin. Show over-all dimensions only. Include a title block and bill of materials. (Time: 6 hr.)

14-13. Make a set of completely dimensioned details of the table jack on an 11- by 17-in. sheet. (Time: 7 hr.)

14-14. Make a two-view general-assembly drawing of the table jack at a suitable enlarged scale on an 11- by 17-in. sheet. Show the base (1) and the collar (2) in full section in the front view. The base (1) is cast iron. The collar (2), the collar screw (3), the adjusting pin (4), and the setscrew (5) are made of steel. Show a title block and bill of materials. Include over-all dimensions only. (Time: 6 hr.)

14-15. Make a two-view working-assembly drawing of the caster. Draw it double size on an 8½- by 11-in. sheet. Dimension completely and include a title block and bill of materials. Show sectioning where desirable. The parts are (1) frame, cast steel; (2) collar, steel; (3) shaft, cold-rolled steel; (4) wheel, cast iron; (5) pin, cold-rolled steel. (Time: 6 hr.)

14-16. Make a two-view general-assembly drawing of the drain cock at double size on an 11- by 17-in. sheet. Show the body (1) in full section in the front view. The parts for the bill of materials are (1) body, (2) handle, (3) special washer, and (4) hex jam nut. All parts made of brass. (Time: 6 hr.)

14-17. Make a two-view working assembly of the pipe support on an 8½- by 11-in. sheet. Show sectioning where helpful. The base (1), lower clamp (2), upper clamp (3), and the screws are made of brass. (Time: 6 hr.)

14-18. Make a two-view general assembly of the adjustable base at double size on an 11- by 17-in. sheet. Employ standard sectioning procedure wherever you feel it will help make the drawing clearer. The assembly includes (1) cast-iron base, (2) cast-iron sliding adjuster, (8) cast-iron wing nut, and standard steel fasteners. Do not dimension the details. Show a title block and a bill of materials that includes all the numbered parts. (Time: 8 hr.)

14-19. Make a two-view general assembly of the special bearing puller on an 11- by 17-in. sheet. Use sectioning where desirable. Treat threads as suggested in Chap. 13. The assembly parts, all made of steel, are (1) jaw holder, (2) top bushing, (3) pulling screw, (4) loose-pin handle, and (5) four adjustable jaws. Show only over-all dimensions. Include a complete title block and bill of materials on the drawing sheet. (Time: 7 hr.)

14-20. Make a drawing showing the details of the valve-lifter unit completely dimensioned on an 11- by 17-in. sheet. (Time: 10 hr.)

14-21. Make a two-view working assembly of the valve-lifter unit at double size on an 11- by 17-in. sheet. The housing and the gaskets may be shown in full or half section. A broken-out section will show the mating of the screw and the follower. A partial view of the follower is shown at the lower left in the illustration. Dimension all details and include a

title block and a bill of materials. (Time: 10 hr.)

14-22. Make a two-view general assembly of the desk lift unit on an 11- by 17-in. sheet. Use sectioning where desirable. The 12-piece assembly consists of various standard steel fasteners identified by their specifications, and (1) cast-iron coupling, (2) steel base bracket, (4) steel extension rod, (5) steel desktop bracket, (7) steel pressure shaft, (8) steel chip-prevention insert, and (9) a wooden handle. Do not dimension. Show a title block with a bill of materials on the drawing sheet. (Time: 12 hr.)

14-23. Make a two-view general assembly of the hand drill on an 11- by 17-in. sheet. Use sectioning where desirable. Show only over-all dimensions. Include a complete title block, bill of materials, and record strip. (Time: 22 hr.)

14-24. Make a two-view general assembly of the hand clamp vise at a suitable scale to fit an 11- by 17-in. sheet. Use sectioning where desirable. Show a title block with a bill of materials in the lower right corner of the problem. Do not dimension. (Time: 12 hr.)

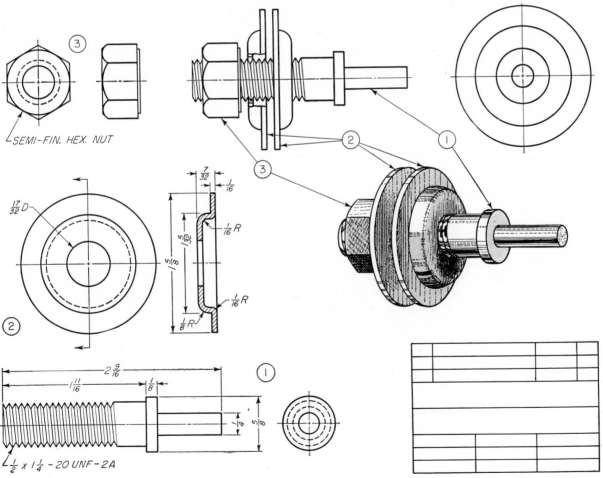

Prob. 14-1. Drill-auger arbor.

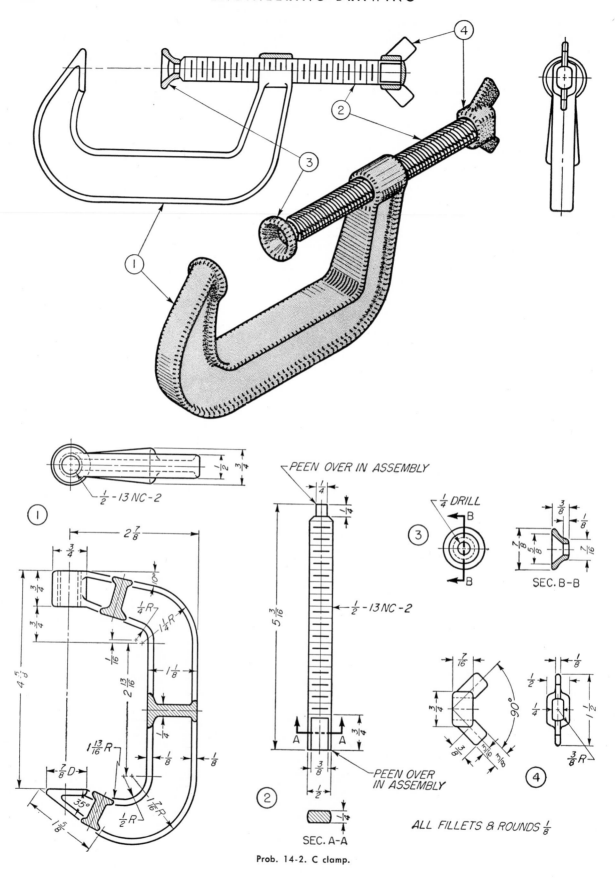

PEEN OVER IN ASSEMBLY

¼ DRILL

SEC. B-B

½-13 NC-2

PEEN OVER
IN ASSEMBLY

SEC. A-A

ALL FILLETS & ROUNDS ⅛

Prob. 14-2. C clamp.

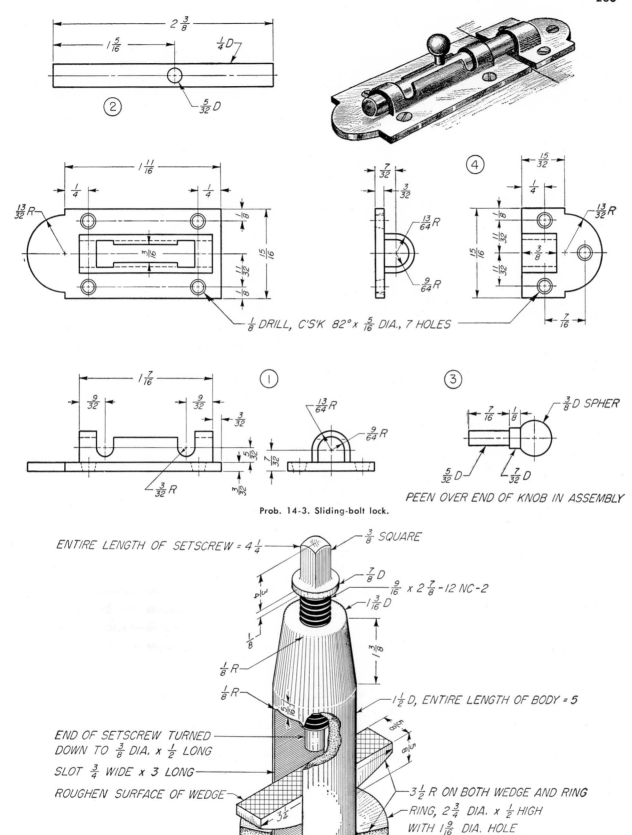

$2\frac{3}{8}$

$1\frac{5}{16}$

$\frac{1}{4}D$

$\frac{5}{32}D$

②

④

$1\frac{11}{16}$

$\frac{1}{4}$ $\frac{1}{4}$

$\frac{13}{32}R$

$\frac{3}{16}$

$\frac{15}{16}$

$\frac{1}{8}$

$\frac{11}{32}$

$\frac{1}{8}$

$\frac{7}{32}$

$\frac{3}{32}$

$\frac{13}{64}R$

$\frac{9}{64}R$

$\frac{15}{32}$

$\frac{1}{4}$

$\frac{1}{8}$

$\frac{11}{32}$

$\frac{3}{8}$

$\frac{15}{16}$

$\frac{11}{32}$

$\frac{13}{32}R$

$\frac{7}{16}$

$\frac{1}{8}$ DRILL, C'S'K 82° x $\frac{5}{16}$ DIA., 7 HOLES

①

③

$1\frac{7}{16}$

$\frac{9}{32}$ $\frac{9}{32}$

$\frac{3}{32}$

$\frac{13}{64}R$

$\frac{9}{64}R$

$\frac{5}{32}$

$\frac{7}{32}$

$\frac{3}{32}R$

$\frac{3}{32}$

$\frac{7}{16}$ $\frac{1}{8}$

$\frac{3}{8}D$ SPHER

$\frac{5}{32}D$

$\frac{7}{32}D$

PEEN OVER END OF KNOB IN ASSEMBLY

Prob. 14-3. Sliding-bolt lock.

ENTIRE LENGTH OF SETSCREW = $4\frac{1}{4}$

$\frac{3}{8}$ SQUARE

$\frac{7}{8}D$

$\frac{9}{16}$ x $2\frac{7}{8}$ -12 NC-2

$\frac{3}{4}$

$1\frac{3}{16}D$

$\frac{1}{8}$

$1\frac{3}{8}$

$\frac{1}{8}R$

$\frac{1}{8}R$

$\frac{5}{16}$

$1\frac{1}{2}D$, ENTIRE LENGTH OF BODY = 5

$\frac{5}{16}$

$\frac{5}{8}$

END OF SETSCREW TURNED
DOWN TO $\frac{3}{8}$ DIA. x $\frac{1}{2}$ LONG

SLOT $\frac{3}{4}$ WIDE x 3 LONG

ROUGHEN SURFACE OF WEDGE

$3\frac{1}{4}$

$3\frac{1}{2}R$ ON BOTH WEDGE AND RING

RING, $2\frac{3}{4}$ DIA. x $\frac{1}{2}$ HIGH
WITH $1\frac{9}{16}$ DIA. HOLE

BLOCK, $2\frac{1}{2}$ SQUARE WITH
CENTERED HOLE $1\frac{9}{16}$ BORE,
C'BORE $1\frac{7}{8}$ DIA. x $\frac{3}{16}$ DEEP

$1\frac{27}{32}D$

$\frac{3}{16}$

$\frac{5}{16}$

$\frac{1}{8}$

Probs. 14-4 and 14-5. Tool post.

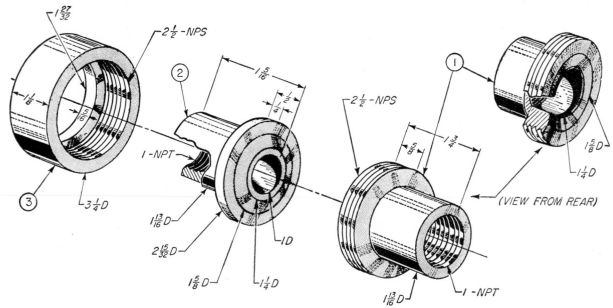

Probs. 14-6 and 14-7. Dilecto union.

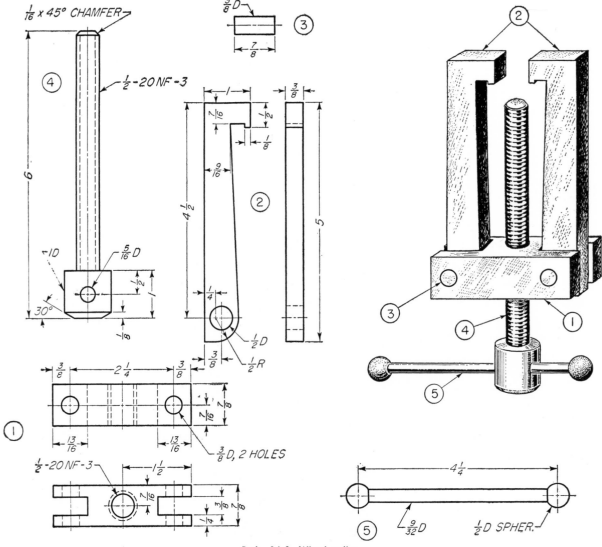

Prob. 14-8. Wheel puller.

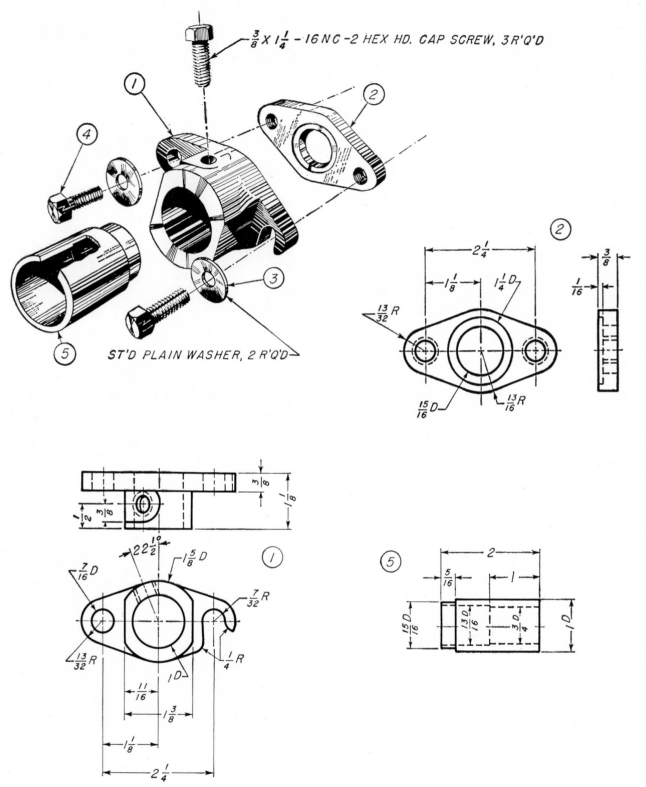

Prob. 14-9. Tool holder.

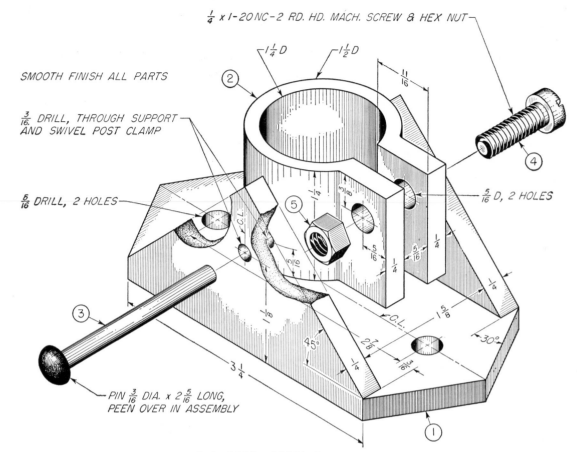

Probs. 14-10 and 14-11. Antenna support.

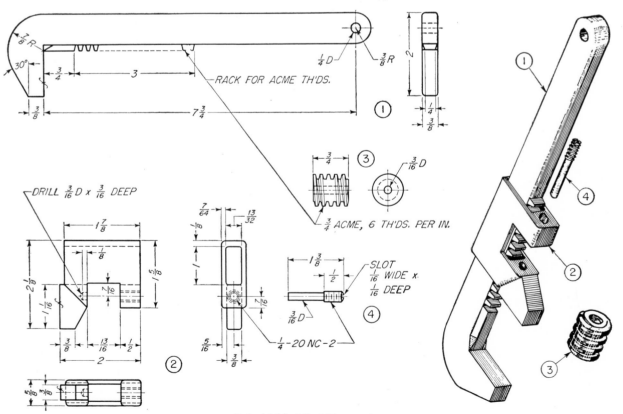

Prob. 14-12. Adjustable wrench.

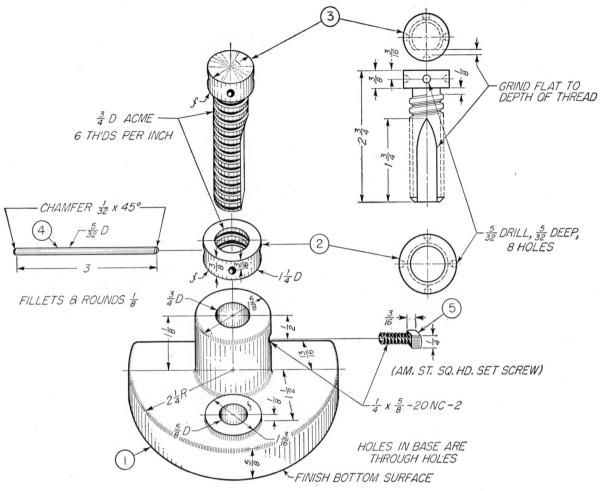

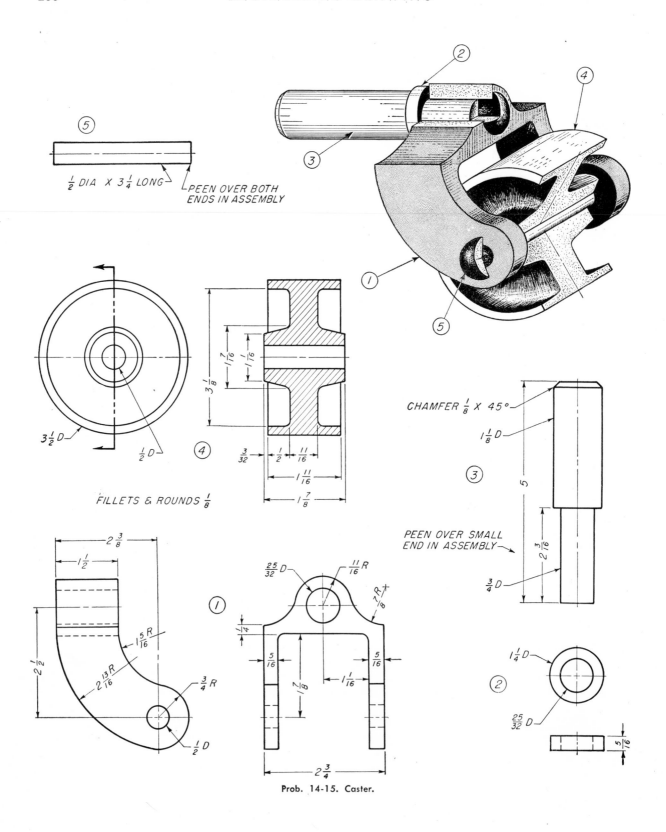

⑤

$\frac{1}{2}$ DIA X 3$\frac{1}{4}$ LONG — PEEN OVER BOTH
ENDS IN ASSEMBLY

3$\frac{1}{2}$ D

$\frac{1}{2}$ D

④

FILLETS & ROUNDS $\frac{1}{8}$

3$\frac{1}{8}$

1$\frac{7}{16}$

$\frac{1}{16}$

$\frac{3}{32}$ $\frac{1}{2}$ $\frac{11}{16}$

1$\frac{11}{16}$

1$\frac{7}{8}$

CHAMFER $\frac{1}{8}$ X 45°

1$\frac{1}{8}$ D

③

5

2$\frac{3}{16}$

$\frac{3}{4}$ D

PEEN OVER SMALL
END IN ASSEMBLY →

2$\frac{3}{8}$

1$\frac{1}{2}$

2$\frac{1}{2}$

1$\frac{5}{16}$ R

2$\frac{13}{16}$ R

$\frac{3}{4}$ R

$\frac{1}{2}$ D

①

$\frac{25}{32}$ D $\frac{11}{16}$ R

$\frac{7}{8}$ R

$\frac{1}{4}$

$\frac{5}{16}$ $\frac{5}{16}$

$\frac{7}{8}$ 1$\frac{1}{16}$

2$\frac{3}{4}$

Prob. 14-15. Caster.

1$\frac{1}{4}$ D

②

$\frac{25}{32}$ D

$\frac{5}{16}$

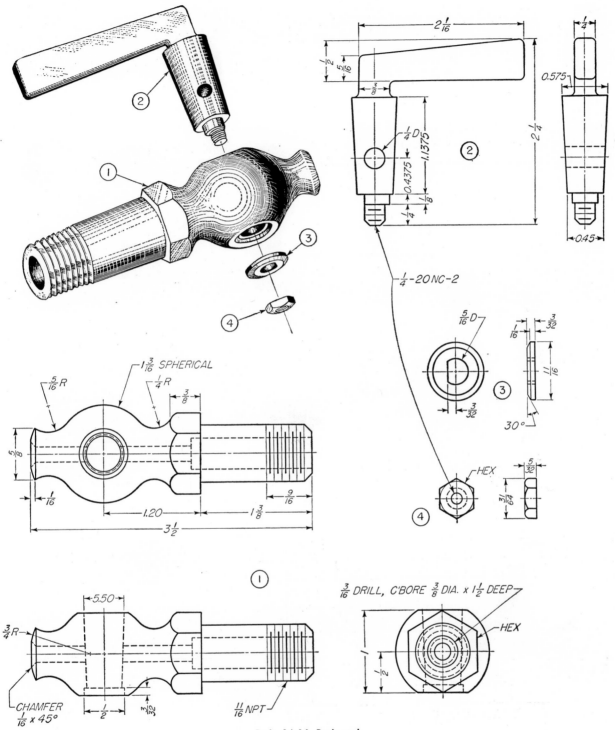

Prob. 14-16. Drain cock.

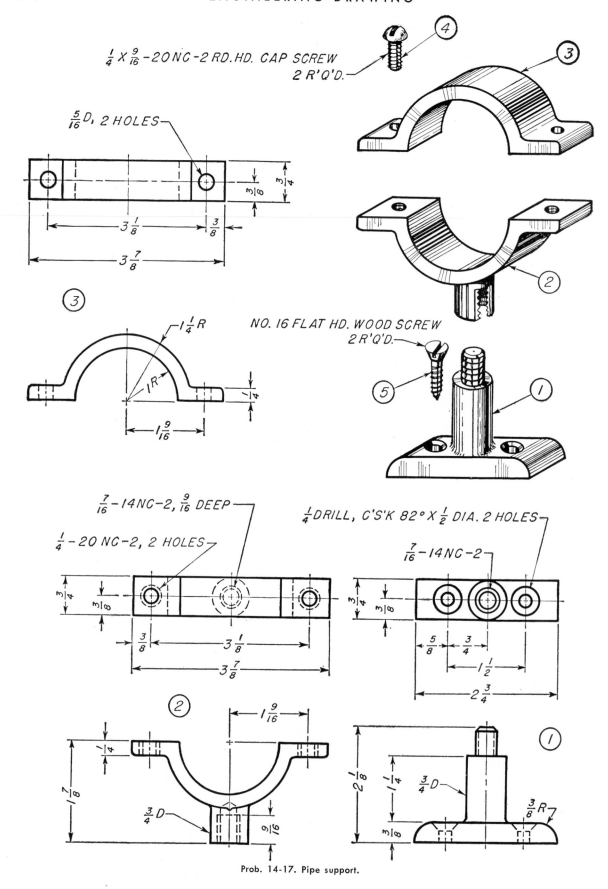

$\frac{1}{4} \times \frac{9}{16} - 20\,NC - 2\,RD.\,HD.\,CAP\,SCREW$
$2\,R'Q'D.$

4

3

$\frac{5}{16}\,D,\,2\,HOLES$

$3\frac{1}{8}$ $\frac{3}{8}$

$\frac{3}{8}$ $\frac{3}{4}$

$3\frac{7}{8}$

2

3

$1\frac{1}{4}\,R$

$1\,R$

$\frac{1}{4}$

$1\frac{9}{16}$

NO. 16 FLAT HD. WOOD SCREW
$2\,R'Q'D.$

5

1

$\frac{7}{16} - 14\,NC - 2,\,\frac{9}{16}\,DEEP$

$\frac{1}{4}\,DRILL,\,C'S'K\,82°\times\frac{1}{2}\,DIA.\,2\,HOLES$

$\frac{1}{4} - 20\,NC - 2,\,2\,HOLES$

$\frac{7}{16} - 14\,NC - 2$

$\frac{3}{4}$ $\frac{3}{8}$

$\frac{3}{8}$ $3\frac{1}{8}$

$3\frac{7}{8}$

$\frac{3}{4}$ $\frac{3}{8}$

$\frac{5}{8}$ $\frac{3}{4}$

$1\frac{1}{2}$

$2\frac{3}{4}$

2

$1\frac{9}{16}$

$\frac{1}{4}$

$\frac{7}{8}$

$\frac{3}{4}\,D$

$\frac{9}{16}$

1

$2\frac{1}{8}$

$1\frac{1}{4}$

$\frac{3}{4}\,D$

$\frac{3}{8}\,R$

$\frac{3}{8}$

Prob. 14-17. Pipe support.

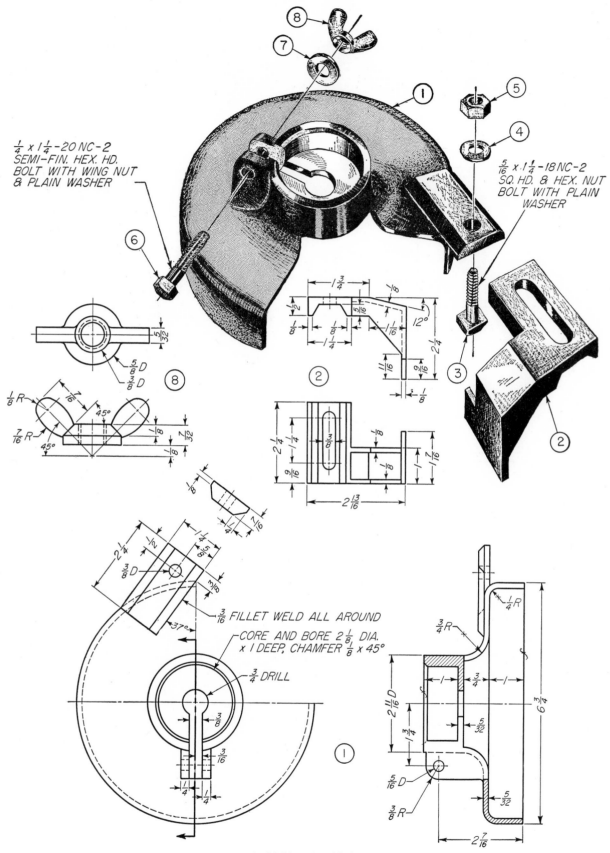

$\frac{1}{4} \times 1\frac{1}{4} - 20\,NC-2$
SEMI-FIN. HEX. HD.
BOLT WITH WING NUT
& PLAIN WASHER

$\frac{5}{16} \times 1\frac{1}{4} - 18\,NC-2$
SQ. HD. & HEX. NUT
BOLT WITH PLAIN
WASHER

FILLET WELD ALL AROUND

CORE AND BORE $2\frac{1}{8}$ DIA.
x I DEEP, CHAMFER $\frac{1}{8}$ x 45°

$\frac{3}{4}$ DRILL

Prob. 14-18. Adjustable base.

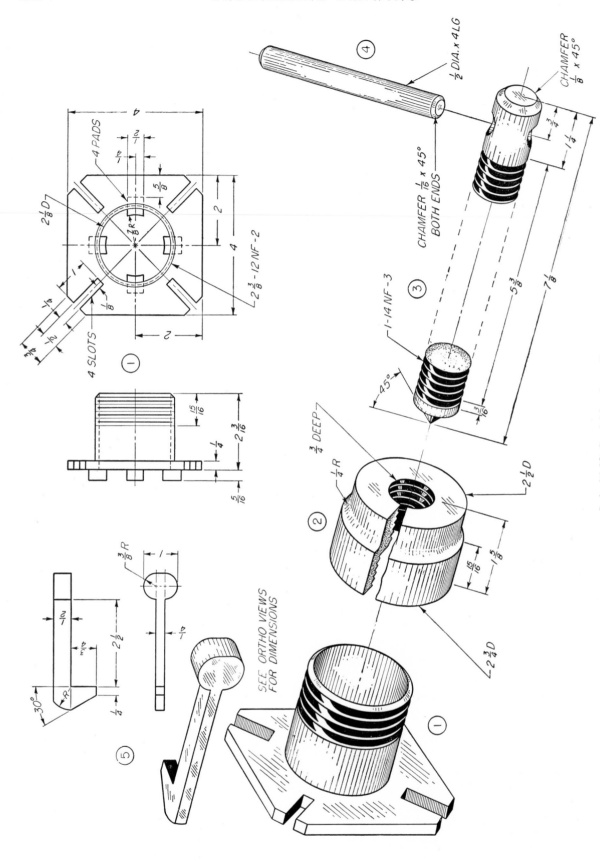

Prob. 14-19. Special bearing puller.

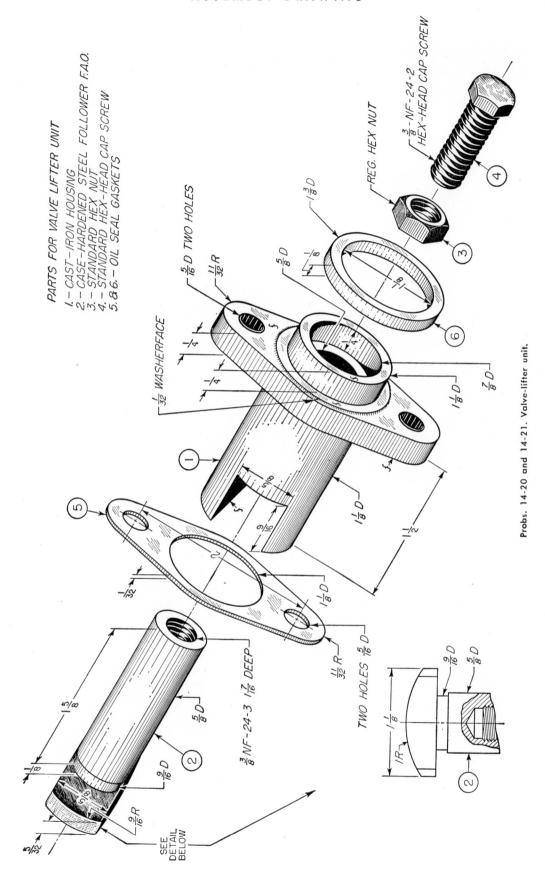

PARTS FOR VALVE LIFTER UNIT

1.- CAST-IRON HOUSING
2.- CASE-HARDENED STEEL FOLLOWER F.A.O.
3.- STANDARD HEX NUT
4.- STANDARD HEX-HEAD CAP SCREW
5.&6.- OIL SEAL GASKETS

REG. HEX NUT

$\frac{3}{8}$-NF-24-2
HEX-HEAD CAP SCREW

$1\frac{3}{8}$ D

$\frac{5}{8}$ D

$\frac{1}{8}$

$\frac{5}{16}$ D TWO HOLES

$\frac{11}{32}$ R

$\frac{1}{32}$ WASHERFACE

$\frac{1}{4}$

$\frac{1}{4}$

$\frac{1}{32}$

$1\frac{1}{8}$ D

$\frac{7}{8}$ D

$1\frac{1}{8}$ D

$1\frac{1}{2}$

$\frac{5}{16}$ D

$\frac{9}{16}$

$\frac{5}{32}$

$1\frac{5}{8}$

$\frac{1}{8}$

$\frac{5}{8}$ D

$\frac{9}{16}$ D

$\frac{9}{16}$ R

SEE DETAIL BELOW

$\frac{3}{8}$ NF-24-3 $1\frac{7}{16}$ DEEP

$\frac{11}{32}$ R

$\frac{1}{32}$

$1\frac{1}{8}$ D

TWO HOLES $\frac{5}{16}$ D

$\frac{9}{16}$ D

$\frac{5}{8}$ D

$1\frac{1}{8}$

1 R

Probs. 14-20 and 14-21. Valve-lifter unit.

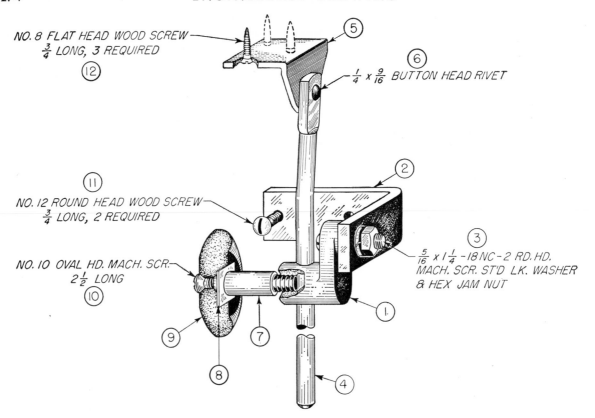

NO. 8 FLAT HEAD WOOD SCREW
$\frac{3}{4}$ LONG, 3 REQUIRED
⑫

⑤

⑥
$\frac{1}{4} \times \frac{9}{16}$ BUTTON HEAD RIVET

②

⑪
NO. 12 ROUND HEAD WOOD SCREW
$\frac{3}{4}$ LONG, 2 REQUIRED

③
$\frac{5}{16} \times 1\frac{1}{4} - 18$ NC - 2 RD. HD.
MACH. SCR. ST'D LK. WASHER
& HEX JAM NUT

NO. 10 OVAL HD. MACH. SCR.
$2\frac{1}{2}$ LONG
⑩

①

⑨

⑦

⑧

④

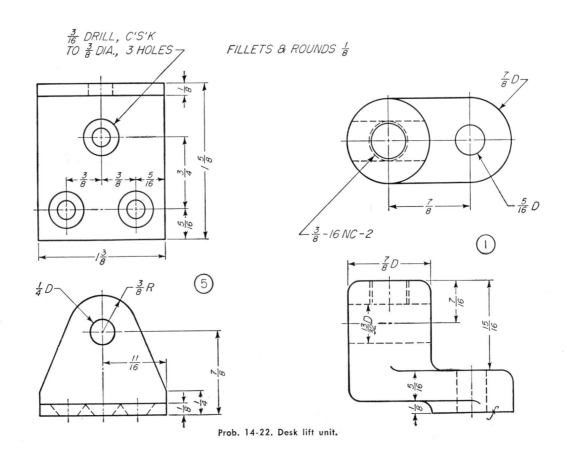

$\frac{3}{16}$ DRILL, C'S'K
TO $\frac{3}{8}$ DIA., 3 HOLES

FILLETS & ROUNDS $\frac{1}{8}$

$\frac{7}{8}$ D

$\frac{3}{8}$
$\frac{3}{8}$
$\frac{5}{16}$

$\frac{3}{4}$
$1\frac{5}{8}$

$\frac{5}{16}$

$1\frac{3}{8}$

$\frac{7}{8}$

$\frac{5}{16}$ D

$\frac{3}{8} - 16$ NC - 2

①

$\frac{1}{4}$ D $\frac{3}{8}$ R

⑤

$\frac{11}{16}$

$\frac{7}{8}$

$\frac{1}{8}$ $\frac{1}{4}$

$\frac{7}{8}$ D

$\frac{7}{16}$

$\frac{13}{32}$ D

$\frac{15}{16}$

$\frac{5}{16}$

$\frac{1}{8}$

Prob. 14-22. Desk lift unit.

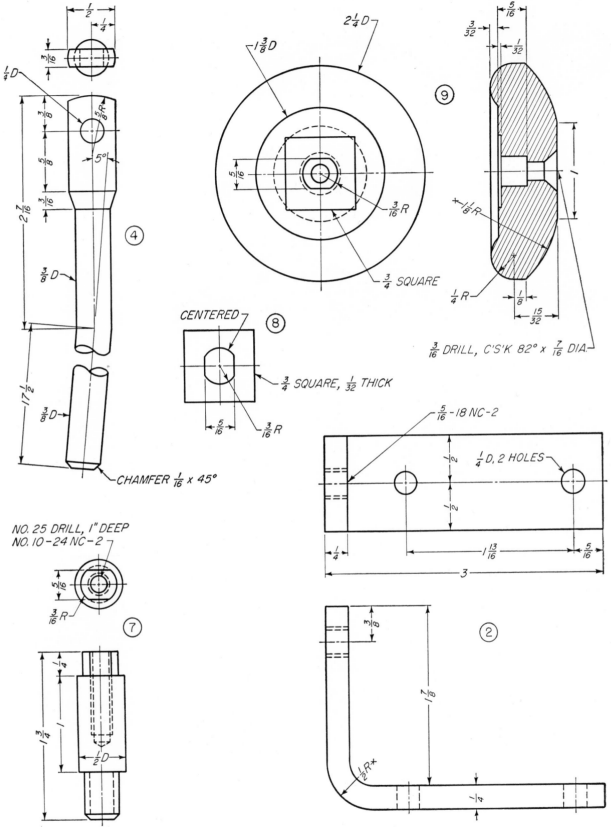

$\frac{1}{2}$

$\frac{1}{4}$

$\frac{3}{16}$

$\frac{1}{4}D$

$\frac{5}{8}R$

$\frac{3}{8}$

$\frac{5}{8}$

$5°$

$2\frac{7}{16}$

$\frac{3}{16}$

$\frac{3}{8}D$

④

$17\frac{1}{2}$

$\frac{3}{8}D$

CHAMFER $\frac{1}{16}$ x 45°

$1\frac{3}{8}D$

$2\frac{1}{4}D$

⑨

$\frac{5}{16}$

$\frac{3}{16}R$

$\frac{3}{4}$ SQUARE

CENTERED

⑧

$\frac{3}{4}$ SQUARE, $\frac{1}{32}$ THICK

$\frac{5}{16}$

$\frac{3}{16}R$

$\frac{5}{16}$

$\frac{3}{32}$

$\frac{1}{32}$

$\frac{1}{8}R$

$\frac{1}{4}R$

$\frac{1}{8}$

$\frac{15}{32}$

$\frac{3}{16}$ DRILL, C'S'K 82° x $\frac{7}{16}$ DIA.

$\frac{5}{16}$-18 NC-2

$\frac{1}{4}D$, 2 HOLES

$\frac{1}{2}$

$\frac{1}{2}$

$\frac{1}{4}$

$1\frac{13}{16}$

$\frac{5}{16}$

3

NO. 25 DRILL, 1" DEEP
NO. 10-24 NC-2

$\frac{5}{16}$

$\frac{3}{16}R$

⑦

$\frac{1}{4}$

$\frac{3}{4}$

1

$\frac{1}{2}D$

$\frac{3}{8}$

②

$1\frac{7}{8}$

$\frac{1}{2}R$

$\frac{1}{4}$

Prob. 14-22. Desk lift unit. (*Continued.*)

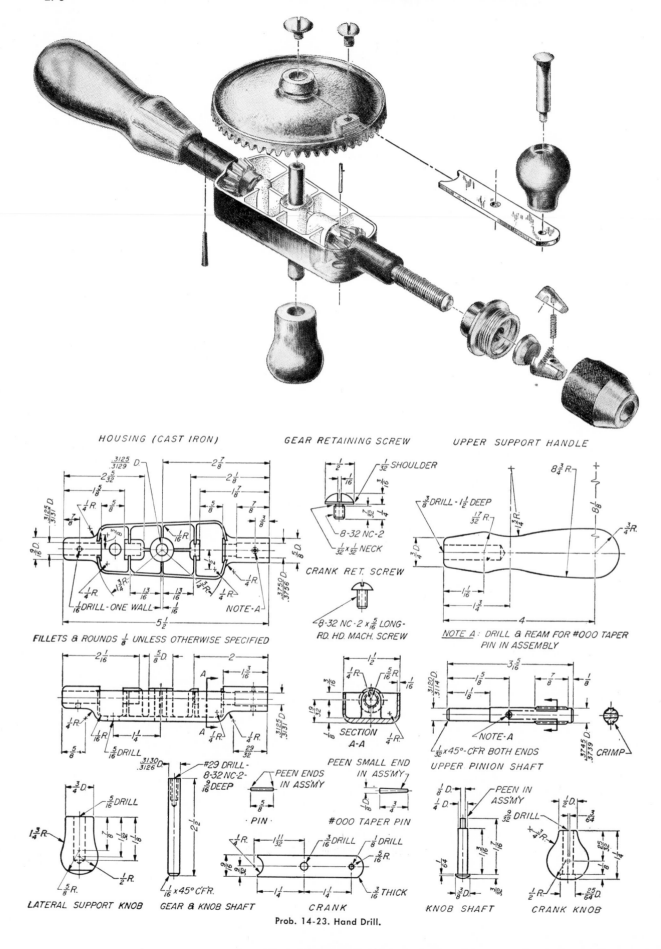

HOUSING (CAST IRON)

GEAR RETAINING SCREW

UPPER SUPPORT HANDLE

SHOULDER

8-32 NC-2

1/32 × 1/32 NECK

CRANK RET. SCREW

8-32 NC-2 × 5/16 LONG-
RD. HD. MACH. SCREW

FILLETS & ROUNDS 1/8 UNLESS OTHERWISE SPECIFIED

3/8 DRILL - 1 1/2 DEEP

NOTE A: DRILL & REAM FOR #000 TAPER
PIN IN ASSEMBLY

1/16 DRILL - ONE WALL

NOTE-A

SECTION
A-A

NOTE-A

UPPER PINION SHAFT

CRIMP

LATERAL SUPPORT KNOB

#29 DRILL-
8-32 NC-2-
9/16 DEEP

1/16 × 45° C'FR.

GEAR & KNOB SHAFT

PEEN ENDS
IN ASS'MY

PIN

PEEN SMALL END
IN ASS'MY

#000 TAPER PIN

3/16 DRILL   1/8 DRILL

3/16 THICK

CRANK

PEEN IN
ASS'MY

KNOB SHAFT

9/32 DRILL

CRANK KNOB

Prob. 14-23. Hand Drill.

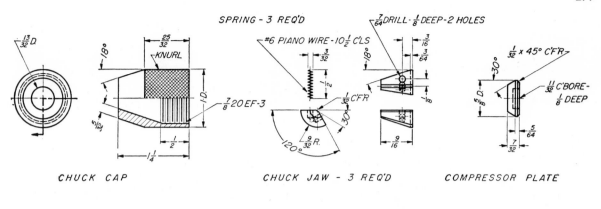

SPRING - 3 REQ'D

CHUCK CAP

CHUCK JAW - 3 REQ'D

COMPRESSOR PLATE

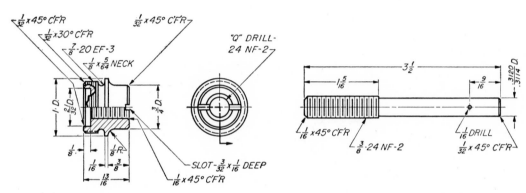

CHUCK RETAINING RING

LOWER PINION SHAFT

PINION - 2 REQ.

GEAR

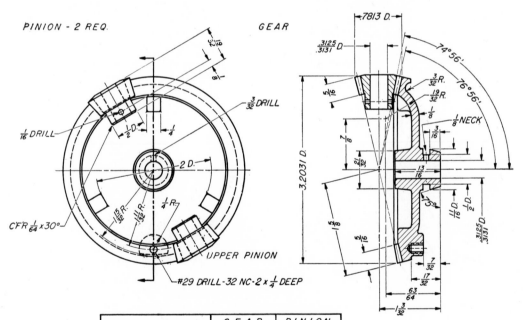

UPPER PINION

#29 DRILL - 32 NC-2 x ¼ DEEP

	GEAR	PINION
NO. OF TEETH	56	13
DIAMETRAL PITCH	18.1	19.2
CHORDAL THICKNESS	.086	.081
CORR. ADDENDUM	.056	.054
WHOLE DEPTH	.119	.112
TOOTH FORM	20° STRAIGHT INV.	
CUTTER NO.	1	8
CUTTING ANGLE	11° 4'	74° 56'

Prob. 14-23. Hand drill. (*Continued.*)

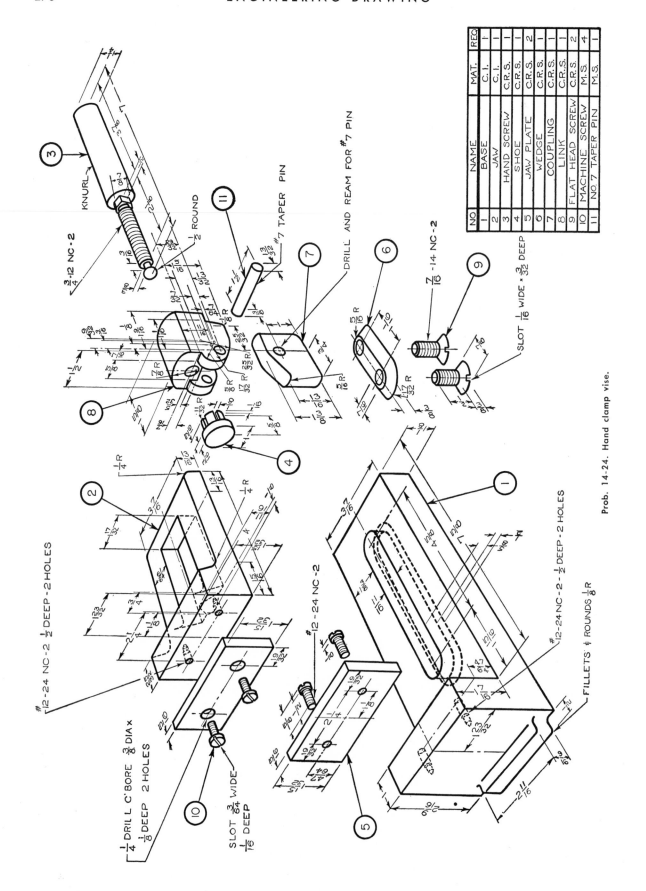

Prob. 14-24. Hand clamp vise.

NO	NAME	MAT.	REQ
1	BASE	C. I.	1
2	JAW	C. I.	1
3	HAND SCREW	C.R.S.	1
4	SHOE	C.R.S.	1
5	JAW PLATE	C.R.S.	2
6	WEDGE	C.R.S.	1
7	COUPLING	C.R.S.	1
8	LINK	C.R.S.	1
9	FLAT HEAD SCREW	C.R.S.	2
10	MACHINE SCREW	M.S.	4
11	NO 7 TAPER PIN	M.S.	1

Chapter 15

INTERSECTIONS AND DEVELOPMENTS

The representation of common intersections, such as those between two plane surfaces, is drawn simply and involves little more than locating two or three points and "guessing in" the remainder of the line of intersection. An intersection between two geometric shapes, such as prisms, cylinders, cones, etc., is much more complex, however, and the exact perimeter, or contour, of the intersection must be accurately determined before the part shown in the drawing can be fabricated. In sheet-metal work especially, it is important to represent such intersections accurately so that the shopworker can transfer the proper dimensions from the drawing to the material he is working on.

The complete line of intersection between two geometric shapes is formed by a series of points located at the intersection of lines lying on one surface with lines lying on the other. The lines are called *elements*. The selection, placement, and method of producing these elements are of prime importance in enabling the draftsman to represent complicated intersections quickly and easily.

15-1. Intersection of two prisms. Figure 15-1 shows two prisms that are to intersect in the general manner illustrated. It is necessary to find the exact line of intersection between them before their surfaces can be developed. In Step I, top view, the intersection points *A, C,* and *E* of the edges can be noted by inspection. From the top view, these points are projected down into the front view to their proper positions on the same straight-line elements that form the edges of the rectangular prism. In Step II, point *H* (where line *HG* of the rectangular prism pierces the upper base of the triangular prism) is found by first passing an imaginary cutting plane perpendicular to the top view, containing the line *HG,* and intersecting the triangular surface *JKL* in the line 1-2. The imaginary cutting plane is called a line projecting plane because it is passed perpendicular to the plane of projection and projects (or appears) as a line or edge in that plane of projection. The line of intesection (line 1-2) between the line-projecting plane and the triangular plane *JKL* is projected into the front view. It will be noted that in the front view the line *GH* that lies in the line-projecting plane pierces *JKL* at the point *H* on the line of intersection 1-2 of the imaginary and given planes. The point *H* is now projected back to line 1-2 in the top view to establish the exact point of intersection of line *GH* in that view. This procedure is the proper method of establishing the location of the piercing point of any line representing an edge or element that intersects an inclined plane surface.

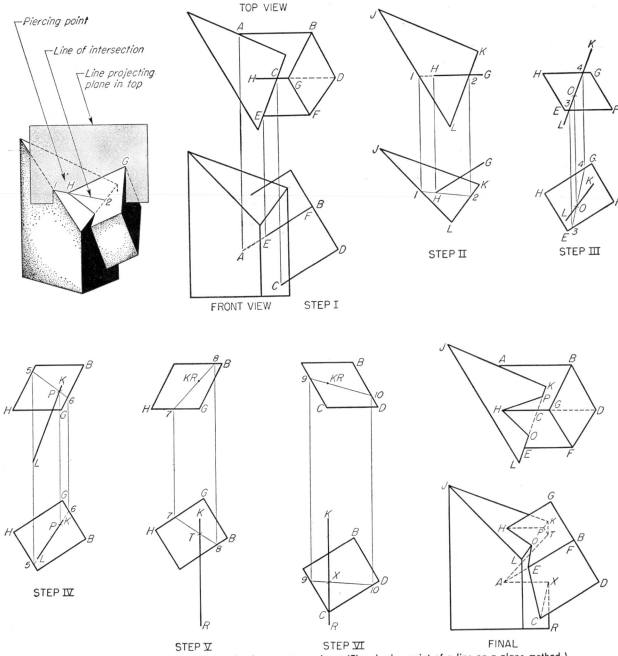

Fig. 15-1. Finding the line of intersection between two prisms. (The piercing point of a line on a plane method.)

Step III illustrates the manner in which line KL of the triangular plane intersects plane $EFGH$ of the rectangular prism. An imaginary line-projecting plane containing the line KL is passed perpendicularly in the top view, where its intersection with $EFGH$ is seen to be line 3-4. In the front view the projection of 3-4 shows that KL pierces $EFGH$ at O. The point O is projected to the top view to establish both views of the piercing point. In Step IV the imaginary line-projecting plane containing KL is passed in the front view where it intersects plane BGH in line 5-6. The procedure outlined in the previous steps is followed to establish point P as the piercing point of KL on this plane.

To find where line KR pierces plane BGH (see Step V), the imaginary line-projecting plane is passed perpendicularly through the point projection of *KR* in the top view. The line of intersection between the two planes is 7-8. In the front view, *T* locates the piercing point of *KR* with *BGH*. The method of establishing the point at which *KR* pierces plane *BCD* is shown in Step VI. The imaginary line-projecting plane is passed through the point projection of *KR* in the top view, where it intersects the given plane in line 9-10. Line 9-10 is projected to the front view and is intersected by *KR* at point *X*, which is the piercing point of *KR* in the plane *BCD*. This determines the final piercing point, and the complete line of intersection of the two prisms is simply established by joining the piercing points with straight lines.

15-2. Intersection of a pyramid and a prism.

The procedure for finding the intersection of a pyramid and a prism is, in general, the same as that used to find the intersection of two prisms. In Fig. 15-2 a line-projecting plane containing line *AO* is passed perpendicular to the front view through the base and apex of the pyramid and through the point projection *BC* of the triangular prism. Line *AO* and point *C* are projected to the top view to establish the exact point of intersection *C* in that view. The other points are located in the same manner and are connected by straight lines to determine the complete line of intersection. When pyramids and cones appear in intersection problems, the line-projecting planes that produce the elements on their surfaces should be passed through

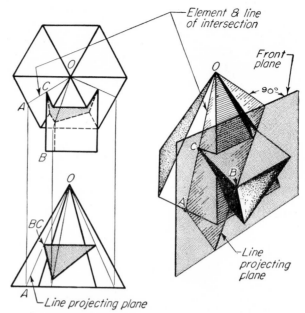

Fig. 15-2. Intersection of a pyramid and a prism.

their bases and apexes to permit positive location of the elements in the adjacent view.

15-3. Intersection of a cylinder and a prism (Fig. 15-3).

To secure the exact line of intersection of a cylinder and prism, pass the line-projecting planes through a right-section view that shows the cross section of the cylinder (perpendicular to its axis). Locate the elements cut by these planes on the surfaces of the prism and cylinder. The points of intersection of the elements lie on the line of intersection of the two forms. When a cylinder appears in an intersection problem, the line-projecting planes should be passed parallel to its axis.

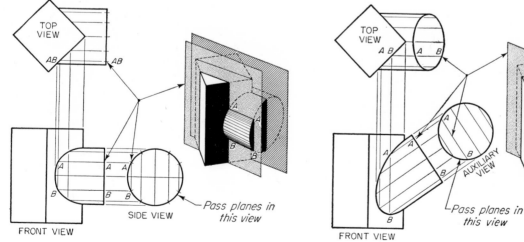

Fig. 15-3. Intersection of a cylinder and a prism.

PLANE IS PARALLEL TO AXES OF BOTH CYLINDERS

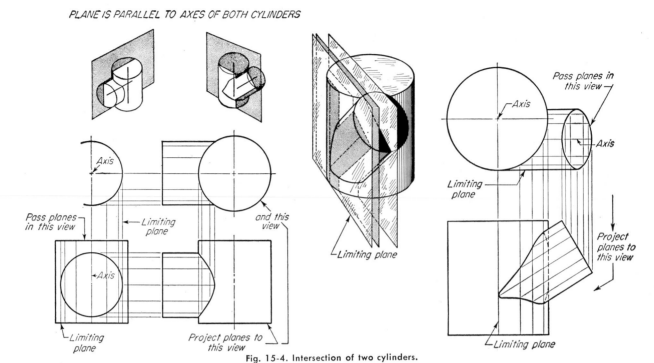

Fig. 15-4. Intersection of two cylinders.

15-4. Intersection of two cylinders (Fig. 15-4).

In order to find the line of intersection between two cylinders, line-projecting planes that cut elements in the surface of both cylinders are passed parallel to their axes. (A view allowing such planes to be passed should be found if not given.) The elements cut by these planes are then located on the surfaces of the cylinders. The intersections of the elements are points on the line of intersection of the cylinders. Limiting line-projecting planes are required in order to locate the extreme points on the line of intersection. Other line-projecting planes should be passed where the line of intersection appears to curve sharply or present an unusual contour. As many line-projecting planes as necessary may be used, provided that they are properly passed parallel to the axes of both cylinders.

15-5. Intersection of a plane and a right cone —conic sections.

The curve of intersection produced by passing a plane perpendicular to the axis of a cone is a circle (see Fig. 15-5a).

If a plane is passed oblique to the axis and it makes a greater angle with the axis than the elements of the cone, the resulting curve of intersection is an ellipse (Fig. 15-5b).

If a plane is passed parallel to the elements of a

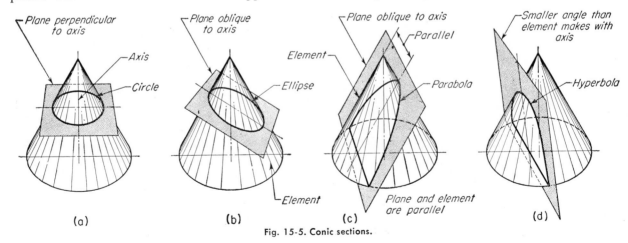

Fig. 15-5. Conic sections.

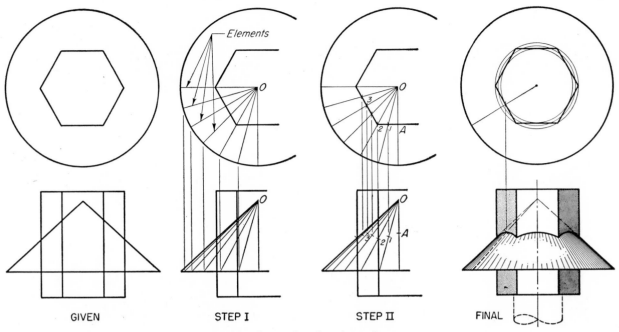

Fig. 15-6. Intersection of a prism and a cone.

cone, the curve of intersection is a parabola (Fig. 15-5c).

If a plane is passed parallel to the axis, or makes a smaller angle with the axis than the elements make, the curve of intersection is a hyperbola (Fig. 15-5d).

15-6. Intersection of a prism and a cone (Fig. 15-6). The line of intersection between the prism and the cone shown in Fig. 15-6 is made up of a series of hyperbolas, since the lateral surfaces of the prism are parallel to the axis of the cone. In the figure, the prism and cone are to intersect as shown. In Step I, pass the line-projecting planes through the apex and base of the cone in the top view and locate them in the front view. In Step II, by inspecting the top view, we note the piercing points of the elements with the sides of the prism along its perimeter. These points are projected to their proper position on the elements in the front view, where they locate the line of intersection of the cone and the prism. Points *A* and 3 are at the same height in the front view. The front view in the final step shows the true hyperbolic curves of the chamfered head of a bolt (which in practice is always shown by a series of circular arcs).

The final step also shows an alternate method of

finding the line of intersection. A series of circles of the cone intersecting and becoming tangent to the prism at selected points are located in the top view, which in turn can be projected to the same circles (cutting planes seen as parallel line projections) in the front view. The location of these points on the line projections produces the required line of intersection.

15-7. Intersection of a cone and a cylinder (Fig. 15-7). To find the line of intersection of a cone and a cylinder, the imaginary cutting planes should be passed through the vertex and base of the cone and parallel to the axis of the cylinder so as to cut the elements in the surfaces of both forms. A view allowing such planes to be passed should be found if not given. A plane creating extreme elements is necessary to locate the boundary point *A* on the line of intersection.

15-8. Developments. Cylinders, ducts, containers, and other similar forms are usually cut from flat metal sheets and then rolled or folded into the required shape. For this reason, the draftsman must represent on the drawing sheet the shape and dimensions of sheet-metal parts not only in their final form but also in their "developed," or "rolled-out," form. As applied to engineering drawing,

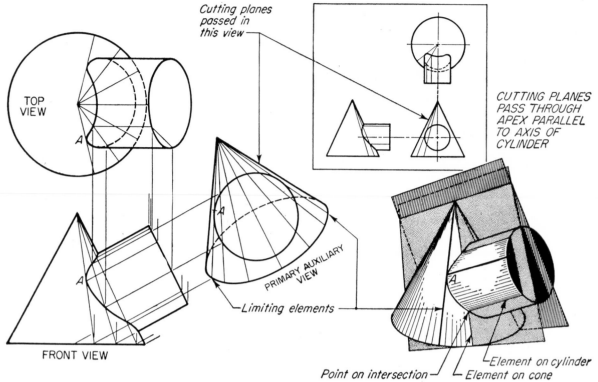

Cutting planes passed in this view

TOP VIEW

A

CUTTING PLANES PASS THROUGH APEX PARALLEL TO AXIS OF CYLINDER

PRIMARY AUXILIARY VIEW

Limiting elements

FRONT VIEW

Element on cylinder
Point on intersection — Element on cone

Fig. 15-7. Intersection of a cone and a cylinder.

therefore, the term "development" refers to the complete surface of an object laid out on a plane (see Fig. 15-8).

The development of the rectangular prism shown pictorially in Fig. 15-8 at (*a*) is simply a matter of opening it up as shown at (*b*) and spreading it out, as shown at (*c*). The inside surface is always placed face up, since the inside dimensions are usually the critical ones. In addition, this procedure simplifies the indication of fold lines, which mark where the metal should be folded in forming the object. The

orthographic view (*d*) shows each surface in its true size and shape joined to its neighboring surface by a common edge, or folding line.

15-9. Development of a hexagonal prism. In the development of the hexagonal prism shown in Fig. 15-9, each side is placed beside its neighbor in its true shape and size and is spread out, inside face up, along a *stretch-out line*, which is equivalent to the perimeter of the base of the prism. Note that dimension *A* of each side is taken from the front view and *B* from the top.

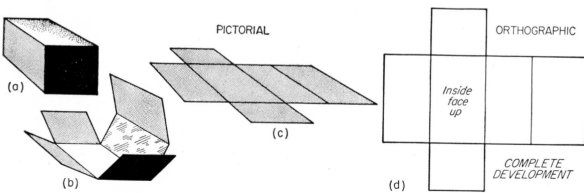

PICTORIAL

ORTHOGRAPHIC

(a)

(c)

Inside face up

(b)

(d)

COMPLETE DEVELOPMENT

Fig. 15-8. Development of a rectangular prism.

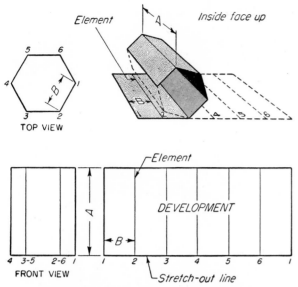

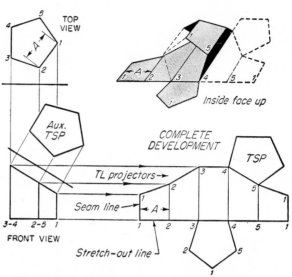

Fig. 15-9. Development of a hexagonal prism.

Fig. 15-10. Development of a truncated pentagonal prism.

15-10. Development of a truncated pentagonal prism. A plane that cuts all elements of the lateral surfaces of any geometric object is said to *truncate* the form. A pentagonal prism that has been truncated is shown in Fig. 15-10. The front and top views and a true-shape auxiliary projection of the top base are given, and it is desired to make a development of the form. On the stretch-out line, which is equal to the perimeter of the base, mark off the distances 1-2, 2-3, etc., shown in the top view. The true lengths of the edges of the sides are seen in the front view and may be either marked off on perpendiculars erected at points 1 to 5 or projected directly from the front view to the development. The true shape of the lower base is taken from the top view and attached to the lateral development; the true shape of the upper base is the auxiliary projection and it is also attached to the lateral development as shown in the figure. In commercial practice, the bases are always attached to the shortest edges of a development in order to save time and materials in making the seams.

15-11. Development of a right cylinder. If the elements lying on the lateral surface of a circular cylinder are perpendicular to a right section parallel to the bases, the cylinder is said to be a right cylinder. The development of the lateral surface of the right cylinder shown in Fig. 15-11 has a

stretch-out line equal to the circumference of a base (as seen in the top view) and a width equal to the height of an element (as seen in the front view).

15-12. Development of a truncated right cylinder. A truncated cylinder is one in which all the lateral elements have been severed by a cutting plane passed in any direction through the cylinder. In Fig. 15-12, the top view of the cylinder is divided into 12 (or 16 or 24) parts, and the points are projected as elements on the lateral surface seen in the front view. The stretch-out line is taken along the intersection of a plane passed perpendicular to the axis and is equal in length to the

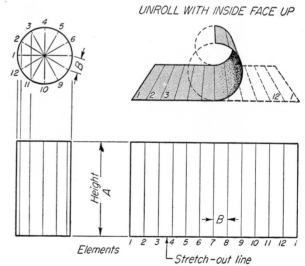

Fig. 15-11. Development of a right cylinder.

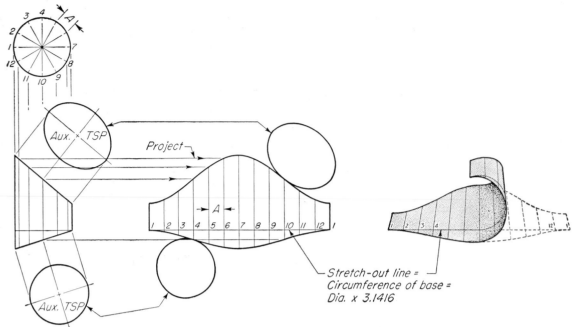

Fig. 15-12. Development of a truncated right cylinder.

circumference of the cylinder. The lengths of the lateral elements are measured or projected from the front view. They are cut off at their true lengths as they extend above and below the stretch-out line. A french curve is used to join the points to complete the lateral development. The auxiliary true-shape projections of the upper and lower bases may be attached to the development of the lateral surface as shown.

A practical application of the principles involved in the development of a truncated right cylinder is seen in the development of the five-piece elbow shown in Fig. 15-13. In order to produce the elbow from sheet metal, the surfaces must be developable; that is, they must lay out flat on a plane surface. Since it is obviously impossible to make a single development for the entire surface of the elbow, it should be divided into a convenient number of

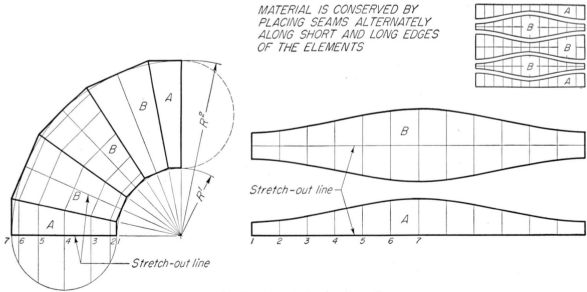

Fig. 15-13. Development of a five-piece elbow.

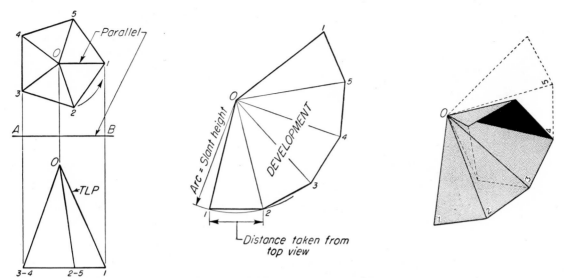

Fig. 15-14. Development of a right pyramid.

smaller segments that are developable which can be joined together in the shop to make the desired piece. In this case, the five segments that make up the elbow are all truncated right cylinders. It will also be noted that the two pieces at the extremities are identical, as are the three intermediate pieces. To develop the segments, first draw the throat radius R^1 and the heel radius R^2. Divide the base into 12, 16, or 24 parts. In this case, the base is divided into 12 parts, 6 of which are visible. Project the points of division as elements on the lateral surface of the five radially proportioned pieces of the elbow. Then draw the stretch-out lines as shown in the figure and at points 1, 2, 3, etc., measure off or project the lengths of the lateral elements. To conserve material, the patterns for the segments are laid out on the flat metal as shown at the upper right corner of the illustration. The shape of the developed segments remains the same, but the seams are placed alternately along the long and short elements of the pieces.

15-13. Development of a right pyramid. A right pyramid is one in which the altitude (a perpendicular from the apex to the base) coincides with the axis (a straight line connecting the apex with the mid-point of the base). The development of a right pyramid consists of drawing the true surface of each side and attaching them together at their edges which intersect at the apex. In Fig.

15-14, the top view shows the true lengths of the edges of the base (distances 1-2, 2-3, etc.). The front view shows the true length of the edge along the sides (distance O-1). From point O (corresponding to the apex), and with a radius equal to the true length of the edge of a side (O-1), strike an arc as shown in the figure. On this arc step off the distances 1-2, 2-3, etc., taken from the top view, and join the points by straight lines. The points are then connected to O to show the elements along which the development is folded to shape the lateral surface of the pyramid.

15-14. Development of a truncated pyramid. A truncated right pyramid is developed in the manner described in Sec. 15-13, except that the true lengths of the edges of the sides (all of which are not evident by inspecting the given views) are found by revolving them parallel to the reference line in the top view and projecting the revolved positions to the front view. In the front view of Fig. 15-15, the edge O-1 is parallel to the projection or picture plane and therefore shows in its true length. With this distance as a radius, strike an arc from point O in the development to form the stretch-out line. On this line mark off the chords 1-2, 2-3, etc., which are the true lengths along the base taken from the top view. Now draw the elements intersecting at the apex O. Along these elements step off the true lengths of the sides 1-6, 2-7, 3-8, etc., as

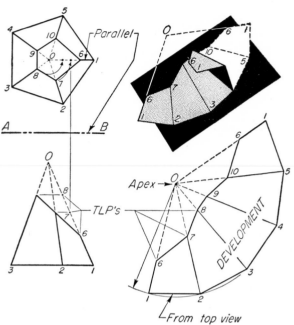

GET TRUE LENGTHS OF ELEMENTS BY REVOLUTION

Fig. 15-15. Development of a truncated pyramid.

to strike an arc from the apex O. The exact extent of the stretch-out line may be computed from the formula given, or the perimeter of the base may be marked off by first dividing the perimeter into a convenient number of segments in the top view and then stepping off these distances with dividers on the stretch-out line.

15-16. Development of the lateral surface of a truncated right cone. In developing a truncated right cone (Fig. 15-17), the first steps are exactly the same as those described in Sec. 15-15. Find the true lengths of the elements by revolving them parallel to the front view, where their projections will show as true lengths along the extreme element O-1. Then mark off the true-length elements on lines O-1, O-2, etc., in the development. An irregular curve is used to draw the curve through the points A, B, C, D, etc., of the development.

15-17. True-length diagram. For the more complicated developments, it is helpful to prepare a separate true-length diagram from which the true lengths of elements can be measured with a pair of dividers and transferred to the progressing development. Figure 15-18 illustrates two ways in which independent true-length projection diagrams may be drawn. The triangular solid with its vertex at O is given in the top and front views. By inspection it

found by revolving the lines in the top view and projecting to the front view. Join points 6, 7, 8, etc., with straight lines to complete the development.

15-15. Development of a right cone. In the development of the right cone shown in Fig. 15-16, the slant height of the cone O-1 is used as a radius

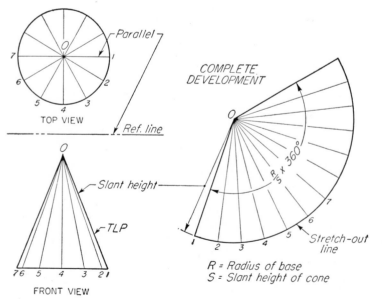

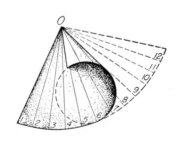

R = Radius of base
S = Slant height of cone

Fig. 15-16. Development of a right cone.

can be seen that the lengths of the edges AB, BC, and CA of the triangular base show in their true lengths in the top view, and so no diagram is needed for them. OA, OB, and OC, however, are not seen in their true length in either of the given views. Therefore, a separate diagram is constructed to show these lines in their true lengths.

One method of finding the true lengths of the lines is based on the principle of *revolution*. In Fig. 15-18a, with O^1 as a center, revolve the lines O^1A^1, O^1B^1, and O^1C^1 until they lie parallel to a frontal reference line drawn through O^1, as shown in the top view. Then project the points vertically down to intersect with lines projected from the front view (points A^2, B^2, and C^2) toward the right parallel to the reference line. The intersections determine the location of the points A, B, and C on the true-length projections drawn from these points through the vertex O^2 in the front view.

If insufficient space is available to allow the revolution procedure just described, it may be necessary to set up a different type of true-length diagram known as the *hypotenuse diagram*. The procedure for developing this type of diagram is illustrated in Fig. 15-18b, and is based on the fact that the true length of each line is the hypotenuse of a triangle in

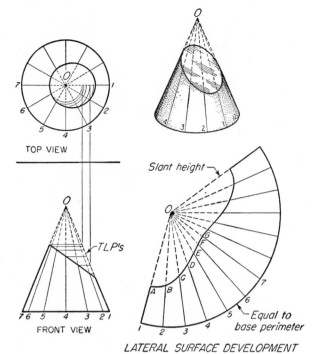

LATERAL SURFACE DEVELOPMENT

Fig. 15-17. Development of the lateral surface of a truncated right cone.

which the altitude is the height of the line in the front view and the base is the length of the projection of the line in the top view. For instance, in triangle A^2O^2P, O^2P is the vertical height of A^2O^2 seen in the front view, the base PA is measured from the top-view projection of the line O^1A^1, and the

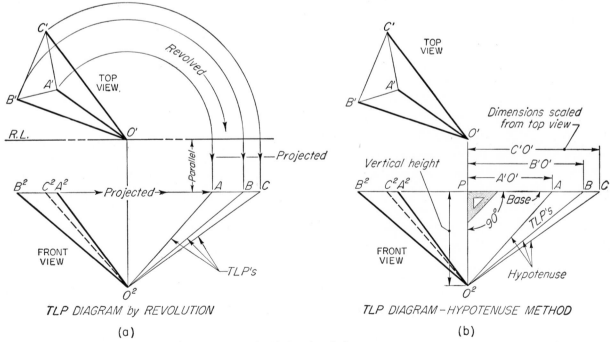

TLP DIAGRAM by REVOLUTION

(a)

TLP DIAGRAM – HYPOTENUSE METHOD

(b)

Fig. 15-18. True length diagrams.

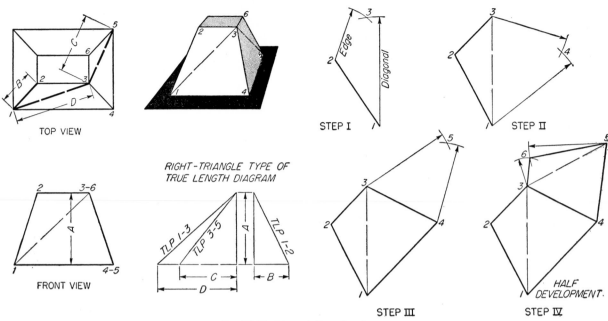

TOP VIEW

RIGHT-TRIANGLE TYPE OF
TRUE LENGTH DIAGRAM

FRONT VIEW

STEP I

STEP II

STEP III

HALF
DEVELOPMENT

STEP IV

Fig. 15-19. Triangulation of surfaces.

hypotenuse O^2A of the right triangle AO^2P seen in the projection is the true-length projection of the line OA.

15-18. Development by triangulation. The lateral surfaces of the form shown in Fig. 15-19 can be developed by arranging suitable triangles on the surface and laying them out side by side to form the development. Such a procedure is called *triangulation*. The true length of each element is determined by the hypotenuse principle discussed in Sec. 15-17, in which it was shown that the true-length projection of an element is the hypotenuse of a right triangle in which one leg is equal to the length of the projection of the line as seen in the top view and the other leg is the altitude of the line as seen in the front view.

In the illustration, the oblique surfaces 1-2-3-4 and 3-4-5-6 are divided into separate, easily developable triangles by the lines 1-3 and 3-5. The true lengths of the lines are determined by the hypotenuse method, as shown, and the required half development is laid out as follows. In Step I, start by laying out edge 1-2 equal to its length taken from the true-length diagram. Then, with a radius equal to the true length of the diagonal 1-3 and with point 1 as a center, strike an arc. Strike another arc intersecting the first by taking the true

distance of 2-3 from the top view and using 2 as the center. The intersection of the arcs determines the location of point 3. In Step II, the procedure is similar, and the two triangles with the diagonal 1-3 as a common side outline the true shape of the lateral side 1-2-3-4 of the pyramid. Steps III and IV continue this process to establish the complete half development.

15-19. Development of an oblique cone. The triangulation method is generally used for the development of an oblique cone. In Fig. 15-20 the front and top views of the cone are shown. The true-shape projection of the base in the top view is divided into a convenient number of parts, and the elements O-1, O-2, etc., are drawn in the top view and projected to the front view. The true-length projections of the elements are then found by revolution. The triangles formed by the elements are laid out consecutively in their true shapes, being joined at the elements that form common edges. Although the final development is only a close approximation of the surface of the cone, it satisfies commercial requirements.

15-20. Development of transition pieces. A transition piece is a form that connects openings of different shapes or different sizes. The transition piece shown in Fig. 15-21 connects two circular

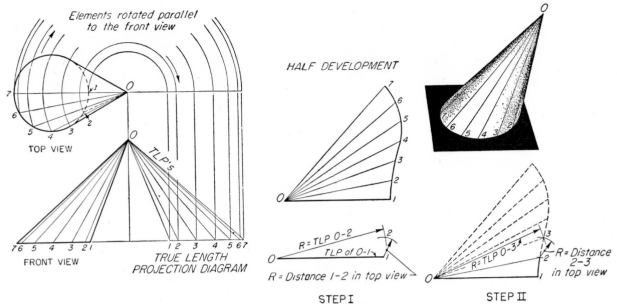

Fig. 15-20. Development of an oblique cone.

pipes of different diameters whose axes intersect. Although this piece is not the frustum of an oblique cone, its development may still be most practically accomplished by triangulation. In triangulating the surfaces, the same number of triangles (in proper projection from one view to the other) are laid out

in both the top and front views. It should also be noted that, since the upper base is not parallel to the plane of projection for the top or front views, the true distances 1-4, 4-6, etc., are taken from the true-shape auxiliary view.

The transition piece shown in Fig. 15-22 con-

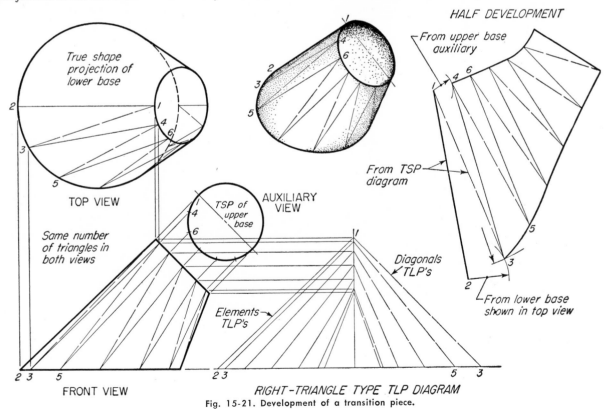

Fig. 15-21. Development of a transition piece.

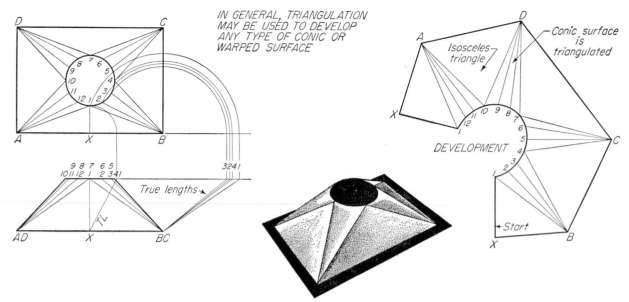

IN GENERAL, TRIANGULATION
MAY BE USED TO DEVELOP
ANY TYPE OF CONIC OR
WARPED SURFACE

Fig. 15-22. Development of a transition piece.

nects a circular pipe with a rectangular duct. A study of the pictorial indicates that the surface may be broken down into four isosceles triangles whose bases connect with the rectangular duct and four conic surfaces whose upper edges form the circle of

connection with the circular pipe. The isosceles triangles are developed by using their outlining edges, and the conic surfaces are triangulated. The length *BX* of the isosceles triangle is taken directly from the top or front views, and a true-length diagram

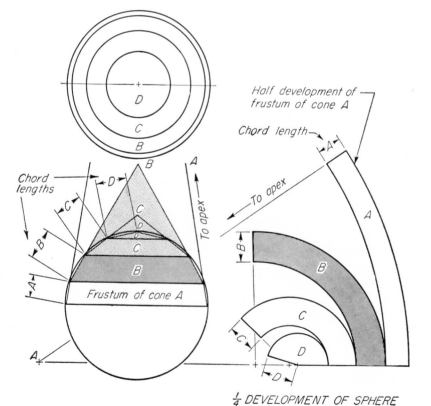

Fig. 15-23. Development of the surface of a sphere.

is produced to show the other required true lengths. Start the development with line 1-X and attach the triangulated portions along their common numbered elements in the regular order.

15-21. Development of the surface of a sphere. The surface of a sphere is a double-curved surface, that is, it is generated by a curved line and contains no straight-line elements. Such surfaces are not, strictly speaking, developable; however, their developments may be approximated by dividing the surfaces into smaller segments that are developable. Accordingly, two different ways in which a sphere may be developed approximately are given here.

In Fig. 15-23, the surface of the sphere has been cut by a series of parallel planes. Each section is considered to be part of the surface of an imaginary cone whose apex may be found by extending the sides (chords). The development pictured is one-quarter of the surface of the sphere (or a half development of the frustums of the cones).

In Fig. 15-24, a series of vertical planes is passed through the axis in the top view cutting meridian

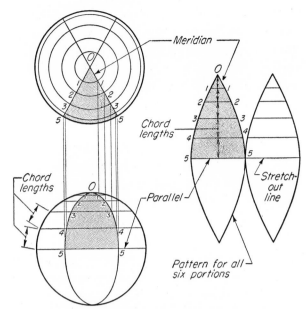

Fig. 15-24. Development of the surface of a sphere.

lines on the surface. Parallel planes are passed perpendicular to the axis in the front view and are projected to, and shown as circles in the top view. The development shows the true shapes of each of the small divisions obtained by rectifying the arcs

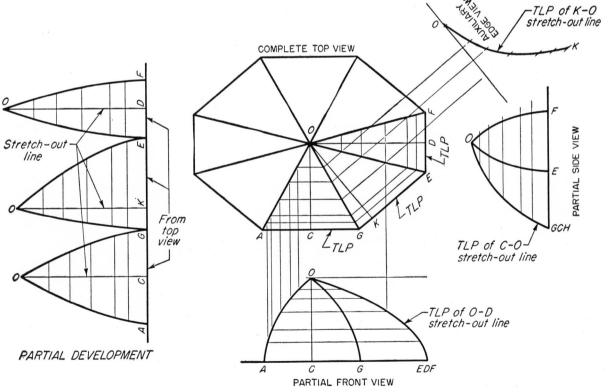

Fig. 15-25. Development of an octagonal dome.

on the circumference of the meridians (from front view) and of the arcs of the circles (from top view). After the pattern of one of the large divisions has been developed, it may be used as a replica for the remaining divisions, which should be placed on a stretch-out line equal to the circumference of the sphere.

15-22. Development of an octagonal dome. It is extremely important for the draftsman to know which procedure to apply in laying out the development for a particular type of surface. In the octagonal dome shown in Fig. 15-25, for example, each piece is a portion of a cylinder, and the method used to develop the cylinder shown in Fig. 15-12 is applicable here (with several additional steps being required in this case).

A series of parallel planes is passed in the front view which cut elements in the surface. These in turn are projected to show in their true lengths in the top view. The true length of the stretch-out line *OC* for surface *AOG* is seen in the side view; the true length of the stretch-out line *OD* for surface *EOF* is seen in the front view. The stretch-out line *KO* for surface *EOG* is found by passing a plane through *O* perpendicular to the elements of that surface in the top view and obtaining its true-length projection in the auxiliary. Rectifying the arcs of the stretch-out lines and stepping off the points of the surfaces on either side of them result in the portion of the development shown at the left in the illustration. These may be used as patterns for the remaining similar surfaces.

PROBLEMS

The problems that follow have been especially selected to offer practice in the application of the principles of intersections and developments. It is suggested that a few of the more complicated objects be drawn and their patterns cut out as a check against the accuracy of the students' work. All the objects may be assumed to be hollow and constructed of thin metal. The drawings may be made on 8½- by 11-in. or 11- by 17-in. sheets, depending on the scale

selected. Numbering the points of the objects will simplify the drafting procedure.

15-1 and 15-2. Find the line of intersection between the prisms. Show correct visibility of lines. Draw the development of the surfaces on another sheet.

15-3 to 15-8. Find the line of intersection between the objects shown. Show correct visibility of lines. The developments are to be shown on another sheet. The squares are ¼ in.

15-9 to 15-11. Show the line of intersection of the given transition pieces. Show the developments on the same sheet. Sheet size, 11 by 17 in.

15-12 to 15-21. Develop the lateral surfaces of the given objects. The squares are ¼ in.

15-22. Develop the surface of the given object. The isometric scale gives points 1/16 in. apart.

15-23 to 15-25. Develop the lateral surfaces of the given objects. The scale shows points ¼ in. apart.

15-26 and 15-27. Develop the lateral surfaces of the given objects. The scale shows points 1/16 in. apart.

15-28 and 15-29. Develop the lateral surfaces of the given objects. The scale shows points ¼ in. apart.

15-30 and 15-31. Develop the lateral surfaces of the forms shown.

15-32 to 15-37. Show the developments of the given transition pieces. Each pattern should be shown on an 11- by 17-in. sheet.

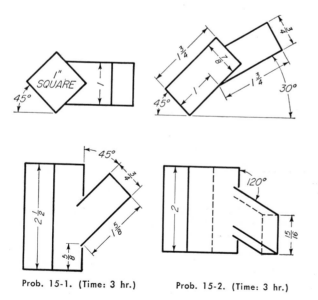

Prob. 15-1. (Time: 3 hr.)   Prob. 15-2. (Time: 3 hr.)

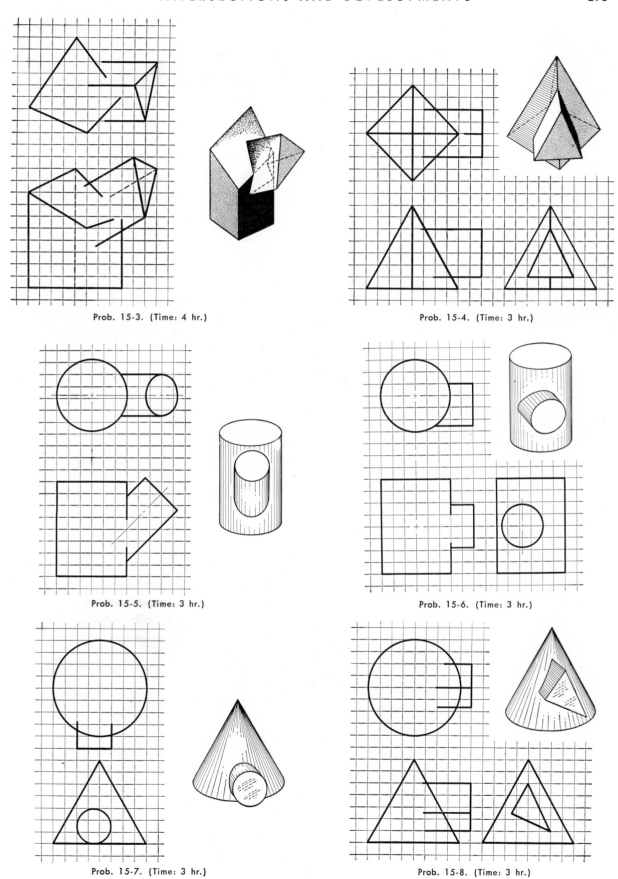

Prob. 15-3. (Time: 4 hr.)

Prob. 15-4. (Time: 3 hr.)

Prob. 15-5. (Time: 3 hr.)

Prob. 15-6. (Time: 3 hr.)

Prob. 15-7. (Time: 3 hr.)

Prob. 15-8. (Time: 3 hr.)

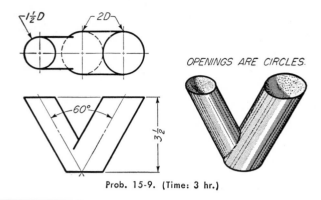

OPENINGS ARE CIRCLES.

Prob. 15-9. (Time: 3 hr.)

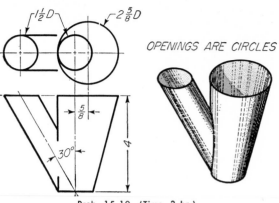

OPENINGS ARE CIRCLES

Prob. 15-10. (Time: 3 hr.)

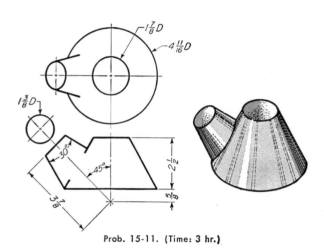

Prob. 15-11. (Time: 3 hr.)

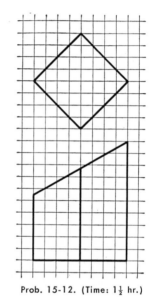

Prob. 15-12. (Time: 1½ hr.)

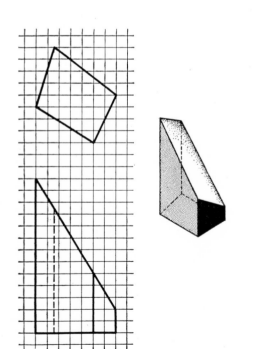

Prob. 15-13. (Time: 1½ hr.)

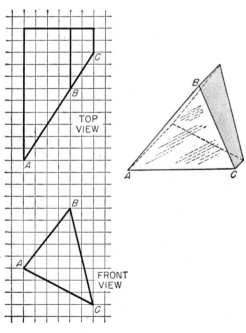

TOP VIEW

FRONT VIEW

Prob. 15-14. (Time: 1½ hr.)

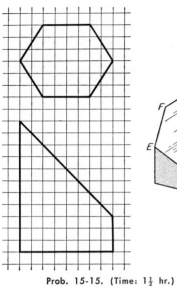

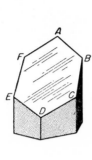

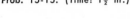

Prob. 15-15. (Time: 1½ hr.)

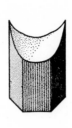

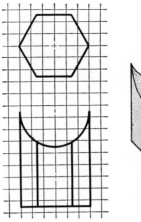

Prob. 15-16. (Time: 2 hr.)

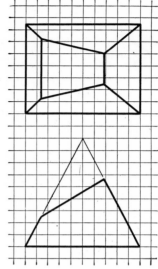

Prob. 15-17. (Time: 2 hr.)

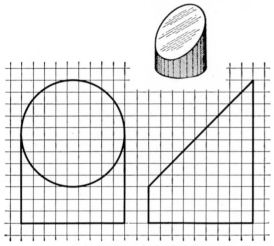

Prob. 15-18. (Time: 1½ hr.)

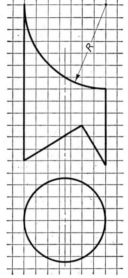

Prob. 15-19. (Time: 2 hr.)

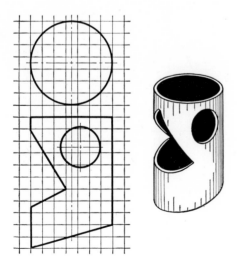

Prob. 15-20. (Time: 2½ hr.)

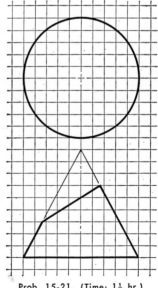

Prob. 15-21. (Time: 1½ hr.)

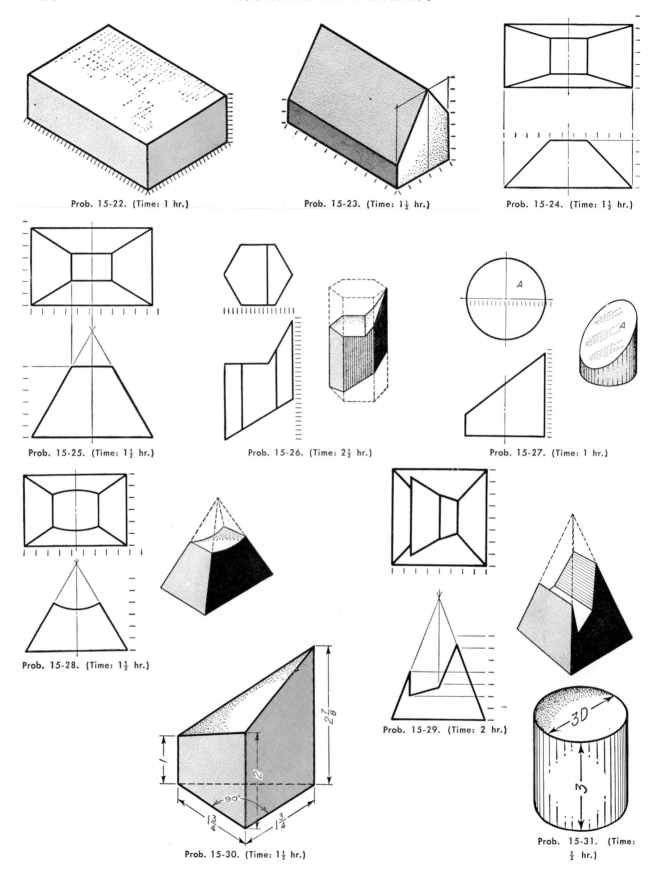

Prob. 15-22. (Time: 1 hr.)

Prob. 15-23. (Time: 1½ hr.)

Prob. 15-24. (Time: 1½ hr.)

Prob. 15-25. (Time: 1½ hr.)

Prob. 15-26. (Time: 2½ hr.)

Prob. 15-27. (Time: 1 hr.)

Prob. 15-28. (Time: 1½ hr.)

Prob. 15-29. (Time: 2 hr.)

Prob. 15-30. (Time: 1½ hr.)

Prob. 15-31. (Time: ½ hr.)

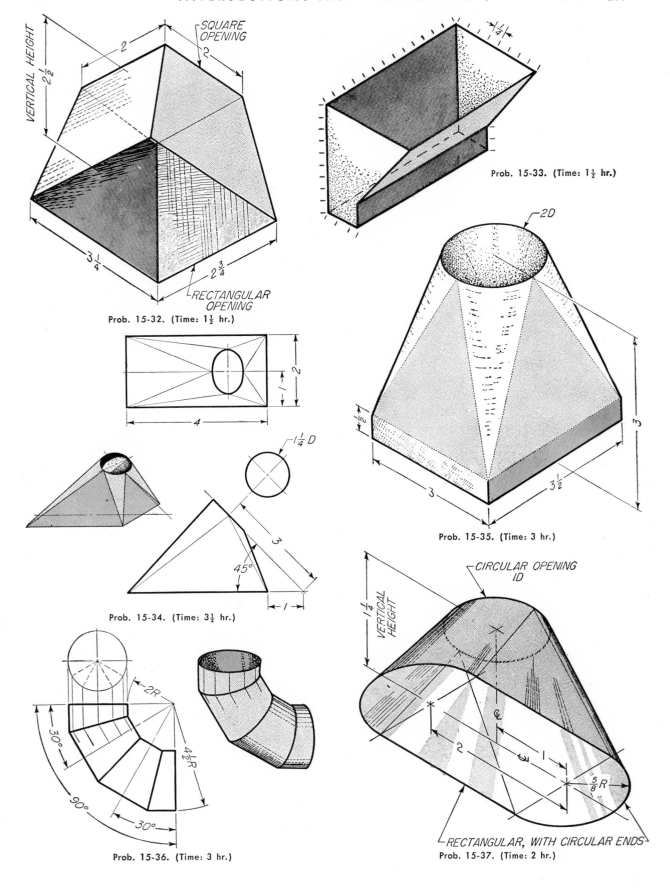

VERTICAL HEIGHT
$2\frac{1}{2}$

SQUARE OPENING
2
2

$3\frac{1}{4}$
$2\frac{3}{4}$

RECTANGULAR OPENING

Prob. 15-32. (Time: $1\frac{1}{2}$ hr.)

2
4

$1\frac{1}{4}$ D
3
45°
1

Prob. 15-34. (Time: $3\frac{1}{2}$ hr.)

Prob. 15-33. (Time: $1\frac{1}{2}$ hr.)

2D

$\frac{1}{2}$
3
3
$3\frac{1}{2}$
3

Prob. 15-35. (Time: 3 hr.)

2R
30°
$4\frac{1}{2}R$
90°
30°

Prob. 15-36. (Time: 3 hr.)

CIRCULAR OPENING ID

VERTICAL HEIGHT
$1\frac{1}{4}$

2
1
$\frac{5}{8}R$

RECTANGULAR, WITH CIRCULAR ENDS
Prob. 15-37. (Time: 2 hr.)

Chapter 16

CAMS AND GEARS

16-1. Cams. A cam is a machine part that produces a continuously repeated rotary motion that is passed on by means of a "follower" to another part of the mechanism as an automatically repeated and timed motion or operation. Cams are fundamental units of automatic machines, such as stamping and shoe machines, screw machines, engines, etc. Typical cams and followers are shown in Fig. 16-1. Figure 16-2 shows a typical cam unit of an internal-combustion engine with an irregularly shaped plate cam mounted on a shaft and a reciprocating valve held in continuous contact with the cam by a spring.

16-2. Cam motions. The path of the motion of the follower lies in a plane perpendicular to the axis of the camshaft if the cam is a disk, plate, or a lever. When the cam is cylindrical, the follower moves in a plane parallel to and in the same general direction as the camshaft axis. The curved surface of a plate cam induces a predetermined motion in the follower. In almost all machine parts, the motion desired for the follower controls the characteristics and shape of the cam. Provided that the shape of a cam remains constant, however, the *kind* of motion imparted to the follower will be the same regardless of the size of the cam.

In order to draw a cam, we must first know its design requirements, that is, the sort of motion the follower must have to produce the desired motions in the mechanism. Follower motions are governed

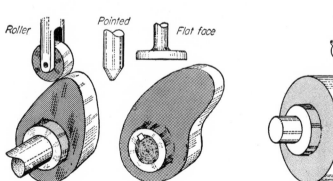

RADIAL CAMS and FOLLOWERS

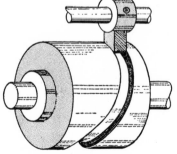

CYLINDRICAL CAM

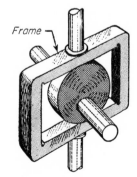

YOKE CAM

Fig. 16-1. Types of cams and followers.

by well-defined natural laws and may be represented graphically. A graphical representation of the movement of a follower is known as a *cam-curve diagram,* or *displacement diagram,* and it is usually desirable to construct such a diagram before attempting to draw the cam representation itself. A cam-curve diagram representing a particular series of follower motions can be developed according to a number of basic laws governing the specific follower motions involved.

Uniform motion, or constant velocity, is represented by a straight line in which the follower travels (or rises) equal distances in equal time intervals.

Constant acceleration is fundamentally the same motion as that of a freely falling body, where the velocity increases with the distance traveled. Decelerated motion is the exact opposite of acceleration and is often used to bring the follower to a gentle stop just before it reaches a period in which the position of the follower remains unchanged. This is called "a period of dwell" (see Fig. 16-6). Accelerated and decelerated motions used together are commonly known as gravity motion.

In simple harmonic motion the maximum velocity is reached at the mid-point of the travel, with the velocity being zero at both ends. It may be likened to the swing of a pendulum obeying the trigonometric sine law.

16-3. Drawing a single-motion diagram. *Constant velocity, Fig. 16-3a.* On the ordinate (the vertical scale) lay off the rise of the follower to either the true or a scaled height. When suitable, the true height should be used. Divide the ordinate into a number of equal parts (six, for instance). Select a convenient length (horizontally) for the abscissa (which shows the position of the cam) and divide this into the same number of parts. As the cam moves through one unit of rotation the follower rises one unit. The straight line of motion produced may be modified at the initial and final points of the motion to provide for smoother movement. The cam curve on the diagram is modified by striking an arc equal to one-third the follower rise at the beginning and final periods, as illustrated.

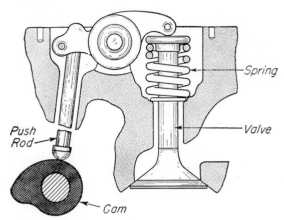

Fig. 16-2. Typical cam unit assembly.

Constant acceleration and deceleration, Fig. 16-3b. In the diagram, the lines representing the rise, or travel, and the cam position are divided into the same number of parts. However, since the distance traveled is proportional to the square of the time, the follower rise is made proportional in increments of 1, 3, 5, 7, 9, etc. Note that the change in velocity occurs at the mid-point of the curve of the motion, and the increments are reversed at this position.

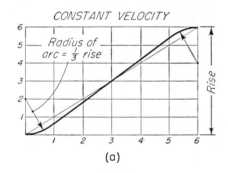

(a)

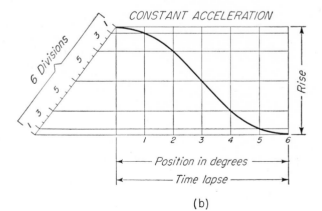

(b)

Fig. 16-3. Cam motion diagrams.

Harmonic motion, Fig. 16-4. The plotting of harmonic motion (sine curve) is shown in Fig. 16-4. The diameter of the semicircle represents the rise of the follower during this motion. Divide the semicircle and the base line into the same number of parts, as shown in Step I. Project the divisional

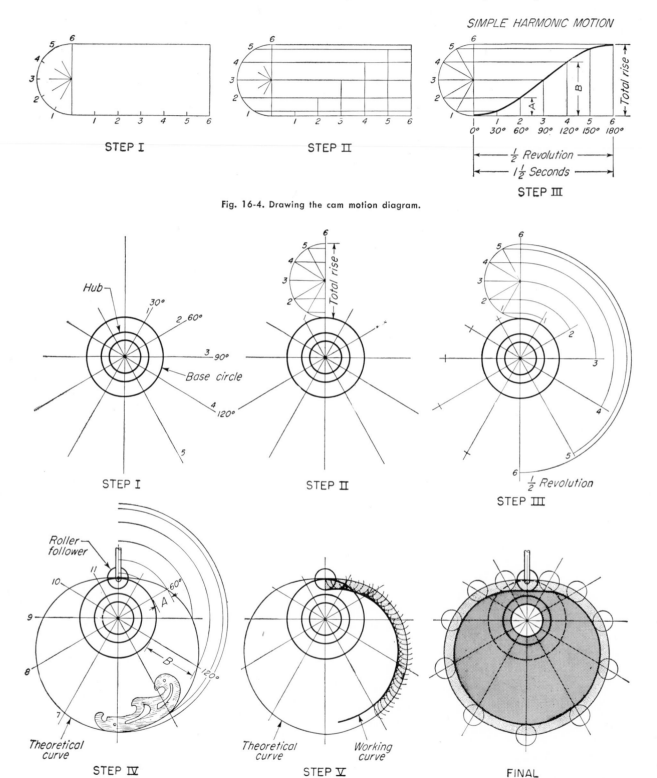

Fig. 16-4. Drawing the cam motion diagram.

Fig. 16-5. Drawing a plate-cam curve.

points to their intersections (Step II). With a french curve, draw a line through the intersections to show the follower motion, as shown in Step III. This motion is the one used in the drawing of the cam curve in Fig. 16-5.

16-4. Drawing a plate-cam curve. The principle involved in the drawing of the cam curve shown in Fig. 16-5 is the same for all types of plate cams (see Fig. 16-6, for example). First draw the circle representing the largest diameter of the hub.

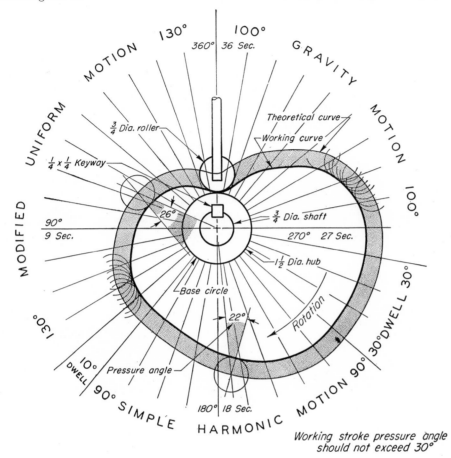

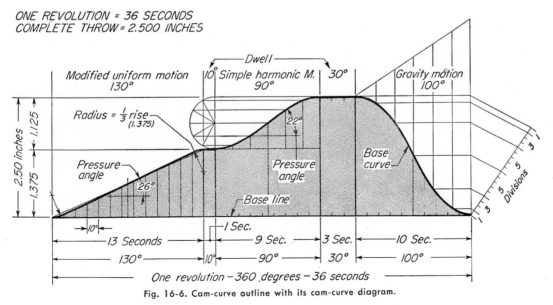

Fig. 16-6. Cam-curve outline with its cam-curve diagram.

Then draw the base circle, the radius of which indicates the nearest approach of the theoretical cam curve to the center of the camshaft. The size of the base circle and the rise of the follower control the size of the cam; the larger the base circle, the larger the cam.

After the hub and the base circles have been laid out, draw radial lines at regular degree intervals through the shaft center, as shown in Step I. These radial lines indicate the rotation of the cam in terms of degrees and time lapse. If the cam curve is designed from a single cam motion, as in this case, the simplest procedure is to transfer the rise to the position of the follower and project by revolving the positions of the follower as it rises (points 1 to 6) to the related degree and time-lapse positions on the radial lines, as shown in Steps II and III. Since this cam revolves one-half turn with this motion and finishes the cycle with the same motion, to complete the drawing of the theoretical cam curve it is only necessary to project the points showing the follower in contact with the cam to the remaining radial lines in reverse order.

The points could have been transferred directly from the motion diagram to the radial lines with dividers if desired. Note that distance A located on line 2 at 60° on the diagram of Fig. 16-4 checks

in length and position on the radial of the cam curve shown in Fig. 16-5. Distance B is located on 4 at 120° in both the diagram of Fig 16-4 and the radial of the cam curve. The cam outline formed by joining the points with a french curve would be that used with a pointed follower, and it is known as the theoretical curve. When adapted to a roller or flat-faced follower, the change in design is termed the working curve. When the follower is a roller, the working curve is developed by describing arcs of the roller radius from points on the theoretical curve and drawing the working curve tangent to the arcs (Step V). The heavily shaded portion in Step VI shows the cam shape for a roller follower, and the lighter portion shows the shape for a pointed follower.

16-5. Pressure angle. The pressure angle is the angle that the follower makes with the cam on the pressure stroke of the cycle. Although the pressure angle varies during the various stages of the cycle, for maximum efficiency the pressure angle should be in the neighborhood of 30°. The pressure angle is measured on the cam outline between a perpendicular drawn through the point of tangency of the follower with the cam and a center line drawn through the follower stem (see Fig. 16-6). It is usually indicated at the mid-point of a working-

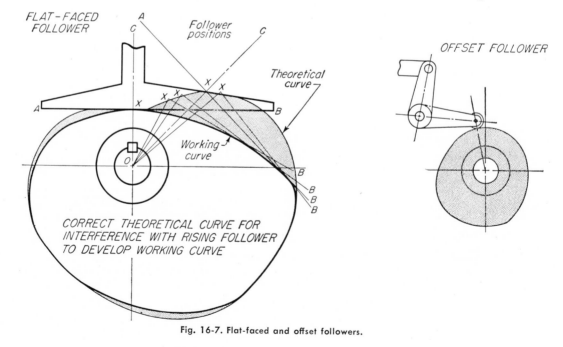

Fig. 16-7. Flat-faced and offset followers.

stroke motion on the displacement diagram. As noted above, in laying out a displacement diagram consisting of one or several motions, the complete rise of the follower is drawn full scale (where possible) and the base line is drawn to any convenient length. However, if the rise of the follower is shown full scale and if the length of the base line is drawn equal to the circumference of a circle whose radius is equal to the distance from the center of the axis of the camshaft to the mid-point of the follower rise, the resulting diagram represents the true development of the pitch surface of the cam.

The cam outline shown in Fig. 16-6 was prepared from the displacement diagram placed below it. This figure illustrates most of the graphic techniques required of the draftsman in the preparation of any cam drawing. With the proper modifications in the procedure, outlines for other types of cams, such as those with offset pivot or roller followers, reciprocating flat-faced followers, etc., may be produced (see Fig. 16-7).

16-6. Cam cutting. Face, peripheral, and cylindrical cams of ordinary size may be cut by outlining the cam curve on the metal blank, drilling holes around the outside of the outline, breaking off the excess metal, and filing to the outline. Cams may also be cut directly on milling machines with the aid of special attachments known as indexing mechanisms.

16-7. Gears. The prime function of gears is to transmit motion uniformly from one shaft to another. Gears are made by casting or cutting cast and forged steel, cast-iron alloys, bronze, brass, or impregnated fabrics and fibers. Figure 16-8 illustrates a number of typical gears. The elements of gear design are extraordinarily complex, and as a rule the draftsman is rarely concerned with the design requirements or with problems of material selection, of strength, fatigue, or wearing qualities. Also the recent adoption of simplified design calculations requiring fewer cutting tools or simpler casting procedures has helped to standardize the drafting procedure that is followed.

16-8. Gear terms and formulas. In discussing and drawing gears, the following terms and formulas will be used.

SPUR PINION & GEAR INTERNAL GEAR

HELICAL GEAR

Fig. 16-8. Typical gears.

Number of teeth (*N*). Multiply pitch diameter by diametral pitch or multiply pitch diameter by 3.1416 and divide the product by the circular pitch.

Circular pitch (*CP*). The distance measured on the arc of the pitch circle between like points on adjacent teeth. Divide 3.1416 by diametral pitch, or multiply pitch diameter by 3.1416 and divide product by number of teeth.

Diametral pitch (*DP*). The number of teeth on the gear for each inch of pitch diameter. Divide 3.1416 by circular pitch, or divide number of teeth by pitch diameter.

Pitch diameter (*PD*). Diameter of pitch circle. Divide number of teeth by diametral pitch, or multiply number of teeth by circular pitch and divide product by 3.1416.

Center distance (*CD*). Distance between the centers of two gears in mesh. Add number of teeth in gear and pinion and divide sum by twice the diametral pitch, or multiply sum of number of teeth in gear and pinion by circular pitch and divide product by 6.2832.

Addendum (*A*). The radial distance from top of teeth to pitch circle. Divide 1 by diametral pitch, or divide circular pitch by 3.1416 (for full-length teeth only).

Clearance (*C*). Radial distance from the top of a tooth to the bottom of the mating tooth space. 0.157 divided by the diametral pitch (for standard involute teeth).

Dedendum (*D*). Radial distance from bottom of tooth space to pitch circle. Add clearance to addendum.

Whole depth (*WD*). Radial distance between the dedendum and addendum circles. Add dedendum to addendum.

Circular thickness (*CT*). Thickness of tooth on pitch circle. Divide 1.5708 by diametral pitch, or divide circular pitch by 2.

Outside diameter (*OD*). Diameter of the addendum circle. Add 2 to the number of teeth and divide sum by diametral pitch for full-length teeth, or add 2 times the addendum to the pitch diameter.

Root diameter (*RD*). Diameter of the dedendum circle. Subtract 2 times the whole depth from the outside diameter.

Base circle diameter (*BCD*). Diameter of base circle. Multiply pitch diameter by cosine of pressure angle.

16-9. Drawing a spur gear. The three more or less standardized gear-tooth forms are the $14\frac{1}{2}°$ full-length tooth involute form, the 20° full-length tooth involute form, and the 20° stub tooth form.

1.- Draw pitch circles tangent on AB.
2.- Draw common tangent CD.
3.- Draw line of action EF through common tangent point.
4.- Draw perpendiculars from O and X to EF intersecting at 1 and 2.
5.- Draw base circles with radii O1 and X2.
6.- Draw addendum circle from calculations.
7.- Draw dedendum circle from calculations.
8.- Divide pitch circle of gear into 26 equal parts and that of pinion into 14 (for circular pitch).
9.- Bisect circular pitch on gear and pinion (no allowance for backlash)
10.- Develope involute for shape of teeth (portion between base and addendum circles). Draw radial line from base circle to dedendum circle to complete flank.

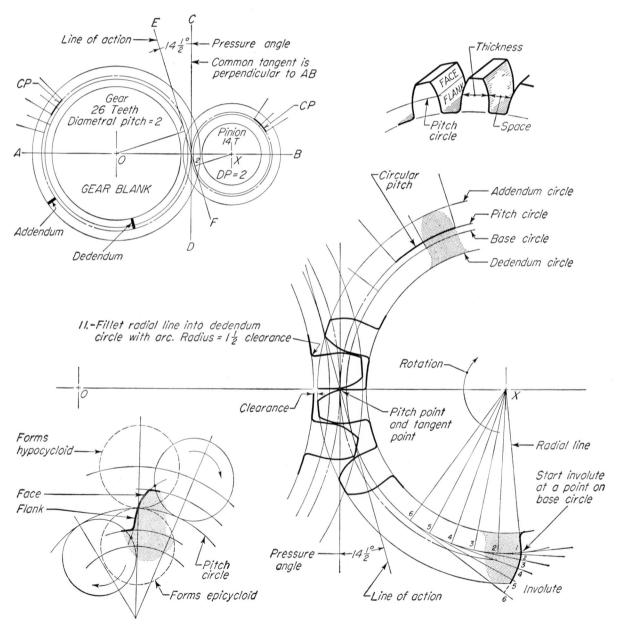

11.- Fillet radial line into dedendum circle with arc. Radius = 1½ clearance

For construction see chapter VI

Fig. 16-9. Drawing a spur gear and pinion.

In drawing a gear it is usually necessary to show only one or two teeth; gears are toothed completely only for display or presentation drawings. If the gear is to be cast, it is necessary to draw only the blank showing the addendum circle, the dedendum circle, the base circle and the outline of one tooth. For cut gears, only the blank and notes concerning the pitch and number of teeth need be given.

Either the cycloid or the involute may be used to develop the shape of the gear tooth. Gear teeth that are shaped by using portions of the involute or the cycloids fullfil the requirements of the fundamental law of toothed gearing, which is a problem of design and cannot suitably be discussed here. The axes of spur gears are parallel to each other. If one of a pair of gears in mesh is much larger than the other, the smaller of the two is called the pinion. The freedom between the teeth of two meshing gears is called *backlash* and is measured in decimal parts of an inch by a feeler gage placed between two meshed teeth when located at the tangent point of the pitch circles of both gears.

Figure 16-9 indicates a step-by-step procedure for laying out and drawing a gear and pinion. The gear has 26 teeth, the pinion has 14 teeth, the diametral pitch is 2, and the pressure angle is 14½°. Note that the circular pitch is the same in both gears, that the gear teeth are in the shape of an involute and start at the base circle, and that a gear must have an integral (whole number) of teeth. The involute shape is determined by the diameter of the base circle. Involutes generated from the same diameter base circles are identical in shape, and the teeth will look the same. Although the contour of the flank and the fillet of a gear are formed by the generating cutter during the manufacturing process, the draftsman may use the method suggested in the illustration for producing them on a drawing.

16-10. Dimensioning a spur gear. The dimensioning of a spur gear and its required cutting data are shown in Fig. 16-10. The chordal thickness is the thickness of the tooth at the pitch circle measured in a straight line. The corrected addendum is the distance from this chord to the top of the finished tooth, measured radially. In the cutting operation, these dimensions are carefully checked with a vernier specially made for measuring gear teeth. The width of the face of the tooth may be given but is not always required. This measurement should not be confused with the width of the gear itself, which is measured on the rim parallel to the axis of the gear.

16-11. Internal gears. The internal gear parts are the same as for an external gear with the exception that an internal diameter is introduced and the outside diameter is eliminated. The addendum and dedendum merely take reverse positions from those they occupy on an external gear (see Fig. 16-8).

16-12. The rack. A rack is a straight bar with teeth cut in it that engage the teeth of a spur gear. Usually the gear revolves and moves the rack in a straight line, although in some mechanisms this is

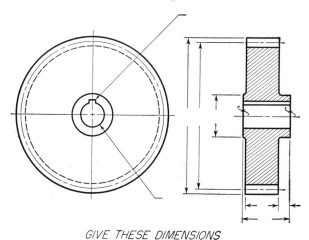

GIVE THESE DIMENSIONS
ON THE DRAWING

NO. OF TEETH	
DIAMETRAL PITCH	
TOOTH FORM	
WHOLE DEPTH	
CHORDAL THICKNESS	
CORRECTED ADDENDUM	

CUTTING DATA

COMPLETE AND SHOW CHART
ON DRAWING

Fig. 16-10. Dimensioning and cutting data for a spur gear.

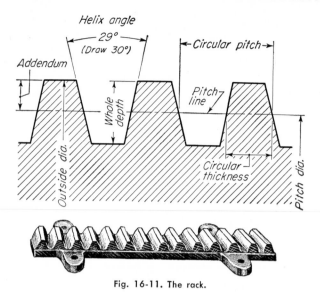

Fig. 16-11. The rack.

Addendum. Multiply circular pitch by 0.318, or divide 1.00 by the diametral pitch.

Dedendum. Divide 1.157 by the diametral pitch, or multiply 0.368 by the circular pitch.

Whole depth of tooth space. Divide 2.157 by the diametral pitch, or multiply 0.687 by the circular pitch.

Thickness of tooth at pitch line. Divide circular pitch by 2, or divide 1.571 by the diametral pitch.

Pitch-cone radius. Divide the pitch diameter by twice the sine of the pitch angle.

Addendum angle. Divide the addendum by the pitch-cone radius to find the trigonometric tangent of the angle.

Dedendum angle. Divide the dedendum by the pitch-cone radius to find the tangent of the angle.

Face angle. Add pitch angle and addendum angle.

Cutting angle. Subtract the dedendum angle from the pitch angle.

Angular addendum. Multiply the cosine of the pitch angle by the addendum.

Outside diameter. Add the pitch diameter and twice the angular addendum.

16-15. Drawing a pair of bevel gears. To draw a pair of bevel gears in mesh follow the procedure outlined in Fig. 16-12.

1. Draw the axis XX of one of the cones as shown in (a).

2. At any convenient distance draw the line DE perpendicular to XX.

3. Through any point O draw the line OE making the required pitch angle with XX.

4. Draw line OD making the same angle with XX to complete the pitch cone. OE corresponds to the pitch circle of a spur gear and is the pitch line between the two bevel gears. Distance OE is the pitch-cone radius. Angle EOF is the pitch angle of the pinion A.

5. To complete the drawing of the frustrum of cone A, draw GH parallel to DE at any desired slant height such as EH.

6. Through O draw axis YY making the required pitch angle with pitch line OE and the required shaft angle with axis XX of the pinion.

7. Through O draw OJ making the same angle with YY as OE.

8. From point E draw EJ perpendicular to YY, and from point H draw HK parallel to EJ to produce the frustum of the cone B. In revolution, B would revolve on its axis YY, A on its axis XX, and the two would come in contact along their common element, indicated by EH, of the pitch line OE. The pitch line, the pitch angles, and the

reversed so that the rack motivates the gear. In designing a rack, the problem is basically one of making the teeth of such shape that the gear will transmit its motion to the rack smoothly and efficiently. The pitch point of the gear is tangent to the pitch line of the rack when the two are in mesh. The thickness of the teeth, the addendum, and the depth of the teeth below the pitch line are calculated in the same manner as for the gear (see Fig. 16-11). In drawing a rack, the number of teeth, the diametral pitch, the linear pitch (equal to circular pitch of gear in mesh), and the whole depth must be specified.

16-13. Bevel gears. The axes of bevel gears (Fig. 6-12) intersect. Although their most common position is at 90°, they may make acute or obtuse angles with each other. Bevel gears in mesh may be likened to a pair of cone frustums whose surfaces are tangent and whose axes intersect at a common apex.

16-14. Terms and formulas. Refer to Fig 16-12 for the graphic representation of the following definitions and rules.

Pitch angle of pinion. Divide the number of teeth in the pinion by the number of teeth in the gear to find the trigonometric tangent of the angle.

Pitch angle of gear. Divide the number of teeth in the gear by the number of teeth in the pinion to find the tangent of the angle.

Pitch diameter. Multiply the number of teeth by the circular pitch and divide by 3.1416, or divide the number of teeth by the diametral pitch.

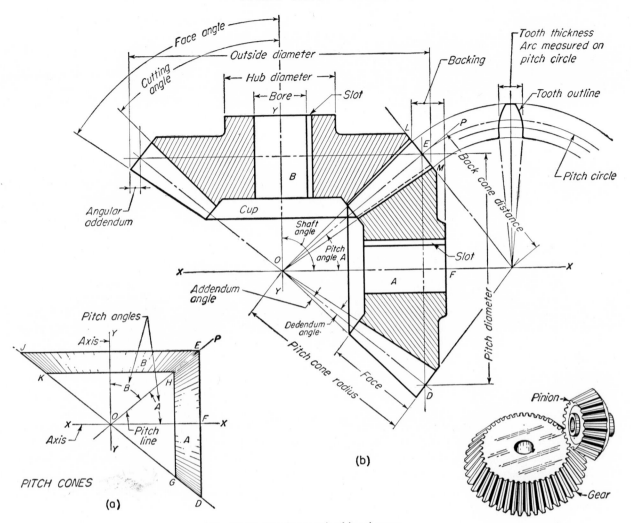

Fig. 16-12. Drawing a pair of bevel gears.

gear axes are fundamental lines in the laying out of bevel gears.

From computations or directly from the given data, draw in the addendum and dedendum angles to show the tooth top lines and the tooth base lines (full depth of tooth) for both gears (see Fig. 16-12b). *LM* is next drawn perpendicular to the pitch line *OE* to intersect the pitch-cone radius to give the outer edge of the tooth. The inner edge of the tooth is located from data giving the length of the tooth. The depth and clearance of the gear cup are also drawn from given data or computations. If the gear is to be cast, the tooth outline should be shown (use same method as for spur gears). If the gear is to be cut, give the cutting data required, as shown in Fig. 16-13.

The dimensioning of a bevel gear blank is dependent on the methods used to produce it. In general, the dimensions shown in Fig. 16-13 would suffice for the majority of the procedures in use.

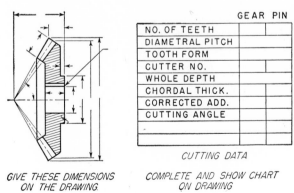

GEAR	PIN
NO. OF TEETH		
DIAMETRAL PITCH		
TOOTH FORM		
CUTTER NO.		
WHOLE DEPTH		
CHORDAL THICK.		
CORRECTED ADD.		
CUTTING ANGLE		

GIVE THESE DIMENSIONS ON THE DRAWING

CUTTING DATA

COMPLETE AND SHOW CHART ON DRAWING

Fig. 16-13. Dimensioning and cutting data for a bevel gear.

PROBLEMS

16-1. Draw a displacement diagram and a cam profile (showing the theoretical curve and the working curve) of a cam that turns clockwise with a modified uniform motion through 180°, returning to the starting point with gravity motion, and raising its vertical roller follower, which is ¾ in. in diameter, through a complete rise of 1 in. Make the base circle of the cam 3 in. in diameter, its hub 1½ in. in diameter, the diameter of the hole through it ⅞ in., and include a key slot for a ³⁄₁₆-in. square key. (Time: 4 hr.)

16-2. Show the working curve for the cam in Prob. 16-1 when acting on a vertical 2-in. flat-faced follower. (Time: 4 hr. for complete problem.)

16-3. A cam raising a vertical roller follower goes through the following sequences. It starts with modified uniform motion, the rise being 1 in. through 120°. It continues with harmonic motion, with a rise of 1 in. through 100°. It dwells through 10°, and completes the cycle with gravity motion in a total time lapse of 90 sec. Construct a displacement diagram, labeling it according to time intervals, angular cam displacement, motion intervals, and types of motion. Construct the front elevation of a plate cam that will provide these motions, showing the locations of the pressure angles, the theoretical curve, and the working curve for a roller follower ⅞ in. in diameter. Make the diameter of the base circle 1¾ in., the diameter of the hub 1½ in., and the diameter of the shaft ¾ in. Show a ¼-in. square key in the assembly. Place dimensions on the cam drawing. (Time: 5 hr.)

16-4. Construct a plate cam with a flat-faced follower to accomplish the desired motions of Prob. 16-3 showing correction for interference. (Time: 5 hr. for complete problem.)

16-5. The following information is available for making a front and side view drawing of a spur gear: 3 DP, 8 PD, 24 teeth, ⅞-in. face, to fit 1-in. shaft, and fixed in place with a ¼-in. square key. Make a suitable working drawing with the addition of the proper computed dimensions. Scale your drawings to fit the size sheet used. (Time: 4 hr.)

16-6. A pinion has 12 teeth; its outside diameter measures 7 in., its face 1 in., and the hub is 2 in. in diameter. The shaft is 1¼ in. in diameter. Included

is a flat key ¼ × ⅜ × 1 in. Make a working drawing showing all required dimensions. (Time: 4 hr.)

16-7. Make an assembly drawing of a spur gear and pinion with specifications as follows: The gear (*A*) has 21 teeth, 3 DP, 7 PD, hub 4 in. in diameter, hole 2 in. in diameter, and face 1½ in. The mating pinion (*B*) has 15 teeth, 5 PD, and a hole 1¾ in. in diameter. Show suitable keys in keyways. Gear is cast iron alloy. Pinion is made of steel. (Time: 7 hr.)

16-8. Draw the mating rack for the gear in Prob. 16-3. The rack is 9 in. long, 2 in. high, and 1½ in. thick. Use suitable scale. (Time: 2 hr.)

16-9. An assembly of an involute bevel gear with its mating pinion set on intersecting shaft centers reveals the following information: 14½° composite system; shaft angle 90°; diametral pitch, 3; teeth in gear, 30; teeth in pinion, 15; pitch diameter of gear, 10; pitch diameter of pinion, 5; face, both gear and pinion, 2 in.; hub diameters, gear 5 in., pinion 3¾ in.; hole in gear hub, 2 in. in diameter × 3¹⁹⁄₃₂ in. long; hole in pinion hub, 1¾ in. in diameter × 3⅞ in. long. Make a layout of a working drawing, which includes at least two teeth from the developed back cones of both the gear and pinion. Supply all other calculations for proper dimensioning. Scale of drawing ½″ = 1″. (Time: 10 hr.)

16-10. On inspection, the bevel gear of a bevel gear and pinion assembly reveals the following data: 14½° composite system intersecting shaft centers placed on a 90° angle; diametral pitch 8; teeth in gear, 40; pitch diameter of gear, 5 in.; pitch diameter of pinion, 2½ in.; gear face, ⅞ in.; hub diameter, 3 in.; hole in hub, 1½ in. in diameter × 1²⁷⁄₃₂ in. long, with a slot for a ¼-in. square key. Make a full-scale section-view drawing of the gear. (Time: 7 hr.)

16-11. Make a layout drawing of a pair of involute bevel gears from the following available data: 14½° composite system; shaft angle, 90°; velocity ratio, 2:1; diametral pitch, 4; pitch diameter of gear, 8 in.; face, 1½ in. Scale ¾″ = 1″. Show both gear and pinion in section, and two teeth of each from their developed back cones. Refer to the illustrations in Chap. 16 to calculate other required dimensions. Assume suitable proportions for webs, hubs, bores, slots, etc. Dimension as a working drawing. (Time: 12 hr.)

Chapter 17

INKING PROCEDURE

The purpose of this chapter is to assist the student or beginning draftsman in preparing a drawing from which a successful print can be made by any of the numerous methods of contact printing in use today. In practically all cases, the working drawing used in the machine shop is a reproduction of an original prepared in the drawing and design room. The original may be either a pencil or an ink drawing executed on tracing paper or tracing cloth. The pencil drawing is prepared directly on the tracing sheet. The ink drawing, on the other hand, is usually prepared by first making a pencil drawing on ordinary drawing paper and then tracing it in ink on transparent tracing paper or cloth placed over the original (see Fig. 17-1). Ink drawings are also prepared by working on the transparent surface with pencil and then inking over the pencil lines.

17-1. Making a print. The basic procedure in making any contact print is to expose the tracing and contact paper to light from one of four main sources—sunlight, arc light, low-pressure tube light, and high-pressure tube light. The success of the print is dependent on the intensity of light and the length of the exposure, the ink or pencil technique employed in making the original drawing (width and firmness of lines, erasures, etc.), the

kind of paper or cloth on which the original has been prepared, and the image-fixing medium employed with the contact paper. There have been many improvements in the mechanical equipment used in print making from tracing cloths and papers since the first blueprint was produced many years ago. Regardless of this fact, however, the success of all methods depends to a large degree on the quality of the original drawing used in making the print.

17-2. Selecting the tracing paper or tracing cloth. Selection of the proper tracing paper or tracing cloth is one of the most important factors

IN MAKING AN INK TRACING FROM A PENCIL ORIGINAL, THE CLOTH IS PLACED OVER THE PENCIL DRAWING

Fig. 17-1. Preparation for ink tracing.

contributing to successful print making. There are two types of tracing paper available on the market. The so-called "natural" paper is, as its name implies, naturally transparent; vellum paper, on the other hand, is transparentized by artificial methods. The natural papers will preserve their transparent quality indefinitely, while some of the vellums may lose it in a very short time. Both take ink or pencil equally well. Whichever type is selected, the paper should be checked for the following qualities: It should have 100 per cent rag content (the strength of the paper depends on its rag content). Check its cloud-producing deficiencies by holding it up to a strong light; if light and dark areas show up, they will be transmitted to the print. Test its ability to withstand erasure; if the surface breaks down too easily, repenciling or re-inking may be impossible. Feel its tooth qualities; if the surface is too rough, ragged lines and excessive dulling of the pencil will result. If the surface is too smooth, a clean, dark, and crisp (good-printing) line cannot be produced. If possible, check with other users on the ability of the paper to withstand discoloration. Because of their general freedom from cloudiness and better transparency, the vellums appear to be more in demand; the heavier weights in the natural papers are longer-lived, however, and are perfectly satisfactory for engineering drawings.

17-3. Tracing cloth. Although tracing cloth is more expensive than tracing paper, it is more durable and frequently more satisfactory for ink work and for drawings that are to be preserved over a number of years. Most tracing cloths permit the use of either pencil or ink, and any properly surfaced linen tracing cloth that is reasonably wax-free and moisture resistant will give satisfactory prints from originals executed in either manner. Of the two types available, the blue-tinted and the white, the white is more popular because it appears to be easier on the eyes and will take both pencil and ink lines with almost equal success. Leads of a good quality ranging from an HB to a 3H will produce acceptable results, but the greater opacity of a good India ink ensures sharper and more even lines on the print. Tracing cloths have a dull side and a glossy side. The pencil or ink work is always done on the dull side.

17-4. Line intensity. In preparing pencil drawings for reproduction, a comparatively soft pencil should be used. The harder pencils (3H to 9H) have a tendency to produce light, weak lines and dig into the drawing surface, and therefore their use is not recommended. For ink work, the ink selected (either black or colored) should be sufficiently opaque to ensure the intensity of line necessary to obtain a clear and sharp print. In general, the line work on tracings should be wider (and blacker when pencil is used) than for ordinary drafting. Often a pencil line (and at times even an ink line) will appear firm, strong, and dark enough on the surface of the sheet when attached to the drawing board, but inspection by reversing the drawing and looking at the line toward a strong light will reveal that its light-stopping properties are insufficient to produce satisfactory results (see Fig. 17-2).

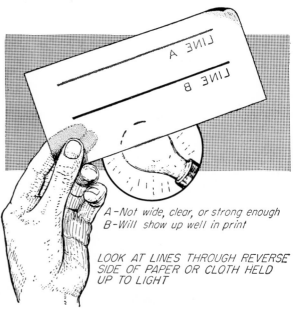

A—Not wide, clear, or strong enough
B—Will show up well in print

LOOK AT LINES THROUGH REVERSE SIDE OF PAPER OR CLOTH HELD UP TO LIGHT

Fig. 17-2. Testing for line quality.

17-5. Standards for ink lines. Figure 17-3 shows the ASA-recommended relative line widths for the preparation of inked drawings. The widths of the lines most commonly employed in drafting have been given also. In general, a good rule to

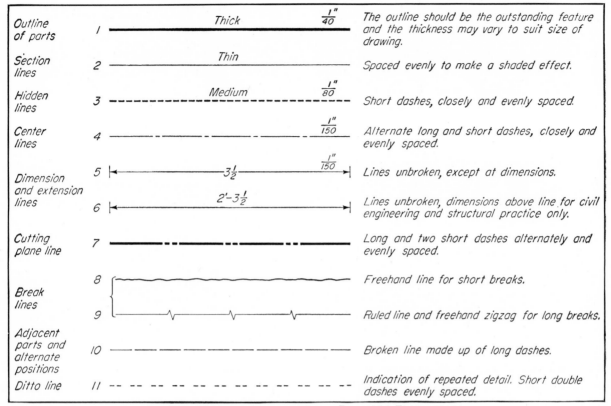

Outline of parts	1	Thick	$\frac{1''}{40}$	The outline should be the outstanding feature and the thickness may vary to suit size of drawing.
Section lines	2	Thin		Spaced evenly to make a shaded effect.
Hidden lines	3	Medium	$\frac{1''}{80}$	Short dashes, closely and evenly spaced.
Center lines	4		$\frac{1''}{150}$	Alternate long and short dashes, closely and evenly spaced.
Dimension and extension lines	5	$3\frac{1}{2}$	$\frac{1''}{150}$	Lines unbroken, except at dimensions.
	6	$2'-3\frac{1}{2}$		Lines unbroken, dimensions above line for civil engineering and structural practice only.
Cutting plane line	7			Long and two short dashes alternately and evenly spaced.
Break lines	8			Freehand line for short breaks.
	9			Ruled line and freehand zigzag for long breaks.
Adjacent parts and alternate positions	10			Broken line made up of long dashes.
Ditto line	11			Indication of repeated detail. Short double dashes evenly spaced.

Fig. 17-3. Width and character of lines. (*From ASA Z14.1—1946.*)

follow is to make center lines, dimension lines, extension lines, and section lining the narrowest, or thinnest, on the sheet; the hidden lines of the object twice as wide as the center lines; and the visible object lines twice as wide as the hidden lines.

17-6. Filling the ruling pen. Remove the stopper from the ink bottle with a turning motion to avoid snapping off the head. Close the blades of the pen and pass the dropper between them near the point formed by the nibs, leaving a drop of ink about ¼ in. above the point (see Fig. 17-4). Be sure that the outside surfaces of the blades are not smeared with ink. If they are, wipe the pen clean of all ink and repeat the operation.

17-7. Adjusting the pen. The width of the ink line depends upon the separation of the pen's blades at the points. The closer together, the narrower the line; the farther apart, the wider the line. The blades are spread apart or brought to-

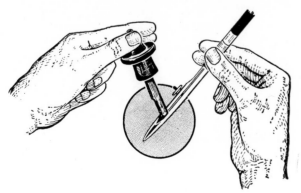

Fig. 17-4. Filling the ruling pen.

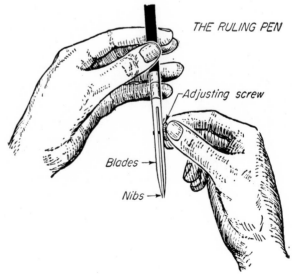

THE RULING PEN

Adjusting screw

Blades

Nibs

Fig. 17-5. Adjusting the pen.

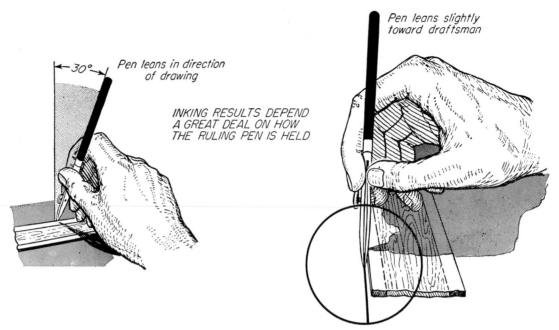

Fig. 17-6. Holding the ruling pen.

gether by manipulating the adjusting screw located just above the points (Fig. 17-5). To adjust the pen to a desired line width, draw trial lines on a piece of scrap paper or cloth (identical with the drawing sheet being used) until the desired line is secured. Trial lines may also be drawn on the outside of the margin along which the sheet is to be trimmed.

17-8. Use of the ruling pen. The ruling pen is always used in conjunction with a guiding instrument, such as the T square, triangles, or ir-

regular curve, to "ink in" or trace penciled lines. It is never used freehand. To hold the pen properly, place it in the hand with the adjusting screw pointing outward. The pen is held by the thumb and first finger and rests against the second finger. The third and little fingers steady and guide the hand. The pen should lean about 30° in the direction of the line being drawn. When using the straightedge, the pen should lean slightly toward the draftsman (see Fig. 17-6). Should the ink fail to flow after filling the pen, draw the point across

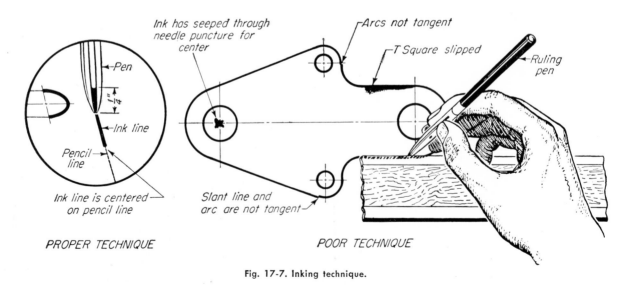

Fig. 17-7. Inking technique.

the nail of the thumb, or a saliva-moistened paper scrap. This should start the pen unless the nibs are improperly shaped.

17-9. Inking technique. Many of the unfortunate occurrences in inking procedure are the result of improper manipulation of the pen, unwillingness on the part of the draftsman to allow enough time for the ink to dry, incorrect treatment of line intersections and junctures, or carelessness in regard to line widths.

In tracing or inking a pencil line, the ink line should be centered over the pencil line as shown in Fig. 17-7. Careful attention to this when inking circles, arcs, irregular curves, and straight lines will assure proper junctures at tangent points. When removing the straightedge from a newly drawn line, avoid pushing it toward the line in the slightest degree, otherwise it will cause the mishap shown in the figure. Ink all center lines for circles and arcs first. If this is not done, the center lines will blot at their intersections when inked over the hole in the drawing sheet made by the compass point. If the pen is held so that it leans too far toward the draftsman, an irregular and uneven line will result because only one nib will touch the drawing surface (see Fig. 17-8a). The pen should not be held so that it leans too far away from the draftsman because the ink will run under the working edge as shown in Fig. 17-8b. If dried ink or dust and particles from the wiping cloth are permitted to accumulate on the pen, a ragged uneven line such as that shown in Fig. 17-8c will result. Too much ink in the pen will cause a drop to form that will blot the drawing (Fig. 17-9a). If the ink carried in the pen is insufficient to finish the line, it will appear split at the extremity (Fig. 17-9b). Sharp corners and intersections are impossible unless the previously inked lines are completely dry (Fig. 17-9c).

The large compass with the ruling pen attachment is employed in inking circles and arcs up to 9 or 10 in. in diameter. For larger circles the ruling-pen attachment and the interchangeable compass joint with extension bar may be used. The ink bow compass will serve for the inking of small circles and arcs (Fig. 17-10).

The various types of french curves are used to ink noncircular and irregular curves. When using a french curve, the pen should lean only very slightly in the direction of the line being drawn, otherwise there will be a tendency for the pen point to stray from the route of the guiding pencil line. Many draftsmen place a triangle under the guiding straightedge or french curve, with the upper instrument's working edge extended just over the edge of the lower instrument, in order to keep the

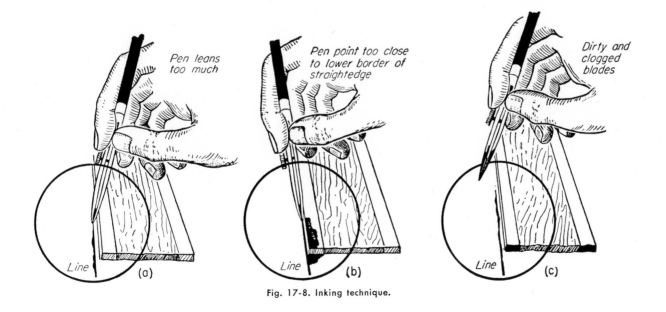

Fig. 17-8. Inking technique.

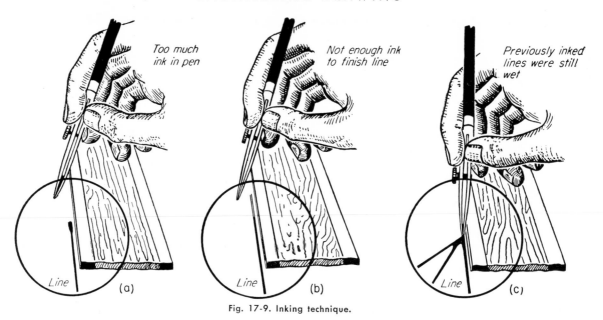

Fig. 17-9. Inking technique.

pen point from coming in contact with the lower border of the guiding instrument and causing dragging and blotting of the lines.

17-10. Cleaning the pen. A new pen should always be wiped with a clean cloth moistened with a vegetable oil, such as olive or corn oil, and then rubbed vigorously until dry. This will prevent rusting of metal parts, particularly the threads on the adjusting screw, and will not affect the functioning of the pen in any way. To obtain the best results while the pen is in use, it should be wiped clean before each refilling. If the draftsman is interrupted, the pen should be wiped dry before it is placed aside, because dried-ink accumulations mixed with fresh ink will cause annoying variations in the width of lines. The setting of the pen point need not be changed with each wiping if a folded linen cloth is passed carefully between the nibs and then pulled gently through (see Fig. 17-11). When the pen is to be put away for the day, it should be

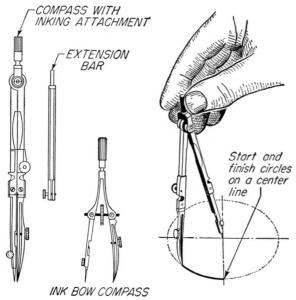

Fig. 17-10. Use of Compass.

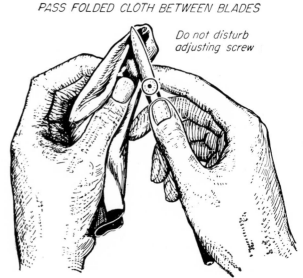

Fig. 17-11. Cleaning the pen.

thoroughly cleaned by washing it in a weak solution of ammonia (the household preparation).

17-11. Sharpening the pen. Sometimes if a pen is new, or has been used constantly over a long period of time, the draftsman may have difficulty producing fine thin lines or lines of even width. In such cases, the pen should be reshaped or resharpened as described below.

Any dried ink that may have accumulated on the blades should be removed by washing the pen in a mild ammonia solution. When clean, turn the adjusting screw until the blades just touch. Then hold the pen vertically over a fine-grained stone and swing it pendulum-like across the stone to sharpen the blades and to equalize their length (see Fig. 17-12a). When satisfied with the result, hold the pen as illustrated in (b), and without touching the adjusting screw, continue the sharpening procedure with a slight circular motion until the points present the elliptical shapes shown at (c) and (d). The pen should be tested at various intervals during the sharpening process to make sure that the ink flows with the proper freedom, that the nibs do not cut into the surface of the paper or cloth, and that even lines of the finest and heaviest desired widths can be obtained. Do not attempt to sharpen the inner surfaces of the blades. Remove

any feathered edges by rubbing the pen on a piece of hard leather.

A pen point that is overly rounded should be avoided for the ink will run too readily from the pen. A point that is too steep will prevent the ink from running at all, and an overly sharp point will cut into the surface of the tracing paper or cloth.

17-12. Use of the freehand pen. The lettering for notes, specifications, the title block, and all dimensions, including whole numbers and fractions, is inked with a lettering, or freehand, pen. When making an ink tracing of a pencil drawing, penciled horizontal and vertical guide lines should be used to preserve verticality and regularity in the height of the letters and figures. It is not advisable to try to trace the individual characters, but rather to use them as guides in arranging and spacing the lettering on the tracing.

No special pen points need be recommended for freehand ink lettering. Overly flexible points should be avoided because they are likely to produce an uneven line, and very stiff points should not be used because they have a tendency to cause the draftsman to "tighten up" and exert excessive pressure. Various types of pens recommended for freehand lettering are shown in Fig. 17-13.

The lettering pen should be held in the hand

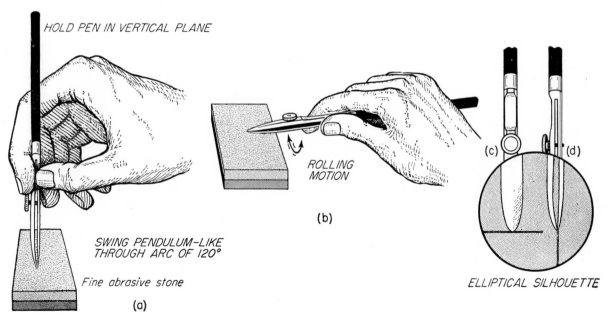

HOLD PEN IN VERTICAL PLANE

SWING PENDULUM-LIKE THROUGH ARC OF 120°

Fine abrasive stone

(a)

ROLLING MOTION

(b)

(c)   (d)

ELLIPTICAL SILHOUETTE

Fig. 17-12. Sharpening the pen.

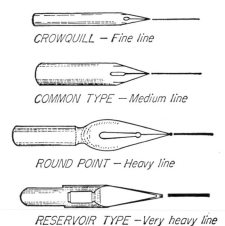

CROWQUILL — Fine line

COMMON TYPE — Medium line

ROUND POINT — Heavy line

RESERVOIR TYPE — Very heavy line

Fig. 17-13. Pens for freehand inking (for lettering, for small fillets and rounds, etc.).

in the same manner as the pencil, loosely enough and gently enough to give the feeling of perfect freedom for easy manipulation (see Fig. 17-14). A sketchy technique is faulty because the strokes will present weak, uneven lines of irregular width. A forthright continuous stroke, which can be produced after a little practice, will yield the desired letter line. If the pen is tilted one way or another from its habitual position, the letter strokes will vary from those inked while the pen was being held properly.

Dipping the pen in the ink bottle is not a good

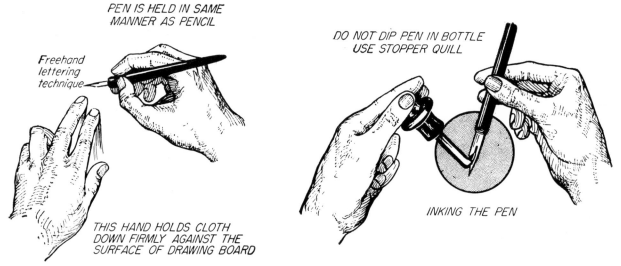

PEN IS HELD IN SAME MANNER AS PENCIL

Freehand lettering technique

THIS HAND HOLDS CLOTH DOWN FIRMLY AGAINST THE SURFACE OF DRAWING BOARD

DO NOT DIP PEN IN BOTTLE USE STOPPER QUILL

INKING THE PEN

Fig. 17-14. Holding the freehand pen and inking it.

THE INKSTAND IS A TIME AND INK SAVER

INDIA INK

Fig. 17-15. The inkstand.

practice. The pen should be inked by putting the stopper to the slot on the under side as shown in Fig. 17-14. If ink is permitted to lodge on the point, or if too much ink is applied, the pen will flow too freely and the lettering will start with a blot or the first stroke lines will be unusually heavy. The lettering pen should be cleaned before using and should be wiped frequently when in use. It should be completely cleaned on being put away in order to remove caked dried ink.

The pen-filling inkstand shown in Fig. 17-15 saves ink and time, and only one hand is necessary to operate it. It may be used to ink either the ruling pen or the lettering pen. Any ¾-oz bottle of drawing ink can be placed under the bottle-holder clamp. A locking device keeps the stopper tight in the neck of the bottle when not in use. The stand is rigid and heavy enough to prevent tipping, and it may be screwed securely to the drawing board or table if desired.

17-13. Erasing. Superfluous pencil lines appearing on an inked drawing may be removed very simply from tracing paper by using a soft rubber or kneaded eraser. Rubbing the paper surface gently will remove the pencil lines without blemishing the ink. The removal of ink from any paper, however, always presents the possibility of so marring the surface that re-inking is impossible. For this reason it is advisable to use tracing cloth for all ink work, because the treated linen can withstand erasures and other abuses it may be subjected to while being worked on in the drafting room or in the print-making department. The better types of water-repellant wax- and oil-free white tracing cloths need no preparations rubbed on or into their surfaces before starting to ink, and they will stand up under the softer abrasive erasers with no appreciable damage to the working surface. The use of an erasing shield will prevent wrinkling of the paper and the defacing of correct line work. A knife or razor blade may be used to remove a minute error in inking, but never where re-inking is to take place for the ink will invariably seep through and run at that spot. Erasing should be done by slipping a hard surface, such as a triangle, under the area to be erased. Eraser crumbs should be removed with a soft brush or clean handkerchief, and the erased surface rubbed with a clean fingertip or a bone burnisher especially made for the purpose. An erased area treated in this manner will normally take ink as well as the undisturbed portions of the drawing, and the chances of the ink running and spreading are reduced to a minimum. Pencil lines, carbon or graphite smudges, and hand moisture are usually removed from the finished cloth tracing with a soft rubber eraser. However, a cloth moistened with benzine or carbon tetrachloride rubbed gently over the drawing surface will serve the same purpose.

The electric erasing machine illustrated in Fig. 5-24 is a convenient time and energy saver. The erasing point is small and it can be used with the erasing shield. Only the soft rubber ink erasers should be employed when erasing ink lines. Care must be taken to exert only very gentle pressure when using the machine, since the heat generated by the rubber point turning at high speed will mar or burn through the surface.

17-14. Order of inking. After the light penciled guide lines for notes, specifications, whole numbers, fractions, title information, etc., have been placed on the tracing, it is well to follow a regular order in the inking procedure. By doing so much time will be saved and the chances of omitting lines will be minimized. The procedure suggested helps to avoid lines of unequal widths by dispensing with frequent resettings of the pen nibs. Also, little time will be lost waiting for the ink to dry. The natural order for the right-handed person is to move across the paper from left to right and from top to bottom. For most drawings, the order of inking should be as follows:

1. Ink all center lines, starting with circular center lines.

2. Ink visible object lines and cutting-plane lines (heavy lines) in the following order: (*a*) small circles, (*b*) large circles, (*c*) small arcs, (*d*) large arcs, (*e*) irregular curves, (*f*) horizontal lines, (*g*) vertical lines, (*h*) slant lines.

3. Ink hidden object lines (medium lines). Using a medium-weight dotted line, start with the small circles and follow the order suggested in item 2 above.

4. Ink the fine lines in the following order: (*a*) extension lines, (*b*) dimension lines, (*c*) section lining. Ink vertical lines first, horizontal lines next, slant lines last.

5. With the lettering pen, ink (*a*) arrowheads, (*b*) dimension figures, (*c*) specific notes, (*d*) general notes.

6. Ink the border and lettering for the title block.

BIBLIOGRAPHY

Aeronautical Drawing

Anderson, N. H.: "Aircraft Layout and Detail Design." McGraw-Hill.

Apalategui, J. J.: "Aircraft Analytical Geometry with Applications to Aircraft." Macmillan.

Faulconer, T. P.: "Introduction to Aircraft Design." McGraw-Hill.

Katz, H. H.: "Aircraft Drafting." Macmillan.

LeMaster, C. A.: "Aircraft Sheet Metal Work." Amer. Tech. Society.

Meadowcroft, N.: "Aircraft Detail Drafting." McGraw-Hill.

Norcross, C., and J. D. Quinn: "How to Do Aircraft Sheet Metal Work." McGraw-Hill.

Sechler, E. E., and L. G. Dunn: "Airplane Structural Analysis and Design." Wiley.

Svensen, S. L.: "A Manual of Aircraft Designing." Van Nostrand.

Titterton, G. F.: "Aircraft Materials and Processes." Pitman.

Architectural and Structural Drawing

Bishop, C. T.: "Structural Design." Wiley.

Bishop, C. T.: "Structural Drafting." Wiley.

Field, W. B.: "An Introduction to Architectural Drawing." McGraw-Hill.

Kenney, J. E., and J. P. McGrail: "Architectural Drawing for the Building Trades." McGraw-Hill.

Morgan, S. W.: "Architectural Drawing." McGraw-Hill.

Pickering, E.: "Architectural Design." Wiley.

Ramsey, C. G., and H. R. Sleeper: "Architectural Specifications." Wiley.

Shedd, T. C., and J. Vawter: "Theory of Simple Structures." Wiley.

Svensen, C. L., and E. D. Shelton: "Architectural Drafting." Van Nostrand.

Williams, C. D., and E. C. Harris: "Structural Design in Metals." Ronald.

Blueprint Reading

Bush, G. F.: "Reading Engineering Drawings." Wiley.

DeVette, W. A., and D. E. Kellogg: "Blueprint Reading for the Metal Trades." Bruce.

Dick, A. A.: "Blueprint Reading." Ronald.

Heine, G. M., and C. H. Dunlap: "How to Read Electrical Blueprints." Amer. Tech. Society.

Hobart, D. E.: "Notes and Problems in Blueprint Reading of Machine Drawings." Harper.

Ihne, R. W., and W. E. Streeter: "Machine Trades Blueprint Reading." Amer. Tech. Society.

Kenney, J. E.: "Blueprint Reading for the Building Trades." McGraw-Hill.

Lincoln Electric Co.: "Simple Blueprint Reading." Cleveland, Ohio.

Owens, A. A., and B. F. Slingluff: "How to Read Blueprints." Winston.

Spencer, H. C., and H. E. Grant: "Blueprint Language of the Machine Industries." Macmillan.

Svensen, C. L., and W. E. Street: "A Manual of Blueprint Reading." Van Nostrand.

Thayer, H. R.: "Blueprint Reading and Sketching." McGraw-Hill.

Weir, J. J.: "Blueprint Reading." McGraw-Hill.

Cams and Gears

Beale, O. J.: "Practical Treatise on Milling." Brown and Sharpe Mfg. Co., Providence, R. I.

Buckingham, E.: "Spur Gears." McGraw-Hill.

Colvin, F. H., and F. A. Stanley: "Gear-cutting Practice." McGraw-Hill.

Fellows Gear Shaper Co.: "Treatise on Gear Shapers." Springfield, Vt.

Furman, F. DeR.: "Cams, Elementary and Advanced." Wiley.

Owen, W. M.: "Spur Gearing." McKnight.

Descriptive Geometry

Grant, H. E.: "Practical Descriptive Geometry." McGraw-Hill.

Higbee, F. G.: "Drawing-board Geometry." Wiley.

Hood, G. J.: "Geometry of Engineering Drawing." McGraw-Hill.

Millar, A. V., and K. G. Shiels: "Descriptive Geometry." Heath.

Miller, H. W.: "Descriptive Geometry." Wiley.

Roever, W. H.: "The Mongean Method of Descriptive Geometry." Macmillan.

Rowe, C. E.: "Engineering Descriptive Geometry." Van Nostrand.

Smith, W. G.: "Practical Descriptive Geometry." McGraw-Hill.

Street, W. E.: "Technical Descriptive Geometry." Van Nostrand.

Vaughn, W.: "Aircraft Descriptive Geometry." Aircraft Publishing Co., Glendale, Calif.

Warner, F. M.: "Applied Descriptive Geometry." McGraw-Hill.

Watts, E. F., and J. T. Rule: "Descriptive Geometry." Prentice-Hall.

Wellman, B. L.: "Technical Descriptive Geometry." McGraw-Hill.

Electrical Drawing

Bishop, C. C.: "Electrical Drafting and Design." McGraw-Hill.

Carini, L. F. B.: "Drafting for Electronics." McGraw-Hill.

Kocher, S. E.: "Electrical Drafting." International Textbook.

Van Gieson, D. W.: "Electrical Drafting." McGraw-Hill.

Engineering Drawing

French, T. E., and C. J. Vierck: "Engineering Drawing." McGraw-Hill.

French, T. E., and C. L. Svenson: "Mechanical Drawing." McGraw-Hill.

Giesecke, F. E., A. Mitchell, and H. C. Spencer: "Technical Drawing." Macmillan.

Hobart, D. E.: "Engineering Drawing." Heath.

Johnson, W. H., and L. V. Newkirk: "Modern Drafting." Macmillan.

Jordan, H. H., and R. P. Hoelscher: "Engineering Drawing." Wiley.

Luzadder, W. J.: "Fundamentals of Engineering Drawing." Prentice-Hall.

Orth, H. D., R. R. Worsencroft, and H. B. Doke: "Basic Engineering Drawing." Ronald.

Rule, J. T., and E. F. Watts: "Engineering Graphics." McGraw-Hill.

Sahag, L. M.: "Engineering Drawing." Ronald.

Schumann, C. H.: "Technical Drafting." Harper.

Svensen, C. L.: "Drafting for Engineers." Van Nostrand.

Svensen, C. L.: "Essentials of Drafting." Van Nostrand.

Turner, W. W., C. P. Buck, and H. P. Ackert: "Basic Engineering Drawing." Ronald.

Engineering Drawing Problems

Higbee, F. G., and J. M. Russ: "Engineering Drawing Problems." Wiley.

Levens, A. S., and A. E. Edstrom: "Problems in Engineering Drawing." McGraw-Hill.

Spencer, H. C., and H. E. Grant: "Technical Drawing Problems." Macmillan.

Vierck, C. J., C. D. Cooper, and P. E. Machovina: "Engineering Drawing Problems." McGraw-Hill. (11″ × 17″)

Vierck, C. J., C. D. Cooper, and P. E. Machovina: "Engineering Drawing—Basic Problems." McGraw-Hill. (8½″ × 11″)

Zozzora, F.: "Engineering Drawing Problems." McGraw-Hill.

Handbooks

"American Civil Engineers' Handbook," T. Merriman and T. H. Wiggin. Wiley.

"American Electricians' Handbook," T. Croft. McGraw-Hill.

"American Machinists' Handbook," F. H. Colvin and F. A. Stanley. McGraw-Hill.

"American Society of Heating and Ventilating Engineers' Guide," (annual).

"Architects' and Builders' Handbook," F. E. Kidder and H. Parker. Wiley.

"Chemical Engineers' Handbook," J. H. Perry. McGraw-Hill.

"Civil Engineering Handbook," L. C. Urquhart. McGraw-Hill.

"Data Book for Civil Engineers," E. E. Seelye. Wiley.

"General Engineering Handbook," C. E. O'Rourke. McGraw-Hill.

"Handbook on Designing for Quantity Production," H. Chase. McGraw-Hill.

"Handbook of Engineering Fundamentals," O. W. Eshbach. Wiley.

"Machinery's Handbook," Industrial Press.

"Machinist's and Draftsman's Handbook," A. M. Wagener. Van Nostrand.

"Materials Handbook," G. S. Brady. McGraw-Hill.

"Mechanical Engineers' Handbook," W. Kent. Wiley.

"Mechanical Engineers' Handbook," L. S. Marks. McGraw-Hill.

"National Electrical Code Handbook," A. L. Abbott. McGraw-Hill.

"Plant Engineering Handbook," W. Staniar. McGraw-Hill.

"SAE Handbook," Society of Automotive Engineers, New York.

"Standard Handbook for Electrical Engineers," A. E. Knowlton. McGraw-Hill.

"Steel Construction," American Institute of Steel Construction, New York.

"Tool Engineers' Handbook," American Society of Tool Engineers, F. W. Wilson, Editor-in-Chief. McGraw-Hill.

Lettering

Benson, J. H., and A. G. Carey: "The Elements of Lettering." McGraw-Hill.

DeGarmo, E. P., and F. Jonassen: "Technical Lettering." Macmillan.

French, T. E., and W. D. Turnbull: "Lessons in Lettering." McGraw-Hill.

Giesecke, F. E., A. Mitchell, and H. C. Spencer: "Lettering Exercises." Macmillan.

Ogg, O.: "An Alphabet Source Book." Harper.

Reinhardt, C. W.: "Lettering for Draftsmen." Van Nostrand.

Svensen, C. L.: "The Art of Lettering." Van Nostrand.

Machine Drawing and Design

Albert, C. D.: "Machine Design and Drawing Room Problems." Wiley.

Faires, V. M.: "Design of Machine Elements." Macmillan.

Guillet, G. L.: "Kinematics of Machines." Wiley.

Ham, C. W., and E. J. Crane: "Mechanics of Machinery." McGraw-Hill.

Hyland, P. H., and J. B. Kommers: "Machine Design." McGraw-Hill.

Jefferson, T. B., and W. J. Brooking: "Introduction to Mechanical Design." Ronald.

Keown, R. M., and V. M. Faires: "Mechanism." McGraw-Hill.

Lent, D.: "Design of Machine Elements." Prentice-Hall.

Maleev, V. L.: "Machine Design." International Textbook.

Norman, C. A., E. S. Ault, and I. F. Zabrosky: "Fundamentals of Machine Design." Macmillan.

Schwamb, P., A. L. Merrill, and W. H. James: "Elements of Mechanism." Wiley.

Snow, G. C., and J. C. Russell: "Machine Drafting." Manual Arts Press.

Spotts, M. F.: "Design of Machine Elements." Prentice-Hall.

Svensen, C. L.: "Machine Drawing." Van Nostrand.

Tozer, E. F., and H. A. Rising: "Machine Drawing." McGraw-Hill.

Vallance, A., and V. L. Doughtie: "Design of Machine Members." McGraw-Hill.

Vallance A., and M. E. Farris: "Principles of Mechanism." Macmillan.

Winston, S. E.: "Machine Design." Van Nostrand.

Map Drawing

Deetz, C. H.: "Elements of Map Projection." U.S. Government Printing Office.

Finch, J. K.: "Topographic Maps and Sketch Mapping." Wiley.

Hinks, A. R.: "Maps and Surveys." Macmillan.

Sloane, R. C., and J. M. Montz: "Topographic Drawing and Mapping." McGraw-Hill.

Whitmore, G. D.: "Advanced Surveying and Mapping." International Textbook.

Patent Drawing

Radzinsky, H.: "Making Patent Drawings." Macmillan.

"Rules of Practice." U.S. Patent Office, Washington, D.C.

Perspective, Sketching, and Illustration

Everett, H. E., and W. H. Lawrence: "Freehand and Perspective Drawing." Amer. Tech. Society.

Freese, E. I.: "Perspective Projection." Reinhold.

Guptill, A. L.: "Sketching and Rendering in Pencil." Reinhold.

Hoelscher, R. P., C. H. Springer, and R. F. Pohle: "Industrial Production Illustration." McGraw-Hill.

Jones, F. D.: "How to Sketch Mechanisms." Industrial Press.

Katz, H.: "Technical Sketching." Macmillan.

Kautsky, T.: "Pencil Rendering." Reinhold.

Lawson, P. J.: "Practical Perspective Drawing." McGraw-Hill.

Lubschez, B. J.: "Perspective." Van Nostrand.

Norling, E.: "Perspective Made Easy." Macmillan.

Tharratt, G.: "Aircraft Production Illustration." McGraw-Hill.

Treacy, J.: "Production Illustration." Wiley.

Turner, W. W.: "Freehand Sketching for Engineers." Ronald.

Turner, W. W.: "Simplified Perspective." Ronald.

Zipprich, A. E.: "Freehand Drafting." Van Nostrand.

Pipe Drawing

Crane & Company Piping Catalogue. Chicago.

Crocker, S.: "Piping Handbook." McGraw-Hill.

Day, L. J.: "Standard Plumbing Details." Wiley.

Littleton, C. T.: "Industrial Piping." McGraw-Hill.

Svensen, C. L.: "A Handbook on Piping." Van Nostrand.

Walworth Company Catalogue. Boston.

Sheet-metal Drawing

Dougherty, J. S.: "Sheet-metal Pattern Drafting." Manual Arts.

Jenkins, R.: "Sheet Metal Pattern Layout." Prentice-Hall.

Kidder, F. S.: "Triangulation Applied to Sheet Metal Pattern Cutting." Sheet Metal Publishing Co., New York.

Kittredge, G. W.: "The New Metal Worker Pattern Book." Scientific Book Corp.

Neubecker, W.: "Sheet Metal Work." Amer. Tech. Society.

O'Rourke, F. J.: "Sheet Metal Pattern Drafting." McGraw-Hill.

Paul, J. H.: "Industrial Sheet Metal Drawing." Van Nostrand.

Smith, R. E.: "Units in Sheet Metal Work." McKnight.

Shop Tools and Shop Processes

Begeman, M. L.: "Manufacturing Processes." Wiley.

Boston, O. W.: "Engineering Shop Practice." Wiley.

Burghardt, H. D., and A. Axelrod: "Machine Tool Operation." McGraw-Hill.

Campbell, H. L.: "Metal Castings." Wiley.

Campbell, H. L.: "The Working, Heat Treating and Welding of Steel." Wiley.

Campbell, J. S.: "Casting and Forming Processes in Manufacturing." McGraw-Hill.

Clapp, W. H., and D. S. Clark: "Engineering Materials and Processes." International Textbook.

Colvin, F. H., and L. L. Haas: "Jigs and Fixtures." Mc-Graw-Hill.

Colvin, F. H., and F. A. Stanley: "Drilling and Surfacing Practice." McGraw-Hill.

Ford Trade School: "Shop Theory." McGraw-Hill.

Hesse, H. C.: "Engineering Tools and Processes." Van Nostrand.

Hine, C. R.: "Machine Tools for Engineers." McGraw-Hill.

Hinman, C. W.: "Pressworking of Metals." McGraw-Hill.

Johnson, C. G.: "Forging Practice." Amer. Tech. Society.

Linsley, H. E.: "Practical Ideas for Machinists." McGraw-Hill.

Marek, C. T.: "The Production and Design of Castings." Wiley.

Schaller, G. S.: "Engineering Manufacturing Methods." McGraw-Hill.

Smith, R. E.: "Machining of Metal." McKnight.

Turner, W. P., and H. F. Owen: "Machine-tool Work." McGraw-Hill.

Wendt, R. E.: "Foundry Work." McGraw-Hill.

Young, J. F.: "Materials and Processes." Wiley.

Tool Design

Bryant, L. A., and T. A. Dickinson: "Jigs and Fixtures." Pitman.

Cole, C. B.: "Tool Design." Amer. Tech. Society.

Donaldson, C., and G. H. LeCain: "Tool Design." Harper.

Hinman, C. W.: "Die Engineering Layouts and Formulas." McGraw-Hill.

Hinman, C. W.: "Practical Designs for Drilling, Milling, and Tapping Tools." McGraw-Hill.

Jones, F. D.: "Jig and Fixture Design." Industrial Press.

Kipers, R.: "Manufacturing Analysis." McGraw-Hill.

Stanley, F. A.: "Punches and Dies." McGraw-Hill.

Woodcock, F. L.: "The Design of Metal-cutting Tools." McGraw-Hill.

Welding

Churchill, H. D., and J. B. Austin: "Weld Design." Prentice-Hall.

Elzea, L. S.: "Aircraft Welding." McGraw-Hill.

Kerwin, H.: "Arc and Acetylene Welding." McGraw-Hill.

Lincoln Electric Co.: "Procedure Handbook of Arc Welding Design and Practice." Cleveland.

Moon, A. R.: "Design of Welded Structures." Pitman.

Plumley, S.: "Oxyacetylene Welding and Cutting." McGraw-Hill.

Rossi, B. E.: "Welding Engineering." McGraw-Hill.

Rossi, B. E.: "Manual of Instructions in Welding and Cutting." McGraw-Hill.

American Standards

Publications of Particular Interest to Draftsmen and Designers

Abbreviations:

Abbreviations for Scientific and Engineering Terms, Z10.1—1941.

Abbreviations for Use on Drawings, Z32.13—1950.

Charts and Graphs:

Engineering and Scientific Charts for Lantern Slides, Z15.1—1947.

Engineering and Scientific Graphs for Publications, Z15.3—1947.

Time Series Charts, Z15.2—1947.

Dimensioning:

Design and Dimensioning, Z14.

Limits and Fits for Engineering and Manufacturing, B4.1—1947.

Drawings and Drafting:

Drawings and Drafting Room Practice, Z14.1—1946.

Fasteners:

Large Rivets, B18.4—1950.

Plow Bolts, B18.9—1950.

Round Head Bolts, B18.5—1952.

Slotted and Recessed Head Screws, Machine, Cap, Wood, Tapping, and Slotted Headless Types, B18.6—1947.

Small Rivets, B18a—1927.

Socket Head Cap Screws and Socket Set Screws, B18.3—1947.

Square and Hexagon Bolts and Nuts, B18.2—1952.

Tinners', Coopers', and Belt Rivets, B18g—1929.

Gears:

Fine-pitch Straight Bevel Gears, B6.8—1950.

Gear Nomenclature, Terms, Definitions, and Illustrations, B6.10—1950.

Gear Tolerances and Inspections, B6.6—1946.

Spur Gear Tooth Form, B6.1—1932.

Graphical Symbols:

Basic Graphical Symbols for Electric Apparatus, Z32.12—1947.

Graphical Symbols for Heating, Ventilating, and Air Conditioning, Z32.2.4—1949.

Graphical Symbols for Pipe Fittings, Valves, and Piping, Z32.2.3—1949.

Graphical Symbols for Plumbing, Z32.2.2—1949.

Graphical Symbols for Use on Drawings in Mechanical Engineering, Z32.2—1941.

Graphical Symbols for Welding, Z32.2.1—1949.

Keys:

Shafting and Stock Keys, B17.1—1943.
Woodruff Keys, Keyslots, and Cutters, B17f—1930.

Machining and Machine Tools:

Jig Bushings, B5.6—1941.
Machine Tapers, Self-holding and Steep Taper Series, B5.10—1943.
Milling Cutters, Nomenclature, Principal Dimensions, etc., B5.3—1950.
Reamers, B5.14—1949.
Taps, Cut and Ground Threads, B5.4—1948.
Twist Drills, Straight Shank and Taper Shank, B5.12—1950.

Pipe and Piping:

Brass or Bronze Screwed Fittings, 125 lb, B16.15—1947.
Cast Iron Pipe Flanges and Flanged Fittings:
25 lb: B16b2—1931.
125 lb: B16.1—1948.
250 lb: B16d—1944.
800 lb: B16b1—1947.
Cast Iron Screwed Fittings, 125 and 250 lb, B16.4—1949.
Ferrous Plugs, Bushings, and Locknuts, B16.14—1949.

Malleable-iron Screwed Fittings, 150 lb, B16.3—1951.
Plumbing Code, A40.7—1949.
Scheme for the Identification of Piping Systems, A13—1947.
Steel Butt-welding Fittings, B16.9—1951.
Steel Pipe Flanges and Flanged Fittings, B16e—1939.
Steel Socket-welding Fittings, B16.11—1946.
Wrought-iron and Wrought-steel Pipe, B36.10—1950.

Screw Threads:

Acme Threads, B1.5—1945.
Nomenclature, Definitions, and Letter Symbols for Screw Threads, B1.7—1949.
Pipe Threads, B2.1—1945.
Screw Threads for High-strength Bolting, B1.4—1945.
Unified and American Screw Threads for Screws, Bolts, Nuts, and Other Threaded Parts, B1.1—1949.

Surface Quality:

Surface Roughness, Waviness, and Lay, 1B46.1—1947.

Washers:

Lock Washers, B27.1—1950.
Plain Washers, B27.2—1949.

LIST OF VISUAL AIDS

The motion pictures and filmstrips listed in this *visual bibliography* can be used to supplement the material presented in this book. It is recommended, however, that each film be reviewed before using in order to determine its suitability for a particular group. For the convenience of users, the films have been grouped under the various chapters in the book. Some films may, of course, be used in the study of different chapters.

Both motion pictures and filmstrips are included in this visual bibliography, and the character of each is indicated by the abbreviations "MP," for motion picture, and "FS," for filmstrip. Immediately following is the name of the producer; if the distributor is different from the producer, the name of the distributor follows. The addresses of these producers and distributors are listed at the end of the bibliography. In most instances, the films can be borrowed or rented from local or state 16-mm. film libraries, a nation-wide list of which is given in *A Directory of 2002 16mm. Film Libraries,* available for 35 cents from the Superintendent of Documents, Washington 26, D.C. Unless otherwise indicated, the motion pictures are 16-mm. sound black-and-white, and the filmstrips are 35-mm. black-and-white silent.

This bibliography is suggestive only, and film users should examine the latest annual edition and quarterly supplements of *Educational Film Guide,* a catalogue of some 10,000 films published by the H. W. Wilson Co., New York. The *Guide,* a standard reference book, is available in most college and public libraries.

Chapter 1—Introduction

According to Plan: Introduction to Engineering Drawing (MP, McGraw, 9 min). Explains and emphasizes the importance of engineering drawing as a "language" of modern construction, production, and industrial development. (Engineering Drawing Series, No. 1)

The Draftsman (MP, VGF, 11 min). A vocational guidance film showing the work of draftsmen in industry; the different types of drafting and the skills required; and the job opportunities for draftsmen (as of 1942, the date of production of the film).

Engineering (MP, VGF, 11 min). Shows the kinds of work performed and the skills required in various engineering professions. A background information film.

Industrial Design (MP, Knaus, 10 min, silent, color). Shows the designing of a radio cabinet from the first thumb-nail sketch to the finished full color drawings.

Chapter 2—Engineering Lettering

Capital Letters (MP, Purdue, 23 min). Demonstrates the construction of single-stroke inclined commercial Gothic capital letters, ampersand, and numerals.

Lower Case Letters (MP, Purdue, 18 min). Explains and demonstrates the construction of each of the 26 lower-case letters.

Practical Lettering (MP, Cocking, 25 min, silent). Demonstrates the construction of each letter and number in commercial Gothic.

Technical Lettering (FS, Handy). A series of five filmstrips, approximately 60 fr each, with the following self-explanatory titles:

Single-Stroke Gothic—Introduction
Vertical Capitals IHT LEF AVW
Vertical Capitals MN YZXK4 OQCG
Vertical Capitals 069 DUJ PRB
Vertical Capitals 725& and Spacing

Chapter 3—Orthographic Projection

Introduction to Mechanical Drawing (MP, Cocking, 20 min, silent). Explains the methods and materials necessary for mechanical drawing, and demonstrates the making of drawings requiring one, two, and three views.

Multi-view Drawing (MP, Purdue, 27 min, silent). Demonstrates the way to represent an object by means of three orthographic views.

Orthographic Projection (MP, McGraw, 18 min). Demonstrates the need for projection of front, top, and side views and the consequent meaning of orthographic projection, and the making and reading of such a drawing. Correlated filmstrip, same title, 40 fr, also available. (Engineering Drawing Series, no. 2)

Shape Description (MP, Purdue 25 min). Demonstrates, for each of five views, the sketching of the pictorial view and the three principal views.

Shape Description, Part 1 (MP, McGraw, 11 min). Describes orthographic projection in terms of three-dimensional effects and shows how the three projected views are combined to represent a three-dimensional object. Correlated filmstrip, same title, 33 fr, also available. (Mechanical Drawing Series, no. 2)

Shape Description, Part 2 (MP, McGraw, 8 min). Demonstrates the step-by-step procedure of constructing an orthographic projection drawing and explains the reasons for each step. Correlated filmstrip same title, 32 fr, also available. (Mechanical Drawing Series, no. 3)

Visualizing an Object (MP, USOE/UWF, 9 min). How a blueprint is developed; how dimensions are shown by different views; and how special information is indicated on a blueprint. Correlated filmstrip, same title, 39 fr, also available.

Chapter 4—Freehand Detail Drafting

Broad Stroke Drawing (MP, Brandon, 10 min). Demonstrates how to manipulate broad-edge crayon, paper, shading, and design in using this technique.

Freehand Drafting (MP, Purdue, 15 min, silent). Shows sketching as an antecedent to drafting, and demonstrates methods and techniques of freehand drawing.

Chapter 5—Instruments and Their Use

Drafting Tips (MP, PSC, 28 min). Consists of two parts: (1) use and care of drafting equipment, with emphasis upon cleanliness, accuracy, and orderliness; and (2) sheet layout, use of alphabet of lines, and procedure for developing a drawing.

The Steel Rule (MP, USOE/UWF, 14 min). How to read steel rules; use flexible hook and rule-type gages; lay out holes with a combination square and scribe them with a divider; and use inside and outside calipers to transfer dimensions to and from steel rules. Correlated filmstrip, same title, 52 fr, also available.

Use of T-Square and Triangles (MP, Purdue, 22 min, silent). Explains the basic principles of using the T-square and triangles, and demonstrates the drawing of a number of kinds of lines and angles.

Chapter 6—Geometrical Constructions

Angles (MP, KB, 12 min). Depicts various types of angles and their relationship to each other. (Practical Geometry Series)

Angles and Arcs in Circles (MP, KB, 10 min). Explains the measurement of central angles, arcs, inscribed angles, and angles formed by two chords. (Practical Geometry Series)

Applied Geometry (MP, Purdue, 18 min, silent). Demonstrates how to perform various geometric constructions such as bisecting a line using T-square and triangles, drawing an arc tangent to a circle and a straight line, etc.

Descriptive Geometry: Finding the Line of Intersection between Two Solids (MP, USN/UWF, 22 min). Methods of determining intersecting lines of a cylinder and a cone by passing planes through the objects on an orthographic drawing.

Plane Geometry (FS, SVE). A series of 12 filmstrips, approximately 50 fr each, with the following self-explanatory titles:

Areas
Basic Triangles
Common Tangents and Tangent Circles
Congruent and Overlapping Triangles
Introduction to Circles
Introduction to Demonstrative Geometry—Axioms, Theorems, Postulates
Introduction to Plane Geometry
Loci
Parallel Lines and Transversals
Quadrilaterals
Similar Polygons
Basic Angles and Experimental Geometry

Chapter 7—Shop Processes

The Drawings and the Shop (MP, McGraw, 15 min). Describes the relationship between the making of engineering drawings and various production operations in shop and factory. Correlated filmstrip, same title, 43 fr, also available. (Engineering Drawing Series, no. 6)

Machine Shop Work (MP, USOE/UWF). A series of more than 100 motion pictures and correlated filmstrips showing in detail the operations on the engine lathes, turret lathes, milling machines, planers, shapers, boring mills, drill presses, etc. Write to the U.S. Office of Education, Washington 25, D.C., for a complete catalog.

Reading a Drawing of a Valve Bonnet (MP, USOE/-UWF, 20 min). How to interpret conventional symbols and tolerance specifications and use the blueprint in planning machine operations. Correlated filmstrip, same title, 30 fr, also available.

Reading a Three-view Drawing (MP, USOE/UWF, 10 min). How to use a blueprint to visualize the object, interpret a blueprint, and make a tool according to specifications shown on a blueprint. Correlated filmstrip, same title, 30 fr, also available.

Shop Procedures (MP, McGraw, 17 min). Shows how finished drawings are used in a pattern shop, foundry, forging shop, machine shop, and assembly line. Correlated filmstrip, same title, 41 fr, also available. (Mechanical Drawing Series, no. 4)

Shop Work (MP, Purdue, 25 min, silent). Explains various machines and the processes and operations they perform.

Chapter 8—Dimensioning

Principal Dimensions, Reference Surfaces, and Tolerances (MP, USOE/UWF, 12 min). Relationship between the blueprint and a rough and finished casting; how to use a blueprint in selecting reference surfaces; interpret tolerances; and check the accuracy of finished work. Correlated filmstrip, same title, 25 fr, also available.

Selection of Dimensions (MP, McGraw, 18 min). Explains the principles governing the choice of dimensions: functional characteristics of the object and manufacturing methods to be used. Correlated filmstrip, Dimensioning Techniques, 48 fr, also available. (Engineering Drawing Series, no. 7)

Size Description (MP, McGraw, 13 min). Explains the choosing of dimensions, uniform practices in dimensioning practice, and the breaking down of complex drawings into simple geometric parts. Correlated filmstrip, same title, 33 fr, also available. (Mechanical Drawing Series, no. 8)

Chapter 9—Sectioning and Conventional Practices

Sectional Views (MP, Purdue, 22 min, silent). Illustrates the principles of sectioning—full section, half section, and offset sections.

Sectional Views and Projections, Finish Marks (MP, USOE/UWF, 15 min). Dimension, center, cross-section, and object lines; projection of a sectional view; uses of finish marks; and meanings of standard cross-section lines. Correlated filmstrip, same title, 29 fr, also available.

Sections (MP, McGraw, 10 min). Explains the need for sectional views, the various symbols used in sectioning, and the construction of a full sectional view. Correlated filmstrip, same title, 32 fr, also available. (Mechanical Drawing Series, no. 5)

Sections and Conventions (MP, McGraw, 15 min). Explains the meaning of sectioning; describes the various types of sections and the meaning of symbols used in sectioning. Correlated filmstrip, same title, 44 fr, also available. (Engineering Drawing Series, no. 5)

Chapters 10 and 11—Primary and Secondary Auxiliaries

Auxiliary Views (MP, Purdue, 18 min, silent). Illustrates principles of auxiliary views and shows the construction of auxiliary views for straight line and curved line figures.

Auxiliary Views, Part 1 (MP, McGraw, 11 min). Explains the need for auxiliary views, defines auxiliary projection, and demonstrates the construction of an auxiliary elevation. Correlated filmstrip, same title, 32 fr, also available. (Mechanical Drawing Series, no. 6)

Auxiliary Views, Part 2 (MP, McGraw, 10 min). Reviews the principles of auxiliary views treated in Part 1; and describes in detail three types of single auxiliaries—auxiliary elevation, right and left auxiliaries, and front and rear auxiliaries. Correlated filmstrip, same title, 34 fr, also available. (Mechanical Drawing Series, no. 7)

Auxiliary Views: Double Auxiliaries (MP, McGraw, 13 min). Reviews the principles of orthographic projection and of single auxiliary views, and explains the necessity for double auxiliary or oblique views in certain cases. Correlated filmstrips, same title, 26 fr, also available. (Engineering Drawing Series, no. 4)

Auxiliary Views: Single Auxiliaries (MP, McGraw, 23 min). Reviews the principles of orthographic projection; explains why the projections of three principal planes do not represent the true shape of an object which has slanting surfaces: and demonstrates the necessity for auxiliary projection. Correlated filmstrip, same title, 38 fr, also available. (Engineering Drawing Series, no. 3)

Chapter 12—Pictorial Drawing

Pictorial Drawing (MP, Purdue, 21 min, silent). Demonstrates the principles of isometric drawing and the construction of objects with isometric and nonisometric lines and circles.

Chapter 13—Fastener

Screw Threads (MP, Purdue, 24 min). Defines important terms associated with screw threads; shows the construction of national and square threads; and explains the meaning of each line of a drawing.

Chapter 15—Intersections and Developments

Development of Surfaces (MP, Purdue, 22 min, silent). Explains the construction of patterns of surfaces, including methods for right prism, oblique prism, right pyramid, right cone, and oblique cone.

Developments (MP, McGraw, 18 min). Explains development of prisms, pyramids, cylinders, cones, and transition pieces. Correlated filmstrip, same title, also available.

Descriptive Geometry: Finding the Lines of Intersection between Two Solids (MP, USN/UWF, 22 min). Methods of determining lines of a cylinder and a cone by passing planes through the objects on an orthographic drawing.

Intersection of Surfaces (MP, Purdue, 10 min, silent). Explains the principles of finding the lines of intersection between surfaces, particularly between two prisms, two cylinders, and a cylinder and a cone.

Pictorial Sketching (MP, McGraw, 12 min). Demonstrates types of pictorial sketches and explains position of object, choice of axes, use of construction lines, methods of sketching circles, etc. Correlated filmstrip, same title, also available.

Chapter 16—Cams and Gears

Principles of Gearing: An Introduction (MP, USOE/-UWF, 18 min). Friction gears and toothed gears; law of gearing, positive driving, involute profiles, pressure angle, cycloid profiles, velocity rates, and circular pitch. Correlated filmstrip, same title, 37 fr, also available.

Chapter 17—Inking Practice

Ink Work and Tracing (MP, Purdue, 34 min, silent). Demonstrates the various steps in making tracings on cloth.

Directory of Sources

Brandon—Brandon Films, Inc., 200 W. 57th St., New York.

Cocking—Floyd W. Cocking, 4757 Constance Drive, San Diego, 15, Calif.

Handy—Jam Handy Organization, 2821 E. Grand Blvd., Detroit 11.

KB—Knowledge Builders, 625 Madison Ave., New York 22.

Knaus—Frank Knaus, 385 Malcolm Drive, Pasadena 2, Calif.

McGraw—McGraw-Hill Book Company, Inc., Text-Film Department, 330 W. 42d St., New York 36.

PSC—Pennsylvania State College, State College, Pa.

Purdue—Purdue University, Lafayette, Ind.

SVE—Society for Visual Education, Inc., 1345 W. Diversey Pkwy., Chicago 14.

UWF—United World Films, Inc., 1445 Park Ave., New York 29.

VGF—Vocational Guidance Films, 215 E. Third St., Des Moines, Ia.

APPENDIX

Contents

Table 1. Trigonometric Functions

Angle	Sine	Cosine	Tan	Cotan	Angle
0°	0.0000	1.0000	0.0000	∞	90°
1°	0.0175	0.9998	0.0175	57.290	89°
2°	0.0349	0.9994	0.0349	28.636	88°
3°	0.0523	0.9986	0.0524	19.081	87°
4°	0.0698	0.9976	0.0699	14.301	86°
5°	0.0872	0.9962	0.0875	11.430	85°
6°	0.1045	0.9945	0.1051	9.5144	84°
7°	0.1219	0.9925	0.1228	8.1443	83°
8°	0.1392	0.9903	0.1405	7.1154	82°
9°	0.1564	0.9877	0.1584	6.3138	81°
10°	0.1736	0.9848	0.1763	5.6713	80°
11°	0.1908	0.9816	0.1944	5.1446	79°
12°	0.2079	0.9781	0.2126	4.7046	78°
13°	0.2250	0.9744	0.2309	4.3315	77°
14°	0.2419	0.9703	0.2493	4.0108	76°
15°	0.2588	0.9659	0.2679	3.7321	75°
16°	0.2756	0.9613	0.2867	3.4874	74°
17°	0.2924	0.9563	0.3057	3.2709	73°
18°	0.3090	0.9511	0.3249	3.0777	72°
19°	0.3256	0.9455	0.3443	2.9042	71°
20°	0.3420	0.9397	0.3640	2.7475	70°
21°	0.3584	0.9336	0.3839	2.6051	69°
22°	0.3746	0.9272	0.4040	2.4751	68°
23°	0.3907	0.9205	0.4245	2.3559	67°
24°	0.4067	0.9135	0.4452	2.2460	66°
25°	0.4226	0.9063	0.4663	2.1445	65°
26°	0.4384	0.8988	0.4877	2.0503	64°
27°	0.4540	0.8910	0.5095	1.9626	63°
28°	0.4695	0.8829	0.5317	1.8807	62°
29°	0.4848	0.8746	0.5543	1.8040	61°
30°	0.5000	0.8660	0.5774	1.7321	60°
31°	0.5150	0.8572	0.6009	1.6643	59°
32°	0.5299	0.8480	0.6249	1.6003	58°
33°	0.5446	0.8387	0.6494	1.5399	57°
34°	0.5592	0.8290	0.6745	1.4826	56°
35°	0.5736	0.8192	0.7002	1.4281	55°
36°	0.5878	0.8090	0.7265	1.3764	54°
37°	0.6018	0.7986	0.7536	1.3270	53°
38°	0.6157	0.7880	0.7813	1.2799	52°
39°	0.6293	0.7771	0.8098	1.2349	51°
40°	0.6428	0.7660	0.8391	1.1918	50°
41°	0.6561	0.7547	0.8693	1.1504	49°
42°	0.6691	0.7431	0.9004	1.1106	48°
43°	0.6820	0.7314	0.9325	1.0724	47°
44°	0.6947	0.7193	0.9657	1.0355	46°
45°	0.7071	0.7071	1.0000	1.0000	45°
Angle	Cosine	Sine	Cotan	Tan	Angle

Table 2. Decimal Equivalents of Inch Fractions

Fraction	Equiv.	Fraction	Equiv.	Fraction	Equiv.	Fraction	Equiv.
1/64	0.015625	17/64	0.265625	33/64	0.515625	49/64	0.765625
1/32	0.03125	9/32	0.28125	17/32	0.53125	25/32	0.78125
3/64	0.046875	19/64	0.296875	35/64	0.546875	51/64	0.796875
1/16	0.0625	5/16	0.3125	9/16	0.5625	13/16	0.8125
5/64	0.078125	21/64	0.328125	37/64	0.578125	53/64	0.828125
3/32	0.09375	11/32	0.34375	19/32	0.59375	27/32	0.84375
7/64	0.109375	23/64	0.359375	39/64	0.609375	55/64	0.859375
1/8	0.1250	3/8	0.3750	5/8	0.6250	7/8	0.8750
9/64	0.140625	25/64	0.390625	41/64	0.640625	57/64	0.890625
5/32	0.15625	13/32	0.40625	21/32	0.65625	29/32	0.90625
11/64	0.171875	27/64	0.421875	43/64	0.671875	59/64	0.921875
3/16	0.1875	7/16	0.4375	11/16	0.6875	15/16	0.9375
13/64	0.203125	29/64	0.453125	45/64	0.703125	61/64	0.953125
7/32	0.21875	15/32	0.46875	23/32	0.71875	31/32	0.96875
15/64	0.234375	31/64	0.484375	47/64	0.734375	63/64	0.984375
1/4	0.2500	1/2	0.5000	3/4	0.7500	1	1.0000

Table 3. Sizes of Numbered and Lettered Drills

Number	Size, in.	Number	Size, in.	Number	Size, in.	Letter	Size, in.
80	0.0135	53	0.0595	26	0.1470	A	0.2340
79	0.0145	52	0.0635	25	0.1495	B	0.2380
78	0.0160	51	0.0670	24	0.1520	C	0.2420
77	0.0180	50	0.0700	23	0.1540	D	0.2460
76	0.0200	49	0.0730	22	0.1570	E	0.2500
75	0.0210	48	0.0760	21	0.1590	F	0.2570
74	0.0225	47	0.0785	20	0.1610	G	0.2610
73	0.0240	46	0.0810	19	0.1660	H	0.2660
72	0.0250	45	0.0820	18	0.1695	I	0.2720
71	0.0260	44	0.0860	17	0.1730	J	0.2770
70	0.0280	43	0.0890	16	0.1770	K	0.2810
69	0.0292	42	0.0935	15	0.1800	L	0.2900
68	0.0310	41	0.0960	14	0.1820	M	0.2950
67	0.0320	40	0.0980	13	0.1850	N	0.3020
66	0.0330	39	0.0995	12	0.1890	O	0.3160
65	0.0350	38	0.1015	11	0.1910	P	0.3230
64	0.0360	37	0.1040	10	0.1935	Q	0.3320
63	0.0370	36	0.1065	9	0.1960	R	0.3390
62	0.0380	35	0.1100	8	0.1990	S	0.3480
61	0.0390	34	0.1110	7	0.2010	T	0.3580
60	0.0400	33	0.1130	6	0.2040	U	0.3680
59	0.0410	32	0.1160	5	0.2055	V	0.3770
58	0.0420	31	0.1200	4	0.2090	W	0.3860
57	0.0430	30	0.1285	3	0.2130	X	0.3970
56	0.0465	29	0.1360	2	0.2210	Y	0.4040
55	0.0520	28	0.1405	1	0.2280	Z	0.4130
54	0.0550	27	0.1440				

Table 4. ASA-preferred Diameter-Pitch Combinations for Acme and Stub Acme Threads*

Nominal (major) diam., in.	Threads per in.	Nominal (major) diam., in.	Threads per in.	Nominal (major) diam., in.	Threads per in.	Nominal (major) diam., in.	Threads per in.
1/4	16	3/4	6	1 1/2	4	3	2
5/16	14	7/8	6	1 3/4	4	3 1/2	2
3/8	12	1	5	2	4	4	2
7/16	12	1 1/8	5	2 1/4	3	4 1/2	2
1/2	10	1 1/4	5	2 1/2	3	5	2
5/8	8	1 3/8	4	2 3/4	3		

* ASA B1.5 and B1.8—1952.

Table 5. American Standard Unified and American Thread Series[a]
Threads per Inch for Coarse, Fine, Extra-fine, 8-thread, 12-thread, and 16-thread Series[b]
Tap-drill Sizes for Approximately 75% Depth of Thread (Not American Standard)

Nominal size (basic major diam.)	Coarse thd series UNC and NC[c] in classes 1A, 1B, 2A, 2B, 3A, 3B, 2, 3		Fine thd series UNF and NF[c] in classes 1A, 1B, 2A, 2B, 3A, 3B, 2, 3		Extra-fine thd series UNEF and NEF[d] in classes 2A, 2B, 2, 3		8-thd series 8N[c] in classes 2A, 2B, 2, 3		12-thd series 12 UN and 12N[d] in classes 2A, 2B, 2, 3		16-thd series 16 UN and 16N[d] in classes 2A, 2B, 2, 3	
	Thds per in.	Tap drill	Thds per in.	Tap drill	Thds per in.	Tap drill	Thds per in.	Tap drill	Thds per in.	Tap drill	Thds per in.	Tap drill
0(0.060)	....	.....	80	$\frac{3}{64}$								
1(0.073)	64	No. 53	72	No. 53								
2(0.086)	56	No. 50	64	No. 50								
3(0.099)	48	No. 47	56	No. 45								
4(0.112)	40	No. 43	48	No. 42								
5(0.125)	40	No. 38	44	No. 37								
6(0.138)	32	No. 36	40	No. 33								
8(0.164)	32	No. 29	36	No. 29								
10(0.190)	24	No. 25	32	No. 21								
12(0.216)	24	No. 16	28	No. 14	32	No. 13						
$\frac{1}{4}$	20	No. 7	28	No. 3	32	$\frac{7}{32}$						
$\frac{5}{16}$	18	Let. F	24	Let. I	32	$\frac{9}{32}$						
$\frac{3}{8}$	16	$\frac{5}{16}$	24	Let. Q	32	$\frac{11}{32}$						
$\frac{7}{16}$	14	Let. U	20	$\frac{25}{64}$	28	$\frac{13}{32}$						
$\frac{1}{2}$	13	$\frac{27}{64}$	20	$\frac{29}{64}$	28	$\frac{15}{32}$	..	....	12	$\frac{27}{64}$		
$\frac{9}{16}$	12	$\frac{31}{64}$	18	$\frac{33}{64}$	24	$\frac{33}{64}$	..	....	12	$\frac{31}{64}$		
$\frac{5}{8}$	11	$\frac{17}{32}$	18	$\frac{37}{64}$	24	$\frac{37}{64}$	..	....	12	$\frac{35}{64}$		
$\frac{11}{16}$	....	.....	..	.....	24	$\frac{41}{64}$	..	....	12	$\frac{39}{64}$		
$\frac{3}{4}$	10	$\frac{21}{32}$	16	$1\frac{1}{16}$	20	$\frac{45}{64}$	..	....	12	$\frac{43}{64}$	16	$1\frac{1}{16}$
$1\frac{3}{16}$	....	.....	..	.....	20	$\frac{49}{64}$	..	....	12	$\frac{47}{64}$	16	$\frac{3}{4}$
$\frac{7}{8}$	9	$\frac{49}{64}$	14	$\frac{13}{16}$	20	$\frac{53}{64}$	..	....	12	$\frac{51}{64}$	16	$\frac{13}{16}$
$\frac{15}{16}$	....	.....	..	.....	20	$\frac{57}{64}$	..	....	12	$\frac{55}{64}$	16	$\frac{7}{8}$
1	....	.....	14	$\frac{15}{16}$	..	.....	8	$\frac{7}{8}$				
1	8	$\frac{7}{8}$	12	$\frac{59}{64}$	20	$\frac{61}{64}$	..	....	12	$\frac{59}{64}$	16	$\frac{15}{16}$
$1\frac{1}{16}$	....	.....	..	.....	18	1	..	....	12	$\frac{63}{64}$	16	1
$1\frac{1}{8}$	7	$\frac{63}{64}$	12	$1\frac{3}{64}$	18	$1\frac{5}{64}$	8	1	12	$1\frac{3}{64}$	16	$1\frac{1}{16}$
$1\frac{3}{16}$	....	.....	..	.....	18	$1\frac{9}{64}$	..	....	12	$1\frac{7}{64}$	16	$1\frac{1}{8}$
$1\frac{1}{4}$	7	$1\frac{7}{64}$	12	$1\frac{11}{64}$	18	$1\frac{3}{16}$	8	$1\frac{1}{8}$	12	$1\frac{11}{64}$	16	$1\frac{3}{16}$
$1\frac{5}{16}$	....	.....	..	.....	18	$1\frac{17}{64}$	..	....	12	$1\frac{15}{64}$	16	$1\frac{1}{4}$
$1\frac{3}{8}$	6	$1\frac{7}{32}$	12	$1\frac{19}{64}$	18	$1\frac{5}{16}$	8	$1\frac{1}{4}$	12	$1\frac{19}{64}$	16	$1\frac{5}{16}$
$1\frac{7}{16}$	....	.....	..	.....	18	$1\frac{3}{8}$	..	....	12	$1\frac{23}{64}$	16	$1\frac{3}{8}$
$1\frac{1}{2}$	6	$1\frac{11}{32}$	12	$1\frac{27}{64}$	18	$1\frac{7}{16}$	8	$1\frac{3}{8}$	12	$1\frac{27}{64}$	16	$1\frac{7}{16}$
$1\frac{9}{16}$	....	.....	..	.....	18	$1\frac{1}{2}$	..	....	..	.....	16	$1\frac{1}{2}$
$1\frac{5}{8}$	....	.....	..	.....	18	$1\frac{9}{16}$	8	$1\frac{1}{2}$	12	$1\frac{35}{64}$	16	$1\frac{9}{16}$
$1\frac{11}{16}$	....	.....	..	.....	18	$1\frac{5}{8}$	..	....	..	.....	16	$1\frac{5}{8}$
$1\frac{3}{4}$	5	$1\frac{9}{16}$	..	.....	16	$1\frac{11}{16}$	8[e]	$1\frac{5}{8}$	12	$1\frac{43}{64}$	16	$1\frac{11}{16}$
$1\frac{13}{16}$	....	.....	..	.....	..	.....	..	....	..	.....	16	$1\frac{3}{4}$
$1\frac{7}{8}$	....	.....	..	.....	..	.....	8	$1\frac{3}{4}$	12	$1\frac{51}{64}$	16	$1\frac{13}{16}$
$1\frac{15}{16}$	....	.....	..	.....	..	.....	..	....	..	.....	16	$1\frac{7}{8}$

Table 5. American Standard Unified and American Thread Series[a]—(*Continued*)

Nominal size (basic major diam.)	Coarse thd series UNC and NC[c] in classes 1A, 1B, 2A, 2B, 3A, 3B, 2, 3		Fine thd series UNF and NF[c] in classes 1A, 1B, 2A, 2B, 3A, 3B, 2, 3		Extra-fine thd series UNEF and NEF[d] in classes 2A, 2B, 2, 3		8-thd series 8N[c] in classes 2A, 2B, 2, 3		12-thd series 12 UN and 12N[d] in classes 2A, 2B, 2, 3		16-thd series 16 UN and 16N[d] in classes 2A, 2B, 2, 3	
	Thds per in.	Tap drill	Thds per in.	Tap drill	Thds per in.	Tap drill	Thds per in.	Tap drill	Thds per in.	Tap drill	Thds per in.	Tap drill
2	**4½**	$1\frac{25}{32}$	..	.....	**16**	$1\frac{15}{16}$	8[e]	$1\frac{7}{8}$	**12**	$1\frac{59}{64}$	**16**	$1\frac{15}{16}$
2 1/16	....	.....	..	.....	..	.....	..	...	..	.....	**16**	2
2 1/8	....	.....	..	.....	..	.....	8	2	**12**	$2\frac{3}{64}$	**16**	$2\frac{1}{16}$
2 3/16	....	.....	..	.....	..	.....	..	...	..	...	**16**	$2\frac{1}{8}$
2 1/4	**4½**	$2\frac{1}{32}$	..	.....	..	.....	8[e]	$2\frac{1}{8}$	**12**	$2\frac{11}{64}$	**16**	$2\frac{3}{16}$
2 5/16	....	.....	..	.....	..	.....	..	...	..	...	**16**	$2\frac{1}{4}$
2 3/8	....	.....	..	.....	..	.....	..	...	**12**	$2\frac{19}{64}$	**16**	$2\frac{5}{16}$
2 7/16	....	.....	..	.....	..	.....	..	...	..	.....	**16**	$2\frac{3}{8}$
2 1/2	**4**	$2\frac{1}{4}$	..	.....	..	.....	8[e]	$2\frac{3}{8}$	**12**	$2\frac{27}{64}$	**16**	$2\frac{7}{16}$
2 5/8	....	.....	..	.....	..	.....	..	...	**12**	$2\frac{35}{64}$	**16**	$2\frac{9}{16}$
2 3/4	**4**	$2\frac{1}{2}$	..	.....	..	.....	8[e]	$2\frac{5}{8}$	**12**	$2\frac{43}{64}$	**16**	$2\frac{11}{16}$
2 7/8	....	.....	..	.....	..	.....	..	...	**12**	$2\frac{51}{64}$	**16**	$2\frac{13}{16}$
3	**4**	$2\frac{3}{4}$	..	.....	..	.....	8[e]	$2\frac{7}{8}$	**12**	$2\frac{59}{64}$	**16**	$2\frac{15}{16}$
3 1/8	....	.....	..	.....	..	.....	..	...	**12**	$3\frac{3}{64}$	**16**	$3\frac{1}{16}$
3 1/4	**4**	3	..	.....	..	.....	8[e]	$3\frac{1}{8}$	**12**	$3\frac{11}{64}$	**16**	$3\frac{3}{16}$
3 3/8	....	.....	..	.....	..	.....	..	...	**12**	$3\frac{19}{64}$	**16**	$3\frac{5}{16}$
3 1/2	**4**	$3\frac{1}{4}$	..	.....	..	.....	8[e]	$3\frac{3}{8}$	**12**	$3\frac{27}{64}$	**16**	$3\frac{7}{16}$
3 5/8	....	.....	..	.....	..	.....	..	...	**12**	$3\frac{35}{64}$	**16**	$3\frac{9}{16}$
3 3/4	**4**	$3\frac{1}{2}$	..	.....	..	.....	8[e]	$3\frac{5}{8}$	**12**	$3\frac{43}{64}$	**16**	$3\frac{11}{16}$
3 7/8	....	.....	..	.....	..	.....	..	...	**12**	$3\frac{51}{64}$	**16**	$3\frac{13}{16}$
4	**4**	$3\frac{3}{4}$	..	.....	..	.....	8[e]	$3\frac{7}{8}$	**12**	$3\frac{59}{64}$	**16**	$3\frac{15}{16}$
4 1/4	....	.....	..	.....	..	.....	8[e]	$4\frac{1}{8}$	**12**	$4\frac{11}{64}$	**16**	$4\frac{3}{16}$
4 1/2	....	.....	..	.....	..	.....	8[e]	$4\frac{3}{8}$	**12**	$4\frac{27}{64}$	**16**	$4\frac{7}{16}$
4 3/4	....	.....	..	.....	..	.....	8[e]	$4\frac{5}{8}$	**12**	$4\frac{43}{64}$	**16**	$4\frac{11}{16}$
5	....	.....	..	.....	..	.....	8[e]	$4\frac{7}{8}$	**12**	$4\frac{59}{64}$	**16**	$4\frac{15}{16}$
5 1/4	....	.....	..	.....	..	.....	8	$5\frac{1}{8}$	**12**	$5\frac{11}{64}$	**16**	$5\frac{3}{16}$
5 1/2	....	.....	..	.....	..	.....	8	$5\frac{3}{8}$	**12**	$5\frac{27}{64}$	**16**	$5\frac{7}{16}$
5 3/4	....	.....	..	.....	..	.....	8	$5\frac{5}{8}$	**12**	$5\frac{43}{64}$	**16**	$5\frac{11}{16}$
6	....	.....	..	.....	..	.....	8	$5\frac{7}{8}$	**12**	$5\frac{59}{64}$	**16**	$5\frac{15}{16}$

[a] ASA B1.1—1949.

[b] Dimensions are in inches. Boldface type indicates unified threads.

[c] Limits of size for classes are based on a length of engagement equal to the nominal diameter.

[d] Limits of size for classes are based on a length of engagement equal to nine times the pitch.

[e] These sizes with specified limits of size based on a length of engagement of 9 threads in classes 2A and 2B are designated UN.

NOTE: If a thread is in both the 8-, 12-, or 16-thread series and the coarse, fine, or extra-fine thread series, the symbols and tolerances of the latter series apply.

Table 6. American Standard Square and Hexagon Bolts and Hexagon Cap Screw*

Nominal size (basic major diameter)	Regular bolts			Heavy bolts		
	Width across flats W, sq† and hex	Height H		Width across flats W	Height H	
		Unfin sq and hex	Semifin hex and hex screw‡		Unfin hex	Semifin hex and hex screw
$\frac{1}{4}$	$\frac{3}{8}$(sq), $\frac{7}{16}$(hex)	$\frac{11}{64}$	$\frac{5}{32}$			
$\frac{5}{16}$	$\frac{1}{2}$	$\frac{7}{32}$	$\frac{13}{64}$			
$\frac{3}{8}$	$\frac{9}{16}$	$\frac{1}{4}$	$\frac{15}{64}$			
$\frac{7}{16}$	$\frac{5}{8}$	$\frac{19}{64}$	$\frac{9}{32}$			
$\frac{1}{2}$	$\frac{3}{4}$	$\frac{11}{32}$	$\frac{5}{16}$	$\frac{7}{8}$	$\frac{7}{16}$	$\frac{13}{32}$
$\frac{9}{16}$	$\frac{13}{16}$	$\frac{25}{64}$	$\frac{23}{64}$	$\frac{15}{16}$	$\frac{15}{32}$	$\frac{7}{16}$
$\frac{5}{8}$	$\frac{15}{16}$	$\frac{27}{64}$	$\frac{25}{64}$	$1\frac{1}{16}$	$\frac{17}{32}$	$\frac{1}{2}$
$\frac{3}{4}$	$1\frac{1}{8}$	$\frac{1}{2}$	$\frac{15}{32}$	$1\frac{1}{4}$	$\frac{5}{8}$	$\frac{19}{32}$
$\frac{7}{8}$	$1\frac{5}{16}$	$\frac{37}{64}$	$\frac{35}{64}$	$1\frac{7}{16}$	$\frac{23}{32}$	$\frac{11}{16}$
1	$1\frac{1}{2}$	$\frac{43}{64}$	$\frac{39}{64}$	$1\frac{5}{8}$	$\frac{13}{16}$	$\frac{3}{4}$
$1\frac{1}{8}$	$1\frac{11}{16}$	$\frac{3}{4}$	$\frac{11}{16}$	$1\frac{13}{16}$	$\frac{29}{32}$	$\frac{27}{32}$
$1\frac{1}{4}$	$1\frac{7}{8}$	$\frac{27}{32}$	$\frac{25}{32}$	2	1	$\frac{15}{16}$
$1\frac{3}{8}$	$2\frac{1}{16}$	$\frac{29}{32}$	$\frac{27}{32}$	$2\frac{3}{16}$	$1\frac{3}{32}$	$1\frac{1}{32}$
$1\frac{1}{2}$	$2\frac{1}{4}$	1	$\frac{15}{16}$	$2\frac{3}{8}$	$1\frac{3}{16}$	$1\frac{1}{8}$
$1\frac{5}{8}$	$2\frac{7}{16}$	$1\frac{1}{16}$	1	$2\frac{9}{16}$	$1\frac{9}{32}$	$1\frac{7}{32}$
$1\frac{3}{4}$	$2\frac{5}{8}$	$1\frac{5}{32}$	$1\frac{3}{32}$	$2\frac{3}{4}$	$1\frac{3}{8}$	$1\frac{5}{16}$
$1\frac{7}{8}$	$2\frac{13}{16}$	$1\frac{7}{32}$	$1\frac{5}{32}$	$2\frac{15}{16}$	$1\frac{15}{32}$	$1\frac{13}{32}$
2	3	$1\frac{11}{32}$	$1\frac{7}{32}$	$3\frac{1}{8}$	$1\frac{9}{16}$	$1\frac{7}{16}$
$2\frac{1}{4}$	$3\frac{3}{8}$	$1\frac{1}{2}$	$1\frac{3}{8}$	$3\frac{1}{2}$	$1\frac{3}{4}$	$1\frac{5}{8}$
$2\frac{1}{2}$	$3\frac{3}{4}$	$1\frac{21}{32}$	$1\frac{17}{32}$	$3\frac{7}{8}$	$1\frac{15}{16}$	$1\frac{13}{16}$
$2\frac{3}{4}$	$4\frac{1}{8}$	$1\frac{13}{16}$	$1\frac{11}{16}$	$4\frac{1}{4}$	$2\frac{1}{8}$	2
3	$4\frac{1}{2}$	2	$1\frac{7}{8}$	$4\frac{5}{8}$	$2\frac{5}{16}$	$2\frac{3}{16}$
$3\frac{1}{4}$	$4\frac{7}{8}$	$2\frac{3}{16}$	2			
$3\frac{1}{2}$	$5\frac{1}{4}$	$2\frac{5}{16}$	$2\frac{1}{8}$			
$3\frac{3}{4}$	$5\frac{5}{8}$	$2\frac{1}{2}$	$2\frac{5}{16}$			
4	6	$2\frac{11}{16}$	$2\frac{1}{2}$			

All dimensions in inches.

* ASA B18.2—1952.

† Square bolts in (nominal) size from $\frac{1}{4}$ to $1\frac{1}{2}$ only.

‡ Hexagon-head cap screw, automotive hexagon-head bolt, and close-tolerance regular bolt; lengths from $\frac{1}{4}$ to 3 in. only.

NOTE. Bolt lengths are not standardized. For diameters $\frac{1}{4}$ to $\frac{1}{2}$ in., increments are $\frac{1}{4}$ in. beyond $\frac{3}{4}$-in. length. For diameters $\frac{1}{2}$ to 1 in., increments are $\frac{1}{2}$ in. beyond 6-in. lengths. For bolts larger than 1 in. in diameter the lengths increase by 2 to 4 in. beyond 12-in. lengths.

Threads are coarse series, class 2A except with hexagon screw which is coarse, fine, or 8-pitch series, class 2A.

Minimum thread length: $2D + \frac{1}{4}$ in. for bolts 6 in. or less in length.

$2D + \frac{1}{2}$ in. for bolts over 6 in. in length.

Bolts too short for formula, thread entire length.

Table 7. American Standard Square and Hexagon Nuts*

Nominal size (basic major diameter)	Regular nuts†						Heavy nuts†					Slot	
	Width across flats W, sq and hex	Thickness T					Width across flats W, sq and hex	Thickness T				Width	Depth
		Unfin sq and hex	Unfin hex jam	Semi-fin hex and hex slotted‡	Semi-fin hex jam	Semi-fin hex thick, thick slotted,‡ and castle		Unfin sq and hex	Unfin hex jam	Semi-fin hex and hex slotted	Semi-fin hex jam		
1/4	7/16	15/64	11/64	7/32	5/32	9/32	1/2	1/4	3/16	15/64	11/64	5/64	3/32
5/16	1/2	9/32	13/64	17/64	3/16	21/64	9/16	5/16	7/32	19/64	13/64	3/32	3/32
3/8	9/16	11/32	15/64	21/64	7/32	13/32	11/16	3/8	1/4	23/64	15/64	1/8	1/8
7/16	11/16	25/64	17/64	3/8	1/4	29/64	3/4	7/16	9/32	27/64	17/64	1/8	5/32
1/2	3/4	29/64	21/64	7/16	5/16	9/16	7/8	1/2	5/16	31/64	19/64	5/32	5/32
9/16	7/8	1/2	21/64	31/64	5/16	39/64	15/16	9/16	11/32	35/64	21/64	5/32	3/16
5/8	15/16	9/16	25/64	35/64	3/8	23/32	1 1/16	5/8	3/8	39/64	23/64	3/16	7/32
3/4	1 1/8	21/32	7/16	41/64	27/64	13/16	1 1/4	3/4	7/16	47/64	27/64	3/16	1/4
7/8	1 5/16	49/64	1/2	3/4	31/64	29/32	1 7/16	7/8	1/2	55/64	31/64	3/16	1/4
1	1 1/2	7/8	9/16	55/64	35/64	1	1 5/8	1	9/16	63/64	35/64	1/4	9/32
1 1/8	1 11/16	1	5/8	31/32	39/64	1 5/32	1 13/16	1 1/8	5/8	1 7/64	39/64	1/4	11/32
1 1/4	1 7/8	1 3/32	3/4	1 1/16	23/32	1 1/4	2	1 1/4	3/4	1 7/32	23/32	5/16	3/8
1 3/8	2 1/16	1 13/64	13/16	1 11/64	25/32	1 3/8	2 3/16	1 3/8	13/16	1 11/32	25/32	5/16	3/8
1 1/2	2 1/4	1 5/16	7/8	1 9/32	27/32	1 1/2	2 3/8	1 1/2	7/8	1 15/32	27/32	3/8	7/16
1 5/8	2 7/16	.....	....	1 25/64	29/32	.....	2 9/16	1 5/8	15/16	1 19/32	29/32	3/8	7/16
1 3/4	2 5/8	.....	....	1 1/2	31/32	.....	2 3/4	1 3/4	1	1 23/32	31/32	7/16	1/2
1 7/8	2 13/16	.....	....	1 39/64	1 1/32	.....	2 15/16	1 7/8	1 1/16	1 27/32	1 1/32	7/16	9/16
2	3	.....	....	1 23/32	1 3/32	.....	3 1/8	2	1 1/8	1 31/32	1 3/32	7/16	9/16
2 1/4	3 3/8	.....	....	1 59/64	1 13/64	.....	3 1/2	2 1/4	1 1/4	2 13/64	1 13/64	7/16	9/16
2 1/2	3 3/4	.....	....	2 9/64	1 29/64	.....	3 7/8	2 1/2	1 1/2	2 29/64	1 29/64	9/16	11/16
2 3/4	2 1/8	.....	....	2 23/64	1 37/64	.....	4 1/4	2 3/4	1 5/8	2 45/64	1 37/64	9/16	11/16
3	4 1/2	.....	....	2 37/64	1 45/64	.....	4 5/8	3	1 3/4	2 61/64	1 45/64	5/8	3/4
3 1/4	.....	.....	....	.....	.....	.....	5	3 1/4	1 7/8	3 3/16	1 13/16	5/8	3/4
3 1/2	.....	.....	....	.....	.....	.....	5 3/8	3 1/2	2	3 7/16	1 15/16	5/8	3/4
3 3/4	.....	.....	....	.....	.....	.....	5 3/4	3 3/4	2 1/8	3 11/16	2 1/16	5/8	3/4
4	.....	.....	....	.....	.....	.....	6 1/8	4	2 1/4	3 15/16	2 3/16	5/8	3/4

All dimensions in inches.
* ASA B18.2—1952.
† Thread for unfinished nuts: coarse series, class 2B; for semifinished nuts: coarse, fine, or 8-pitch series, class 2B.
‡ Slot dimensions for regular slotted nuts are same as for heavy slotted nuts.

Table 8. American Standard Cap Screws, Socket and Slotted Heads*

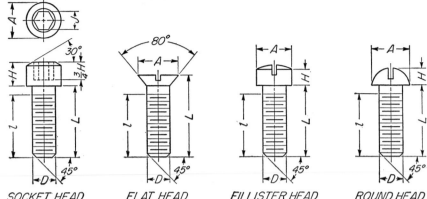

SOCKET HEAD FLAT HEAD FILLISTER HEAD ROUND HEAD

Nominal diameter	Socket head†			Flat head‡	Fillister head		Round head‡	
	A	H	J	A	A	H	A	H
2	0.140	0.086	1/16					
3	0.161	0.099	5/64					
4	0.183	0.112	5/64					
5	0.205	0.125	3/32					
6	0.226	0.138	3/32					
8	0.270	0.164	1/8					
10	5/16	0.190	5/32					
12	11/32	0.216	5/32					
1/4	3/8	1/4	3/16	1/2	3/8	11/64	7/16	3/16
5/16	7/16	5/16	7/32	5/8	7/16	13/64	9/16	15/64
3/8	9/16	3/8	5/16	3/4	9/16	1/4	5/8	17/64
7/16	5/8	7/16	5/16	13/16	5/8	19/64	3/4	5/16
1/2	3/4	1/2	3/8	7/8	3/4	21/64	13/16	11/32
9/16	13/16	9/16	3/8	1	13/16	3/8	15/16	13/32
5/8	7/8	5/8	1/2	1 1/8	7/8	27/64	1	7/16
3/4	1	3/4	9/16	1 3/8	1	1/2	1 1/4	17/32
7/8	1 1/8	7/8	9/16	1 5/8	1 1/8	19/32		
1	1 5/16	1	5/8	1 7/8	1 5/16	21/32		
1 1/8	1 1/2	1 1/8	3/4					
1 1/4	1 3/4	1 1/4	3/4					
1 3/8	1 7/8	1 3/8	3/4					
1 1/2	2	1 1/2	1					

All dimensions in inches.

Slot proportions vary with size of screw; see text for empirical formulas.

* ASA B18.3—1947 and ASA B18.6—1947.

† Body length increments: For screw lengths 1/4 to 1 in. = 1/8 in.

For screw lengths 1 to 4 in. = 1/4 in.

For screw lengths 4 to 6 in. = 1/2 in.

Thread length, l: For coarse thread: $2D + \frac{1}{2}$ in.

For fine thread: $1\frac{1}{2}D + \frac{1}{2}$ in.

‡ Thread either coarse or fine, class 3.

Thread length, l: $2D + \frac{1}{4}$ in.

Body length increments may be taken the same as for socket-head screws.

Table 9. American Standard Machine Screws*
Heads May Be Slotted or Recessed†

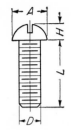 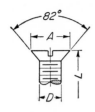 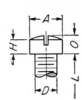 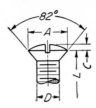 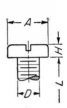 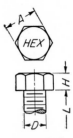

ROUND HEAD   FLAT HEAD   FILLISTER HEAD   OVAL HEAD   PAN HEAD   HEX HEAD

Nominal diameter	Round head		Flat head	Fillister head			Oval head		Pan head		Hexagon head	
	A	H	A	A	H	O	A	C	A	H	A	H
0	0.113	0.053	0.119	0.096	0.045	0.059	0.119	0.021				
1	0.138	0.061	0.146	0.118	0.053	0.071	0.146	0.025				
2	0.162	0.069	0.172	0.140	0.062	0.083	0.172	0.029	0.167	0.053	0.125	0.050
3	0.187	0.078	0.199	0.161	0.070	0.095	0.199	0.033	0.193	0.060	0.187	0.055
4	0.211	0.086	0.225	0.183	0.079	0.107	0.225	0.037	0.219	0.068	0.187	0.060
5	0.236	0.095	0.252	0.205	0.088	0.120	0.252	0.041	0.245	0.075	0.187	0.070
6	0.260	0.103	0.279	0.226	0.096	0.132	0.279	0.045	0.270	0.082	0.250	0.080
8	0.309	0.120	0.332	0.270	0.113	0.156	0.332	0.052	0.322	0.096	0.250	0.110
10	0.359	0.137	0.385	0.313	0.130	0.180	0.385	0.060	0.373	0.110	0.312	0.120
12	0.408	0.153	0.438	0.357	0.148	0.205	0.438	0.068	0.425	0.125	0.312	0.155
¼	0.472	0.175	0.507	0.414	0.170	0.237	0.507	0.079	0.492	0.144	0.375	0.190
⁵⁄₁₆	0.590	0.216	0.635	0.518	0.211	0.295	0.635	0.099	0.615	0.178	0.500	0.230
⅜	0.708	0.256	0.762	0.622	0.253	0.355	0.762	0.117	0.740	0.212	0.562	0.295
⁷⁄₁₆	0.750	0.328	0.812	0.625	0.265	0.368	0.812	0.122				
½	0.813	0.355	0.875	0.750	0.297	0.412	0.875	0.131				
⁹⁄₁₆	0.938	0.410	1.000	0.812	0.336	0.466	1.000	0.150				
⅝	1.000	0.438	1.125	0.875	0.375	0.521	1.125	0.169				
¾	1.250	0.547	1.375	1.000	0.441	0.612	1.375	0.206				

Dimensions given are maximum values, all in inches.

* ASA B18.6—1947.

† Except hexagon head which is plain or may be slotted if so specified. Slot and recess proportions vary with size of fastener; see text for empirical formulas.

Thread length: For screws 2 in. long or less, thread entire length.

For screws 2 in. long or more, thread length (l) = 1¾ in.

Threads are coarse or fine series, class 2.

Table 10. American Standard Hexagon Sockets, Slotted Headless, and Square-head Setscrews*

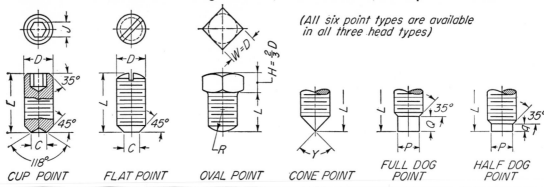

(All six point types are available in all three head types)

CUP POINT FLAT POINT OVAL POINT CONE POINT FULL DOG POINT HALF DOG POINT

Diameter D	Cup and flat-point diameter C	Oval-point radius R	Cone-point angle Y		Full and half dog points			Socket width J
			118° for these lengths and shorter	90° for these lengths and longer	Diameter P	Length Full Q	Half q	
5	1/16	3/32	1/8	3/16	0.083	0.06	0.03	1/16
6	0.069	7/64	1/8	3/16	0.092	0.07	0.03	1/16
8	5/64	1/8	3/16	1/4	0.109	0.08	0.04	5/64
10	3/32	9/64	3/16	1/4	0.127	0.09	0.04	3/32
12	7/64	5/32	3/16	1/4	0.144	0.11	0.06	3/32
1/4	1/8	3/16	1/4	5/16	5/32	1/8	1/16	1/8
5/16	11/64	15/64	5/16	3/8	13/64	5/32	5/64	5/32
3/8	13/64	9/32	3/8	7/16	1/4	3/16	3/32	3/16
7/16	15/64	21/64	7/16	1/2	19/64	7/32	7/64	7/32
1/2	9/32	3/8	1/2	9/16	11/32	1/4	1/8	1/4
9/16	5/16	27/64	9/16	5/8	25/64	9/32	9/64	1/4
5/8	23/64	15/32	5/8	3/4	15/32	5/16	5/32	5/16
3/4	7/16	9/16	3/4	7/8	9/16	3/8	3/16	3/8
7/8	33/64	21/32	7/8	1	21/32	7/16	7/32	1/2
1	19/32	3/4	1	1 1/8	3/4	1/2	1/4	9/16
1 1/8	43/64	27/32	1 1/8	1 1/4	27/32	9/16	9/32	9/16
1 1/4	3/4	15/16	1 1/4	1 1/2	15/16	5/8	5/16	5/8
1 3/8	53/64	1 1/32	1 3/8	1 5/8	1 1/32	11/16	11/32	5/8
1 1/2	29/32	1 1/8	1 1/2	1 3/4	1 1/8	3/4	3/8	3/4
1 3/4	1 1/16	1 5/16	1 3/4	2	1 5/16	7/8	7/16	1
2	1 7/32	1 1/2	2	2 1/4	1 1/2	1	1/2	1

All dimensions are in inches.

* ASA B18.3—1947, ASA B18.6—1947, and ASA B18—1951.

Length increments: For screw lengths 1/4 to 5/8 in. = 1/16 in.

For screw lengths 5/8 to 1 in. = 1/8 in.

For screw lengths 1 to 4 in. = 1/4 in.

For screw lengths 4 to 6 in. = 1/2 in.

Threads are coarse or fine series, classes 2 or 2A.

Slotted headless screws standardized in sizes No. 5 to 3/4 in. only. Slot proportions vary with diameter; see text for empirical formulas.

Square-head setscrews are standardized in sizes No. 10 to 1 1/2 in. only.

Table 11. American Standard Wood Screws*

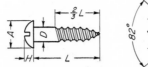

ROUND HEAD   FLAT HEAD   OVAL HEAD

Nominal size	Basic diameter of screw D	No. of threads per in.†	Slot width‡ (all heads)	Round head		Flat head	Oval head	
				A	H	A	A	C
0	0.060	32	0.023	0.113	0.053	0.119	0.119	0.021
1	0.073	28	0.026	0.138	0.061	0.146	0.146	0.025
2	0.086	26	0.031	0.162	0.069	0.172	0.172	0.029
3	0.099	24	0.035	0.187	0.078	0.199	0.199	0.033
4	0.112	22	0.039	0.211	0.086	0.225	0.225	0.037
5	0.125	20	0.043	0.236	0.095	0.252	0.252	0.041
6	0.138	18	0.048	0.260	0.103	0.279	0.279	0.045
7	0.151	16	0.048	0.285	0.111	0.305	0.305	0.049
8	0.164	15	0.054	0.309	0.120	0.332	0.332	0.052
9	0.177	14	0.054	0.334	0.128	0.358	0.358	0.056
10	0.190	13	0.060	0.359	0.137	0.385	0.385	0.060
12	0.216	11	0.067	0.408	0.153	0.438	0.438	0.068
14	0.242	10	0.075	0.457	0.170	0.491	0.491	0.076
16	0.268	9	0.075	0.506	0.187	0.544	0.544	0.084
18	0.294	8	0.084	0.555	0.204	0.597	0.597	0.092
20	0.320	8	0.084	0.604	0.220	0.650	0.650	0.100
24	0.372	7	0.094	0.702	0.254	0.756	0.756	0.116

Dimensions given are maximum values, all in inches. Heads may be slotted or recessed as specified.
* ASA B18.6—1947.   † Thread length = $\frac{2}{3}L$.   ‡ Slots vary with type and size of screw; draw to look well.

Table 12. Dimensions of Taper Pins—Taper $\frac{1}{4}''$ per Foot

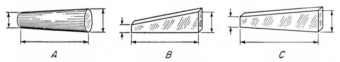

Size No.	Diameter, large end	Drill size for reamer	Max length	Size No.	Diameter, large end	Drill size for reamer	Max length
000000	0.072	53	$\frac{5}{8}$	5	0.289	$\frac{1}{4}$	$2\frac{1}{4}$
00000	0.092	47	$\frac{5}{8}$	6	0.341	$\frac{9}{32}$	$3\frac{1}{4}$
0000	0.108	42	$\frac{3}{4}$	7	0.409	$\frac{11}{32}$	$3\frac{3}{4}$
000	0.125	37	$\frac{3}{4}$	8	0.492	$\frac{13}{32}$	$4\frac{1}{2}$
00	0.147	31	1	9	0.591	$\frac{31}{64}$	$5\frac{1}{4}$
0	0.156	28	1	10	0.706	$\frac{19}{32}$	6
1	0.172	25	$1\frac{1}{4}$	11	0.857	$\frac{23}{32}$	$7\frac{1}{4}$
2	0.193	19	$1\frac{1}{2}$	12	1.013	$\frac{55}{64}$	$8\frac{3}{4}$
3	0.219	12	$1\frac{3}{4}$	13	1.233	$1\frac{1}{64}$	$10\frac{3}{4}$
4	0.250	3	2				

All dimensions in inches.

Table 13. ASA-approved Widths and Heights of Standard Square and Flat Keys with Corresponding Shaft Diameters*

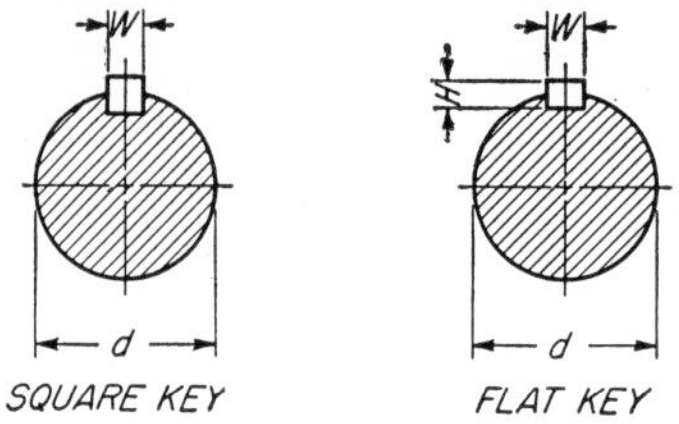

SQUARE KEY　　　　FLAT KEY

Shaft diameter d (inclusive)	Square-stock keys W	Flat-stock keys, $W \times H$	Shaft diameter d (inclusive)	Square-stock keys W	Flat-stock keys, $W \times H$
½ − 9/16	⅛	⅛ × 3/32	2 5/16−2¾	⅝	⅝ × 7/16
⅝ − ⅞	3/16	3/16 × ⅛	2⅞ −3¼	¾	¾ × ½
15/16−1¼	¼	¼ × 3/16	3⅜ −3¾	⅞	⅞ × ⅝
1 5/16−1⅜	5/16	5/16 × ¼	3⅞ −4½	1	1 × ¾
1 7/16−1¾	⅜	⅜ × ¼	4¾ −5½	1¼	1¼ × ⅞
1 13/16−2¼	½	½ × ⅜	5¾−6	1½	1½ × 1

Dimensions in inches.
* ASA B17.1—1943.

Table 14. ASA-approved Dimensions of Standard Gib-head Keys, Square and Flat*

$L = 4W$ (MIN.)
$L = 16W$ (MAX.)

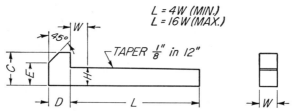

TAPER ⅛" in 12"

Diameters of shafts	Square type					Flat type				
	Key		Gib head			Key		Gib head		
	W	H	C	D	E	W	H	C	D	E
½ − 9/16	⅛	⅛	¼	7/32	5/32	⅛	3/32	3/16	⅛	⅛
⅝ − ⅞	3/16	3/16	5/16	9/32	7/32	3/16	⅛	¼	3/16	5/32
15/16−1¼	¼	¼	7/16	11/32	11/32	¼	3/16	5/16	¼	3/16
1 5/16−1⅜	5/16	5/16	9/16	13/32	13/32	5/16	¼	⅜	5/16	¼
1 7/16−1¾	⅜	⅜	11/16	15/32	15/32	⅜	¼	7/16	⅜	5/16
1 13/16−2¼	½	½	⅞	19/32	⅝	½	⅜	⅝	½	7/16
2 5/16−2¾	⅝	⅝	1 1/16	23/32	¾	⅝	7/16	¾	⅝	½
2 ⅞ −3¼	¾	¾	1 ¼	⅞	⅞	¾	½	⅞	¾	⅝
3 ⅜ −3¾	⅞	⅞	1 ½	1	1	⅞	⅝	1 1/16	⅞	¾
3 ⅞ −4½	1	1	1 ¾	1 3/16	1 3/16	1	¾	1¼	1	1 3/16
4 ¾ −5½	1¼	1¼	2	1 7/16	1 7/16	1¼	⅞	1½	1¼	1
5 ¾ −6	1½	1½	2 ½	1 ¾	1 ¾	1½	1	1¾	1½	1 ¼

Dimensions in inches.
* ASA B17.1—1943.

Table 15. Woodruff Key and Key-slot Dimensions

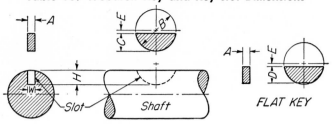

ROUND KEY

FLAT KEY

Key No.*	Nominal size $A \times B$	Max width of key A	Max diam of key B	Max height of key		Distance below center E	Key slot			
				C	D		Max width, W	Min width, W	Max depth, H	Min depth, H
204	$\frac{1}{16} \times \frac{1}{2}$	0.0635	0.500	0.203	0.194	$\frac{3}{64}$	0.0630	0.0615	0.1718	0.1668
304	$\frac{3}{32} \times \frac{1}{2}$	0.0948	0.500	0.203	0.194	$\frac{3}{64}$	0.0943	0.0928	0.1561	0.1511
305	$\frac{3}{32} \times \frac{5}{8}$	0.0948	0.625	0.250	0.240	$\frac{1}{16}$	0.0943	0.0928	0.2031	0.1981
404	$\frac{1}{8} \times \frac{1}{2}$	0.1260	0.500	0.203	0.194	$\frac{3}{64}$	0.1255	0.1240	0.1405	0.1355
405	$\frac{1}{8} \times \frac{5}{8}$	0.1260	0.625	0.250	0.240	$\frac{1}{16}$	0.1255	0.1240	0.1875	0.1825
406	$\frac{1}{8} \times \frac{3}{4}$	0.1260	0.750	0.313	0.303	$\frac{1}{16}$	0.1255	0.1240	0.2505	0.2455
505	$\frac{5}{32} \times \frac{5}{8}$	0.1573	0.625	0.250	0.240	$\frac{1}{16}$	0.1568	0.1553	0.1719	0.1669
506	$\frac{5}{32} \times \frac{3}{4}$	0.1573	0.750	0.313	0.303	$\frac{1}{16}$	0.1568	0.1553	0.2349	0.2299
507	$\frac{5}{32} \times \frac{7}{8}$	0.1573	0.875	0.375	0.365	$\frac{1}{16}$	0.1568	0.1553	0.2969	0.2919
606	$\frac{3}{16} \times \frac{3}{4}$	0.1885	0.750	0.313	0.303	$\frac{1}{16}$	0.1880	0.1863	0.2193	0.2143
607	$\frac{3}{16} \times \frac{7}{8}$	0.1885	0.875	0.375	0.365	$\frac{1}{16}$	0.1880	0.1863	0.2813	0.2763
608	$\frac{3}{16} \times 1$	0.1885	1.000	0.438	0.428	$\frac{1}{16}$	0.1880	0.1863	0.3443	0.3393
609	$\frac{3}{16} \times 1\frac{1}{8}$	0.1885	1.125	0.484	0.475	$\frac{5}{64}$	0.1880	0.1863	0.3903	0.3853
807	$\frac{1}{4} \times \frac{7}{8}$	0.2510	0.875	0.375	0.365	$\frac{1}{16}$	0.2505	0.2487	0.2500	0.2450
808	$\frac{1}{4} \times 1$	0.2510	1.000	0.438	0.428	$\frac{1}{16}$	0.2505	0.2487	0.3130	0.3080
809	$\frac{1}{4} \times 1\frac{1}{8}$	0.2510	1.125	0.484	0.475	$\frac{5}{64}$	0.2505	0.2487	0.3590	0.3540
810	$\frac{1}{4} \times 1\frac{1}{4}$	0.2510	1.250	0.547	0.537	$\frac{5}{64}$	0.2505	0.2487	0.4220	0.4170
811	$\frac{1}{4} \times 1\frac{3}{8}$	0.2510	1.375	0.594	0.584	$\frac{3}{32}$	0.2505	0.2487	0.4690	0.4640
812	$\frac{1}{4} \times 1\frac{1}{2}$	0.2510	1.500	0.641	0.631	$\frac{7}{64}$	0.2505	0.2487	0.5160	0.5110
1008	$\frac{5}{16} \times 1$	0.3135	1.000	0.438	0.428	$\frac{1}{16}$	0.3130	0.3111	0.2818	0.2768
1009	$\frac{5}{16} \times 1\frac{1}{8}$	0.3135	1.125	0.484	0.475	$\frac{5}{64}$	0.3130	0.3111	0.3278	0.3228
1010	$\frac{5}{16} \times 1\frac{1}{4}$	0.3135	1.250	0.547	0.537	$\frac{5}{64}$	0.3130	0.3111	0.3908	0.3858
1011	$\frac{5}{16} \times 1\frac{3}{8}$	0.3135	1.375	0.594	0.584	$\frac{3}{32}$	0.3130	0.3111	0.4378	0.4328
1012	$\frac{5}{16} \times 1\frac{1}{2}$	0.3135	1.500	0.641	0.631	$\frac{7}{64}$	0.3130	0.3111	0.4848	0.4798
1210	$\frac{3}{8} \times 1\frac{1}{4}$	0.3760	1.250	0.547	0.537	$\frac{5}{64}$	0.3755	0.3735	0.3595	0.3545
1211	$\frac{3}{8} \times 1\frac{3}{8}$	0.3760	1.375	0.594	0.584	$\frac{3}{32}$	0.3755	0.3735	0.4060	0.4015
1212	$\frac{3}{8} \times 1\frac{1}{2}$	0.3760	1.500	0.641	0.631	$\frac{7}{64}$	0.3755	0.3735	0.4535	0.4485

All dimensions in inches.

* Key numbers indicate the nominal key dimensions. The last two digits give the nominal diameter B in eighths of an inch and the digits preceding the last two give the nominal width A in thirty-seconds of an inch. Thus, 406 indicates a key $\frac{4}{32}$ by $\frac{6}{8}$, or $\frac{1}{8}$ by $\frac{3}{4}$ in.

Key-slot Cutters. Two series of key-slot cutters, fine and coarse teeth, are standard. Both have a shank diameter of $\frac{1}{2}$ in. for all sizes. They are designated by the key numbers used to specify the size of the key.

Table 16. Dimensions of Pratt and Whitney Keys

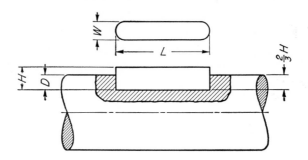

Key No.	L^*	W	H	D	Key No.	L^*	W	H	D
1	$\frac{1}{2}$	$\frac{1}{16}$	$\frac{3}{32}$	$\frac{1}{16}$	22	$1\frac{3}{8}$	$\frac{1}{4}$	$\frac{3}{8}$	$\frac{1}{4}$
2	$\frac{1}{2}$	$\frac{3}{32}$	$\frac{9}{64}$	$\frac{3}{32}$	23	$1\frac{3}{8}$	$\frac{5}{16}$	$\frac{15}{32}$	$\frac{5}{16}$
3	$\frac{1}{2}$	$\frac{1}{8}$	$\frac{3}{16}$	$\frac{1}{8}$	F	$1\frac{3}{8}$	$\frac{3}{8}$	$\frac{9}{16}$	$\frac{3}{8}$
4	$\frac{5}{8}$	$\frac{3}{32}$	$\frac{9}{64}$	$\frac{3}{32}$	24	$1\frac{1}{2}$	$\frac{1}{4}$	$\frac{3}{8}$	$\frac{1}{4}$
5	$\frac{5}{8}$	$\frac{1}{8}$	$\frac{3}{16}$	$\frac{1}{8}$	25	$1\frac{1}{2}$	$\frac{5}{16}$	$\frac{15}{32}$	$\frac{5}{16}$
6	$\frac{5}{8}$	$\frac{5}{32}$	$\frac{15}{64}$	$\frac{5}{32}$	G	$1\frac{1}{2}$	$\frac{3}{8}$	$\frac{9}{16}$	$\frac{3}{8}$
7	$\frac{3}{4}$	$\frac{1}{8}$	$\frac{3}{16}$	$\frac{1}{8}$	51	$1\frac{3}{4}$	$\frac{1}{4}$	$\frac{3}{8}$	$\frac{1}{4}$
8	$\frac{3}{4}$	$\frac{5}{32}$	$\frac{15}{64}$	$\frac{5}{32}$	52	$1\frac{3}{4}$	$\frac{5}{16}$	$\frac{15}{32}$	$\frac{5}{16}$
9	$\frac{3}{4}$	$\frac{3}{16}$	$\frac{9}{32}$	$\frac{3}{16}$	53	$1\frac{3}{4}$	$\frac{3}{8}$	$\frac{9}{16}$	$\frac{3}{8}$
10	$\frac{7}{8}$	$\frac{5}{32}$	$\frac{15}{64}$	$\frac{5}{32}$	26	2	$\frac{3}{16}$	$\frac{9}{32}$	$\frac{3}{16}$
11	$\frac{7}{8}$	$\frac{3}{16}$	$\frac{9}{32}$	$\frac{3}{16}$	27	2	$\frac{1}{4}$	$\frac{3}{8}$	$\frac{1}{4}$
12	$\frac{7}{8}$	$\frac{7}{32}$	$\frac{21}{64}$	$\frac{7}{32}$	28	2	$\frac{5}{16}$	$\frac{15}{32}$	$\frac{5}{16}$
A	$\frac{7}{8}$	$\frac{1}{4}$	$\frac{3}{8}$	$\frac{1}{4}$	29	2	$\frac{3}{8}$	$\frac{9}{16}$	$\frac{3}{8}$
13	1	$\frac{3}{16}$	$\frac{9}{32}$	$\frac{3}{16}$	54	$2\frac{1}{4}$	$\frac{1}{4}$	$\frac{3}{8}$	$\frac{1}{4}$
14	1	$\frac{7}{32}$	$\frac{21}{64}$	$\frac{7}{32}$	55	$2\frac{1}{4}$	$\frac{5}{16}$	$\frac{15}{16}$	$\frac{5}{16}$
15	1	$\frac{1}{4}$	$\frac{3}{8}$	$\frac{1}{4}$	56	$2\frac{1}{4}$	$\frac{3}{8}$	$\frac{9}{16}$	$\frac{3}{8}$
B	1	$\frac{5}{16}$	$\frac{15}{32}$	$\frac{5}{16}$	57	$2\frac{1}{4}$	$\frac{7}{16}$	$\frac{21}{32}$	$\frac{7}{16}$
16	$1\frac{1}{8}$	$\frac{3}{16}$	$\frac{9}{32}$	$\frac{3}{16}$	58	$2\frac{1}{2}$	$\frac{5}{16}$	$\frac{15}{32}$	$\frac{5}{16}$
17	$1\frac{1}{8}$	$\frac{7}{32}$	$\frac{21}{64}$	$\frac{7}{32}$	59	$2\frac{1}{2}$	$\frac{3}{8}$	$\frac{9}{16}$	$\frac{3}{8}$
18	$1\frac{1}{8}$	$\frac{1}{4}$	$\frac{3}{8}$	$\frac{1}{4}$	60	$2\frac{1}{2}$	$\frac{7}{16}$	$\frac{21}{32}$	$\frac{7}{16}$
C	$1\frac{1}{8}$	$\frac{5}{16}$	$\frac{15}{32}$	$\frac{5}{16}$	61	$2\frac{1}{2}$	$\frac{1}{2}$	$\frac{3}{4}$	$\frac{1}{2}$
19	$1\frac{1}{4}$	$\frac{3}{16}$	$\frac{9}{32}$	$\frac{3}{16}$	30	3	$\frac{3}{8}$	$\frac{9}{16}$	$\frac{3}{8}$
20	$1\frac{1}{4}$	$\frac{7}{32}$	$\frac{21}{64}$	$\frac{7}{32}$	31	3	$\frac{7}{16}$	$\frac{21}{32}$	$\frac{7}{16}$
21	$1\frac{1}{4}$	$\frac{1}{4}$	$\frac{3}{8}$	$\frac{1}{4}$	32	3	$\frac{1}{2}$	$\frac{3}{4}$	$\frac{1}{2}$
D	$1\frac{1}{4}$	$\frac{5}{16}$	$\frac{15}{32}$	$\frac{5}{16}$	33	3	$\frac{9}{16}$	$\frac{27}{32}$	$\frac{9}{16}$
E	$1\frac{1}{4}$	$\frac{3}{8}$	$\frac{9}{16}$	$\frac{3}{8}$	34	3	$\frac{5}{8}$	$\frac{15}{16}$	$\frac{5}{8}$

All dimensions in inches.

Key is two-thirds in shaft; one-third in hub.

Keys are 0.001 inch oversize in width to ensure proper fitting in keyway.

Keyway size: width = W; depth = $H - D$.

* Length L may vary but should never be less than $2W$.

Table 17. Wire and Sheet-metal Gages

Number of gage	American or Brown and Sharpe[a]	Washburn & Moen or American Steel and Wire Co.[b]	Music wire[c]	Imperial wire gage[d]	U.S. Std. for plate[e]
0000000	. . . . .	0.4900	. . . . .	0.5000	0.5000
000000	0.5800	0.4615	0.004	0.4640	0.4688
00000	0.5165	0.4305	0.005	0.4320	0.4375
0000	0.4600	0.3938	0.006	0.4000	0.4063
000	0.4096	0.3625	0.007	0.3720	0.3750
00	0.3648	0.3310	0.008	0.3480	0.3438
0	0.3249	0.3065	0.009	0.3240	0.3125
1	0.2893	0.2830	0.010	0.3000	0.2813
2	0.2576	0.2625	0.011	0.2760	0.2656
3	0.2294	0.2437	0.012	0.2520	0.2500
4	0.2043	0.2253	0.013	0.2320	0.2344
5	0.1819	0.2070	0.014	0.2120	0.2188
6	0.1620	0.1920	0.016	0.1920	0.2031
7	0.1443	0.1770	0.018	0.1760	0.1875
8	0.1285	0.1620	0.020	0.1600	0.1719
9	0.1144	0.1483	0.022	0.1440	0.1563
10	0.1019	0.1350	0.024	0.1280	0.1406
11	0.0907	0.1205	0.026	0.1160	0.1250
12	0.0808	0.1055	0.029	0.1040	0.1094
13	0.0720	0.0915	0.031	0.0920	0.0938
14	0.0641	0.0800	0.033	0.0800	0.0781
15	0.0571	0.0720	0.035	0.0720	0.0703
16	0.0508	0.0625	0.037	0.0640	0.0625
17	0.0453	0.0540	0.039	0.0560	0.0563
18	0.0403	0.0475	0.041	0.0480	0.0500
19	0.0359	0.0410	0.043	0.0400	0.0438
20	0.0320	0.0348	0.045	0.0360	0.0375
21	0.0285	0.0317	0.047	0.0320	0.0344
22	0.0253	0.0286	0.049	0.0280	0.0313
23	0.0226	0.0258	0.051	0.0240	0.0281
24	0.0201	0.0230	0.055	0.0220	0.0250
25	0.0179	0.0204	0.059	0.0200	0.0219
26	0.0159	0.0181	0.063	0.0180	0.0188
27	0.0142	0.0173	0.067	0.0164	0.0172
28	0.0126	0.0162	0.071	0.0148	0.0156
29	0.0113	0.0150	0.075	0.0136	0.0141
30	0.0100	0.0140	0.080	0.0124	0.0125
31	0.0089	0.0132	0.085	0.0116	0.0109
			0.090	0.0108	0.0102
32	0.0080	0.0128			
33	0.0071	0.0118	0.095	0.0100	0.0094
34	0.0063	0.0104	0.100	0.0092	0.0086
35	0.0056	0.0095	0.106	0.0084	0.0078
36	0.0050	0.0090	0.112	0.0076	0.0070
37	0.0045	0.0085	0.118	0.0068	0.0066
38	0.0040	0.0080	0.124	0.0060	0.0063
39	0.0035	0.0075	0.130	0.0052	
40	0.0031	0.0070	0.138	0.0048	

All dimensions in decimal parts of an inch.

[a] Recognized standard in the United States for wire and sheet metal of copper and other metals except steel and iron.

[b] Recognized standard for steel and iron wire. Called the "U.S. steel wire gage."

[c] American Steel & Wire Company's music or piano wire gage. Recommended by U.S. Bureau of Standards.

[d] Official British Standard.

[e] Legalized U.S. Standard for iron and steel plate, although plate is now always specified by its thickness in decimals of an inch.

Preferred thicknesses for uncoated thin flat metals (under 0.250 in.), ASA B32—1941, gives recommended sizes for sheets.

Table 18. Approximate Proportions for Drawing American Standard Small Rivets*

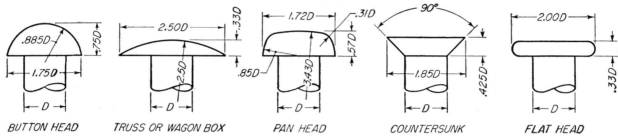

BUTTON HEAD   TRUSS OR WAGON BOX   PAN HEAD   COUNTERSUNK   FLAT HEAD

Diameters, ³⁄₃₂, ⅛, ⁵⁄₃₂, ³⁄₁₆, ⁷⁄₃₂, ¼, ⁹⁄₃₂, ⁵⁄₁₆, ¹¹⁄₃₂, ⅜, ⁷⁄₁₆. Lengths not standardized.

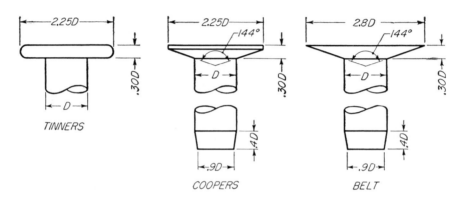

TINNERS   COOPERS   BELT

	Tinner's			Cooper's			Belt	
Size No.†	Body diam.	Length	Size No.†	Body diam.	Length	Size No.‡	Body diam.	Length
8 oz	0.089	0.16	1 lb	0.109	0.219	7	0.180	From ⅜″ to ¾″ by
12	0.105	0.19	1½	0.127	0.256	8	0.165	⅛″ increments
1 lb	0.111	0.20	2	0.141	0.292	9	0.148	
1½	0.130	0.23	2½	0.148	0.325	10	0.134	
2	0.144	0.27	3	0.156	0.358	11	0.120	
2½	0.148	0.28	4	0.165	0.392	12	0.109	
3	0.160	0.31	6	0.203	0.466	13	0.095	
4	0.176	0.34	8	0.238	0.571			
6	0.203	0.39	10	0.250	0.606			
8	0.224	0.44	12	0.259	0.608			
10	0.238	0.47	14	0.271	0.643			
12	0.259	0.50	16	0.281	0.677			
14	0.284	0.52						
16	0.300	0.53						

Dimensions in inches.
* From American Institute of Bolt, Nut, and Rivet Manufacturers. (1944)
† Size numbers refer to weight of 1,000 rivets.
‡ Size number refers to the Stubs iron wire gage number of the stock used in the body of the rivet.

Table 19. Approximate Proportions for Selected American Standard Large Rivets*

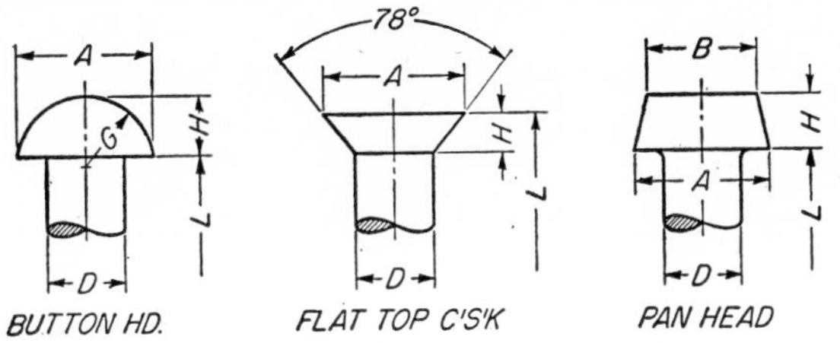
78°
A
G
H
L
D
BUTTON HD.
FLAT TOP C'S'K
B
PAN HEAD

Diameter D	Button head			Countersunk head		Pan head		
	A	H	G	A	H	A	B	H
½	0.875	0.375	0.443	0.905	0.250	0.875	0.500	0.350
⅝	1.094	0.469	0.553	1.131	0.313	1.094	0.625	0.438
¾	1.313	0.563	0.664	1.358	0.375	1.313	0.750	0.525
⅞	1.531	0.656	0.775	1.584	0.438	1.531	0.875	0.613
1	1.750	0.750	0.885	1.810	0.500	1.750	1.000	0.700
1⅛	1.969	0.844	0.996	2.036	0.563	1.969	1.125	0.788
1¼	2.189	0.938	1.107	2.263	0.625	2.189	1.250	0.875
1⅜	2.406	1.031	1.217	2.489	0.688	2.406	1.375	0.963
1½	2.625	1.125	1.328	2.715	0.750	2.625	1.500	1.050
1⅝	2.844	1.219	1.439	2.941	0.813	2.844	1.625	1.138
1¾	3.063	1.313	1.549	3.168	0.875	3.063	1.750	1.225

All dimensions in inches (these are basic sizes).
* American Standard B18.4—1937.
Fillets under heads not more than $\frac{1}{16}$ in. radius. Large rivet lengths range from ½ to 8 in.

Table 20. Gage and Maximum Rivet Size for Angles*

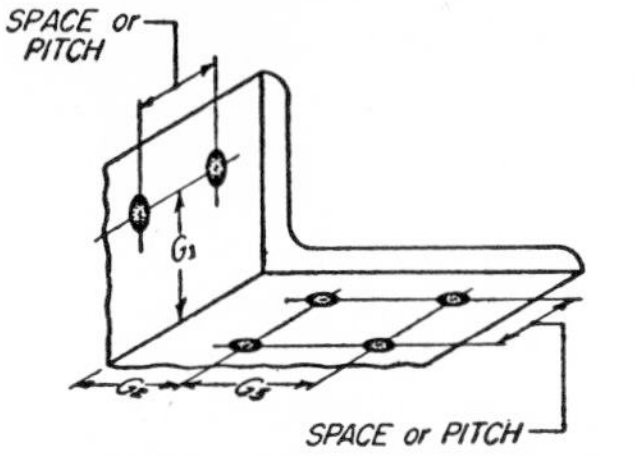
SPACE or PITCH
G_1
G_2
G_3
SPACE or PITCH

Length of leg	Max rivet size	G_1	G_2	G_3
1¾	½	1		
2	⅝	1⅛		
2½	¾	1⅜		
3	⅞	1¾		
3½	⅞	2		
4	⅞	2½		
5	1	3	2	1¾
6	1	3½	2¼	2½
7	1⅛	4	2½	3
8	1⅛	4½	3	3

Dimensions in inches.
* For spacing (or pitch) and other information see "Riveting and Riveted Joints" in Machinery's Handbook and catalogue of American Institute of Bolt, Nut, and Rivet Manufacturers.

Table 21. American Standard Plain Washers*

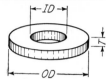

Size	Light			Medium			Heavy			Extra heavy		
	ID	OD	Thickness	ID	OD	Thickness	ID	OD	Thickness	ID	OD	Thickness
0	5/64	3/16	0.020									
1	3/32	7/32	0.020									
2	3/32	1/4	0.020									
3	1/8	1/4	0.022									
4	1/8	1/4	0.022	1/8	5/16	0.032						
5	5/32	5/16	0.035	5/32	3/8	0.049						
6	5/32	5/16	0.035	5/32	3/8	0.049						
7	11/64	13/32	0.049	3/16	3/8	0.049						
8	3/16	3/8	0.049	3/16	7/16	0.049						
9	13/64	15/32	0.049	7/32	1/2	0.049						
3/16	7/32	7/16	0.049	7/32	1/2	0.049	1/4	9/16	0.049			
10	7/32	7/16	0.049	1/4	9/16	0.049	1/4	9/16	0.065			
11	15/64	17/32	0.049	1/4	9/16	0.049	1/4	9/16	0.065			
12	1/4	1/2	0.049	1/4	9/16	0.049	1/4	9/16	0.065			
14	17/64	5/8	0.049	5/16	3/4	0.065	5/16	7/8	0.065			
1/4	9/32	5/8	0.065	5/16	3/4	0.065	5/16	3/4	0.065	5/16	7/8	0.065
16	9/32	5/8	0.065	5/16	3/4	0.065	5/16	7/8	0.065	5/16	7/8	0.065
18	5/16	3/4	0.065	3/8	3/4	0.065	3/8	7/8	0.083	3/8	1 1/8	0.065
5/16	11/32	11/16	0.065	3/8	3/4	0.065	3/8	7/8	0.083	3/8	1 1/8	0.065
20	11/32	11/16	0.065	3/8	3/4	0.065	3/8	7/8	0.083	3/8	1 1/8	0.065
24	13/32	13/16	0.065	7/16	7/8	0.083	7/16	1	0.083	7/16	1 3/8	0.083
3/8	13/32	13/16	0.065	7/16	7/8	0.083	7/16	1	0.083	7/16	1 3/8	0.083
7/16	15/32	59/64	0.065	1/2	1 1/8	0.083	1/2	1 1/4	0.083	1/2	1 5/8	0.083
1/2	17/32	1 1/16	0.095	9/16	1 1/4	0.109	9/16	1 3/8	0.109	9/16	1 7/8	0.109
9/16	19/32	1 3/16	0.095	5/8	1 3/8	0.109	5/8	1 1/2	0.109	5/8	2 1/8	0.134
5/8	21/32	1 5/16	0.095	11/16	1 1/2	0.134	11/16	1 3/4	0.134	11/16	2 3/8	0.165
3/4	13/16	1 1/2	0.134	13/16	1 3/4	0.148	13/16	2	0.148	13/16	2 7/8	0.165
7/8	15/16	1 3/4	0.134	15/16	2	0.165	15/16	2 1/4	0.165	15/16	3 3/8	0.180
1	1 1/16	2	0.134	1 1/16	2 1/4	0.165	1 1/16	2 1/2	0.165	1 1/16	3 7/8	0.238
1 1/8	.....	.....	.....	1 3/16	2 1/2	0.165	1 1/4	2 3/4	0.165			
1 1/4	.....	.....	.....	1 5/16	2 3/4	0.165	1 3/8	3	0.165			
1 3/8	.....	.....	.....	1 7/16	3	0.180	1 1/4	3 1/4	0.180			
1 1/2	.....	.....	.....	1 9/16	3 1/4	0.180	1 5/8	3 1/2	0.180			
1 5/8	.....	.....	.....	1 11/16	3 1/2	0.180	1 3/4	3 3/4	0.180			
1 3/4	.....	.....	.....	1 13/16	3 3/4	0.180	1 7/8	4	0.180			
1 7/8	.....	.....	.....	1 15/16	4	0.180	2	4 1/4	0.180			
2	.....	.....	.....	2 1/16	4 1/4	0.180	2 1/8	4 1/2	0.180			
2 1/4	.....	.....	.....	.....	.....	.....	2 3/8	4 3/4	0.220			
2 1/2	.....	.....	.....	.....	.....	.....	2 5/8	5	0.238			
2 3/4	.....	.....	.....	.....	.....	.....	2 7/8	5 1/4	0.259			
3	.....	.....	.....	.....	.....	.....	3 1/8	5 1/2	0.284			

All dimensions in inches.
* ASA B27.2—1949.

Table 22. American Standard Lock Washers*

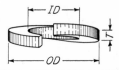

Nominal size	Inside diam., min	Light		Medium		Heavy		Extra heavy	
		Min thickness	Outside diam, max	Min thickness	Outside diam, max	Min thickness	Outside diam, max	Min thickness	Outside diam, max
2 (0.086)	0.088	0.015	0.165	0.020	0.175	0.025	0.185	0.027	0.211
3 (0.099)	0.102	0.020	0.188	0.025	0.198	0.031	0.212	0.034	0.242
4 (0.112)	0.115	0.020	0.202	0.025	0.212	0.031	0.226	0.034	0.256
5 (0.125)	0.128	0.025	0.225	0.031	0.239	0.040	0.255	0.045	0.303
6 (0.138)	0.141	0.025	0.239	0.031	0.253	0.040	0.269	0.045	0.317
8 (0.164)	0.168	0.031	0.280	0.040	0.296	0.047	0.310	0.057	0.378
10 (0.190)	0.194	0.040	0.323	0.047	0.337	0.056	0.353	0.068	0.437
12 (0.216)	0.221	0.047	0.364	0.056	0.380	0.063	0.394	0.080	0.500
$\frac{1}{4}$	0.255	0.047	0.489	0.062	0.493	0.077	0.495	0.084	0.539
$\frac{5}{16}$	0.319	0.056	0.575	0.078	0.591	0.097	0.601	0.108	0.627
$\frac{3}{8}$	0.382	0.070	0.678	0.094	0.688	0.115	0.696	0.123	0.746
$\frac{7}{16}$	0.446	0.085	0.780	0.109	0.784	0.133	0.792	0.143	0.844
$\frac{1}{2}$	0.509	0.099	0.877	0.125	0.879	0.151	0.889	0.162	0.945
$\frac{9}{16}$	0.573	0.113	0.975	0.141	0.979	0.170	0.989	0.182	1.049
$\frac{5}{8}$	0.636	0.126	1.082	0.156	1.086	0.189	1.100	0.202	1.164
$\frac{11}{16}$	0.700	0.138	1.178	0.172	1.184	0.207	1.200	0.221	1.266
$\frac{3}{4}$	0.763	0.153	1.277	0.188	1.279	0.226	1.299	0.241	1.369
$\frac{13}{16}$	0.827	0.168	1.375	0.203	1.377	0.246	1.401	0.261	1.473
$\frac{7}{8}$	0.890	0.179	1.470	0.219	1.474	0.266	1.504	0.285	1.586
$\frac{15}{16}$	0.954	0.191	1.562	0.234	1.570	0.284	1.604	0.308	1.698
1	1.017	0.202	1.656	0.250	1.672	0.306	1.716	0.330	1.810
1 $\frac{1}{16}$	1.081	0.213	1.746	0.266	1.768	0.326	1.820	0.352	1.922
1 $\frac{1}{8}$	1.144	0.224	1.837	0.281	1.865	0.345	1.921	0.375	2.031
1 $\frac{3}{16}$	1.208	0.234	1.923	0.297	1.963	0.364	2.021	0.396	2.137
1 $\frac{1}{4}$	1.271	0.244	2.012	0.312	2.058	0.384	2.126	0.417	2.244
1 $\frac{5}{16}$	1.335	0.254	2.098	0.328	2.156	0.403	2.226	0.438	2.350
1 $\frac{3}{8}$	1.398	0.264	2.183	0.344	2.253	0.422	2.325	0.458	2.453
1 $\frac{7}{16}$	1.462	0.273	2.269	0.359	2.349	0.440	2.421	0.478	2.555
1 $\frac{1}{2}$	1.525	0.282	2.352	0.375	2.446	0.458	2.518	0.496	2.654

All dimensions in inches.
ASA B27.1—1950.

Table 23. Limits for Cylindrical Fits*

Size of hole or external member, inclusive	Clearance Fits							
	Class 1 Loose fit				Class 2 Free fit			
	Hole or external member		Shaft or internal member		Hole or external member		Shaft or internal member	
	+		−	−	+		−	−
0–3/16	0.001	0.000	0.001	0.002	0.0007	0.0000	0.0004	0.0011
3/16–5/16	0.002	0.000	0.001	0.003	0.0008	0.0000	0.0006	0.0014
5/16–7/16	0.002	0.000	0.001	0.003	0.0009	0.0000	0.0007	0.0016
7/16–9/16	0.002	0.000	0.002	0.004	0.0010	0.0000	0.0009	0.0019
9/16–11/16	0.002	0.000	0.002	0.004	0.0011	0.0000	0.0010	0.0021
11/16–13/16	0.002	0.000	0.002	0.004	0.0012	0.0000	0.0012	0.0024
13/16–15/16	0.002	0.000	0.002	0.004	0.0012	0.0000	0.0013	0.0025
15/16–1 1/16	0.003	0.000	0.003	0.006	0.0013	0.0000	0.0014	0.0027
1 1/16–1 3/16	0.003	0.000	0.003	0.006	0.0014	0.0000	0.0015	0.0029
1 3/16–1 3/8	0.003	0.000	0.003	0.006	0.0014	0.0000	0.0016	0.0030
1 3/8–1 5/8	0.003	0.000	0.003	0.006	0.0015	0.0000	0.0018	0.0033
1 5/8–1 7/8	0.003	0.000	0.004	0.007	0.0016	0.0000	0.0020	0.0036
1 7/8–2 1/8	0.003	0.000	0.004	0.007	0.0016	0.0000	0.0022	0.0038
2 1/8–2 3/8	0.003	0.000	0.004	0.007	0.0017	0.0000	0.0024	0.0041
2 3/8–2 3/4	0.003	0.000	0.005	0.008	0.0018	0.0000	0.0026	0.0044
2 3/4–3 1/4	0.004	0.000	0.005	0.009	0.0019	0.0000	0.0029	0.0048
3 1/4–3 3/4	0.004	0.000	0.006	0.010	0.0020	0.0000	0.0032	0.0052
3 3/4–4 1/4	0.004	0.000	0.006	0.010	0.0021	0.0000	0.0035	0.0056
4 1/4–4 3/4	0.004	0.000	0.007	0.011	0.0021	0.0000	0.0038	0.0059
4 3/4–5 1/2	0.004	0.000	0.007	0.011	0.0022	0.0000	0.0041	0.0063
5 1/2–6 1/2	0.005	0.000	0.008	0.013	0.0024	0.0000	0.0046	0.0070
6 1/2–7 1/2	0.005	0.000	0.009	0.014	0.0025	0.0000	0.0051	0.0076
7 1/2–8 1/2	0.005	0.000	0.010	0.015	0.0026	0.0000	0.0056	0.0082

Size of hole or external member, inclusive	Class 3 Medium fit				Class 4 Snug fit			
	Hole or external member		Shaft or internal member		Hole or external member		Shaft or internal member	
	+		−	−	+			−
0–3/16	0.0004	0.0000	0.0002	0.0006	0.0003	0.0000	0.0000	0.0002
3/16–5/16	0.0005	0.0000	0.0004	0.0009	0.0004	0.0000	0.0000	0.0003
5/16–7/16	0.0006	0.0000	0.0005	0.0011	0.0004	0.0000	0.0000	0.0003
7/16–9/16	0.0006	0.0000	0.0006	0.0012	0.0005	0.0000	0.0000	0.0003
9/16–11/16	0.0007	0.0000	0.0007	0.0014	0.0005	0.0000	0.0000	0.0003
11/16–13/16	0.0007	0.0000	0.0007	0.0014	0.0005	0.0000	0.0000	0.0004
13/16–15/16	0.0008	0.0000	0.0008	0.0016	0.0006	0.0000	0.0000	0.0004
15/16–1 1/16	0.0008	0.0000	0.0009	0.0017	0.0006	0.0000	0.0000	0.0004
1 1/16–1 3/16	0.0008	0.0000	0.0010	0.0018	0.0006	0.0000	0.0000	0.0004
1 3/16–1 3/8	0.0009	0.0000	0.0010	0.0019	0.0006	0.0000	0.0000	0.0004
1 3/8–1 5/8	0.0009	0.0000	0.0012	0.0021	0.0007	0.0000	0.0000	0.0005
1 5/8–1 7/8	0.0010	0.0000	0.0013	0.0023	0.0007	0.0000	0.0000	0.0005
1 7/8–2 1/8	0.0010	0.0000	0.0014	0.0024	0.0008	0.0000	0.0000	0.0005
2 1/8–2 3/8	0.0010	0.0000	0.0015	0.0025	0.0008	0.0000	0.0000	0.0005
2 3/8–2 3/4	0.0011	0.0000	0.0017	0.0028	0.0008	0.0000	0.0000	0.0005
2 3/4–3 1/4	0.0012	0.0000	0.0019	0.0031	0.0009	0.0000	0.0000	0.0006
3 1/4–3 3/4	0.0012	0.0000	0.0021	0.0033	0.0009	0.0000	0.0000	0.0006
3 3/4–4 1/4	0.0013	0.0000	0.0023	0.0036	0.0010	0.0000	0.0000	0.0006
4 1/4–4 3/4	0.0013	0.0000	0.0025	0.0038	0.0010	0.0000	0.0000	0.0007
4 3/4–5 1/2	0.0014	0.0000	0.0026	0.0040	0.0010	0.0000	0.0000	0.0007
5 1/2–6 1/2	0.0015	0.0000	0.0030	0.0045	0.0011	0.0000	0.0000	0.0007
6 1/2–7 1/2	0.0015	0.0000	0.0033	0.0048	0.0011	0.0000	0.0000	0.0008
7 1/2–8 1/2	0.0016	0.0000	0.0036	0.0052	0.0012	0.0000	0.0000	0.0008

Table 23. Limits for Cylindrical Fits*—(Continued)

Interference Fits

Size of hole or external member, inclusive	Class 5 Wringing fit				Class 6 Tight fit			
	Hole or external member		Shaft or internal member		Hole or external member		Shaft or internal member	
	+		+		+		+	
0–3/16	0.0003	0.0000	0.0002	0.0000	0.0003	0.0000	0.0003	0.0000
3/16–5/16	0.0004	0.0000	0.0003	0.0000	0.0004	0.0000	0.0005	0.0001
5/16–7/16	0.0004	0.0000	0.0003	0.0000	0.0004	0.0000	0.0005	0.0001
7/16–9/16	0.0005	0.0000	0.0003	0.0000	0.0005	0.0000	0.0006	0.0001
9/16–11/16	0.0005	0.0000	0.0003	0.0000	0.0005	0.0000	0.0007	0.0002
11/16–13/16	0.0005	0.0000	0.0004	0.0000	0.0005	0.0000	0.0007	0.0002
13/16–15/16	0.0006	0.0000	0.0004	0.0000	0.0006	0.0000	0.0008	0.0002
15/16–1 1/16	0.0006	0.0000	0.0004	0.0000	0.0006	0.0000	0.0009	0.0003
1 1/16–1 3/16	0.0006	0.0000	0.0004	0.0000	0.0006	0.0000	0.0009	0.0003
1 3/16–1 3/8	0.0006	0.0000	0.0004	0.0000	0.0006	0.0000	0.0009	0.0003
1 3/8–1 5/8	0.0007	0.0000	0.0005	0.0000	0.0007	0.0000	0.0011	0.0004
1 5/8–1 7/8	0.0007	0.0000	0.0005	0.0000	0.0007	0.0000	0.0011	0.0004
1 7/8–2 1/8	0.0008	0.0000	0.0005	0.0000	0.0008	0.0000	0.0013	0.0005
2 1/8–2 3/8	0.0008	0.0000	0.0005	0.0000	0.0008	0.0000	0.0014	0.0006
2 3/8–2 3/4	0.0008	0.0000	0.0005	0.0000	0.0008	0.0000	0.0014	0.0006
2 3/4–3 1/4	0.0009	0.0000	0.0006	0.0000	0.0009	0.0000	0.0017	0.0008
3 1/4–3 3/4	0.0009	0.0000	0.0006	0.0000	0.0009	0.0000	0.0018	0.0009
3 3/4–4 1/4	0.0010	0.0000	0.0006	0.0000	0.0010	0.0000	0.0020	0.0010
4 1/4–4 3/4	0.0010	0.0000	0.0007	0.0000	0.0010	0.0000	0.0021	0.0011
4 3/4–5 1/2	0.0010	0.0000	0.0007	0.0000	0.0010	0.0000	0.0023	0.0013
5 1/2–6 1/2	0.0011	0.0000	0.0007	0.0000	0.0011	0.0000	0.0026	0.0015
6 1/2–7 1/2	0.0011	0.0000	0.0008	0.0000	0.0011	0.0000	0.0029	0.0018
7 1/2–8 1/2	0.0012	0.0000	0.0008	0.0000	0.0012	0.0000	0.0032	0.0020

Size of hole or external member	Class 7 Medium force fit				Class 8 Heavy force and shrink fit			
	Hole or external member		Shaft or internal member		Hole or external member		Shaft or internal member	
	+		+	+	+		+	+
0–3/16	0.0003	0.0000	0.0004	0.0001	0.0003	0.0000	0.0004	0.0001
3/16–5/16	0.0004	0.0000	0.0005	0.0001	0.0004	0.0000	0.0007	0.0003
5/16–7/16	0.0004	0.0000	0.0006	0.0002	0.0004	0.0000	0.0008	0.0004
7/16–9/16	0.0005	0.0000	0.0008	0.0003	0.0005	0.0000	0.0010	0.0005
9/16–11/16	0.0005	0.0000	0.0008	0.0003	0.0005	0.0000	0.0011	0.0006
11/16–13/16	0.0005	0.0000	0.0009	0.0004	0.0005	0.0000	0.0013	0.0008
13/16–15/16	0.0006	0.0000	0.0010	0.0004	0.0006	0.0000	0.0015	0.0009
15/16–1 1/16	0.0006	0.0000	0.0010	0.0005	0.0006	0.0000	0.0016	0.0010
1 1/16–1 3/16	0.0006	0.0000	0.0012	0.0006	0.0006	[0.0000	0.0017	0.0011
1 3/16–1 3/8	0.0006	0.0000	0.0012	0.0006	0.0006	0.0000	0.0019	0.0013
1 3/8–1 5/8	0.0007	0.0000	0.0015	0.0008	0.0007	0.0000	0.0022	0.0015
1 5/8–1 7/8	0.0007	0.0000	0.0016	0.0009	0.0007	0.0000	0.0025	0.0018
1 7/8–2 1/8	0.0008	0.0000	0.0018	0.0010	0.0008	0.0000	0.0028	0.0020
2 1/8–2 3/8	0.0008	0.0000	0.0019	0.0011	0.0008	0.0000	0.0031	0.0023
2 3/8–2 3/4	0.0008	0.0000	0.0021	0.0013	0.0008	0.0000	0.0033	0.0025
2 3/4–3 1/4	0.0009	0.0000	0.0024	0.0015	0.0009	0.0000	0.0039	0.0030
3 1/4–3 3/4	0.0009	0.0000	0.0027	0.0018	0.0009	0.0000	0.0044	0.0035
3 3/4–4 1/4	0.0010	0.0000	0.0030	0.0020	0.0010	0.0000	0.0050	0.0040
4 1/4–4 3/4	0.0010	0.0000	0.0033	0.0023	0.0010	0.0000	0.0055	0.0045
4 3/4–5 1/2	0.0010	0.0000	0.0035	0.0025	0.0010	0.0000	0.0060	0.0050
5 1/2–6 1/2	0.0011	0.0000	0.0041	0.0030	0.0011	0.0000	0.0071	0.0060
6 1/2–7 1/2	0.0011	0.0000	0.0046	0.0035	0.0011	0.0000	0.0081	0.0070
7 1/2–8 1/2	0.0012	0.0000	0.0052	0.0040	0.0012	0.0000	0.0092	0.0080

All dimensions in inches.   * Compiled from ASA B4.1—1947.

Table 24. American Standard Pipe[a]
Welded Wrought Iron

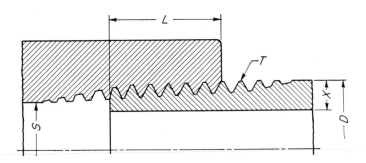

Nominal pipe size	Actual outside diam D	Tap-drill size S	Thds per in. T	Distance pipe enters fittings L	Wall thickness X			Weight—pounds per foot[e]		
					Standard 40[b]	Extra strong 80[c]	Double extra strong[d]	Standard 40[b]	Extra strong 80[c]	Double extra strong[d]
⅛	0.405	11/32	27	3/16	0.070	0.098	. . . . .	0.25	0.32	
¼	0.540	7/16	18	9/32	0.090	0.122	. . . . .	0.43	0.54	
⅜	0.675	37/64	18	19/64	0.093	0.129	. . . . .	0.57	0.74	
½	0.840	23/32	14	3/8	0.111	0.151	0.307	0.86	1.09	1.714
¾	1.050	59/64	14	13/32	0.115	0.157	0.318	1.14	1.48	2.440
1	1.315	1 5/32	11½	½	0.136	0.183	0.369	1.68	2.18	3.659
1¼	1.660	1 ½	11½	35/64	0.143	0.195	0.393	2.28	3.00	5.214
1½	1.900	1 47/64	11½	9/16	0.148	0.204	0.411	2.72	3.64	6.408
2	2.375	2 7/32	11½	37/64	0.158	0.223	0.447	3.66	5.03	9.029
2½	2.875	2 ⅝	8	⅞	0.208	0.282	0.565	5.80	7.67	13.695
3	3.5	3 ¼	8	15/16	0.221	0.306	0.615	7.58	10.3	18.583
3½	4.0	3 ¾	8	1	0.231	0.325	. . . . .	9.11	12.5	. . . . .
4	4.5	4 ¼	8	1 1/16	0.242	0.344	0.690	10.8	15.0	27.451
5	5.563	5 5/16	8	1 5/32	0.263	0.383	0.768	14.7	20.8	38.552
6	6.625	6 5/16	8	1 ¼	0.286	0.441	0.884	19.0	28.6	53.160
8	8.625	. . . . .	8	1 15/32	0.329	0.510	0.895	28.6	43.4	72.424
10	10.75	. . . . .	8	1 43/64	0.372	0.606	. . . . .	40.5	64.4	
12	12.75	. . . . .	8	1 ⅞	0.414	0.702	. . . . .	53.6	88.6	
14 OD	14.0	. . . . .	8	2	0.437	0.750	. . . . .	62.2	104.	
16 OD	16.0	. . . . .	8	2 13/64	0.500	. . . . .	. . . . .	81.2		
18 OD	18.0	. . . . .	8	2 13/32	0.562	. . . . .	. . . . .	103.		
20 OD	20.0	. . . . .	8	2 19/32	0.562	. . . . .	. . . . .	115.		
24 OD	24.0	. . . . .	8	3						

All dimensions in inches.

A pipe size may be designated by giving the nominal pipe size and wall thickness, or by giving the nominal pipe size and weight per linear foot.

[a] For welded and seamless steel pipe see ASA B36.10—1939.

[b] Refers to American Standard schedule numbers, approximate values for the expression $1,000 \times P/S$. Schedule 40—standard weight.

[c] Schedule 80—extra strong.

[d] Not American Standard, but commercially available in both wrought iron and steel.

[e] Plain ends.

Table 25. American Standard Graphical Symbols*

PIPING

Piping, in general_____(Lettered with name of material conveyed)

Non-intersecting pipes ——————

(To differentiate lines of piping on a drawing the following symbols may be used)

Air	Cold water	Steam
Gas	Hot water	Condensate
Oil	Vacuum	Refrigerant

PIPE FITTINGS AND VALVES

	Flanged	Screwed	Bell and spigot	Welded	Soldered
Joint					
Elbow – 90 deg.					
Elbow – 45 deg.					
Elbow – turned up					
Elbow – turned down					
Elbow – long radius					
Side outlet elbow, outlet down					
Side outlet elbow, outlet up					
Base elbow					
Double branch elbow					
Reducing elbow					
Reducer					
Eccentric reducer					
Tee – outlet up					
Tee – outlet down					
Tee					
Side outlet tee, outlet up					
Side outlet tee, outlet down					
Single sweep tee					
Double sweep tee					
Cross					
Lateral					
Gate valve					

Table 25. American Standard Graphical Symbols—(*Continued*)

PIPING	Flanged	Screwed	Bell and spigot	Welded	Soldered
Globe valve					
Angle globe valve					
Angle gate valve					
Check valve					
Angle check valve					
Stop cock					
Safety valve					
Quick opening valve					
Float operating valve					
Motor operated gate valve					
Motor operated globe valve					
Expansion joint, flanged					
Reducing flange					
Union	(See joint)				
Sleeve					
Bushing					

HEATING AND VENTILATING

Lock and shield valve	Tube radiator (Plan) (Elev.)	Exhaust duct section	
Reducing valve	Wall radiator (Plan) (Elev.)	Butterfly damper (Plan or elev.) (Plan or elev.)	
Diaphragm valve	Pipe coil (Plan) (Elev.)	Deflecting damper, rectangular pipe	
Thermostat (T)	Indirect radiator (Plan) (Elev.)	Vanes	
Radiator trap (Plan) (Elev.)	Supply duct, section	Air supply outlet / Exhaust inlet	

HEAT-POWER APPARATUS

Flue gas reheater (Intermediate superheater)	Steam turbine	Automatic by-pass valve
Steam generator (Boiler)	Condensing turbine	Automatic valve operated by governor
Live steam superheater	Open tank	Pumps— Air
Feed heater with air outlet	Closed tank	Service Boiler feed Condensate Circulating water Reciprocating
Surface condenser	Automatic reducing valve	Dynamic pump (Air ejector)

* ASA Z14.2—1935.

Table 26. American Standard Plumbing Symbols*

Corner bath	Recessed bath	Roll rim bath	Sitz bath
Foot bath	Bidet	Shower stall	(Plan) (Elev.) Shower head
Overhead gang shower	Manicure lavatory Medical lavatory	Corner lavatory	Wall lavatory
Dental lavatory	Plain kitchen sink	Kitchen sink R. & L. drain board	Pedestal lavatory
Kitchen sink L.H. drain board	Combination sink and dishwasher	Combination sink and laundry tray	Service sink
Laundry tray	Wash sink (wall type)	Water closet (no tank)	Wash sink
Water closet (low tank)	Urinal (pedestal type)	Urinal (corner type)	Urinal (wall type)
Drinking fountain (pedestal type)	Drinking fountain (wall type)	Urinal (stall type)	Urinal (trough type)

Drinking fountain (trough type)	Hot water tank	Water heater	Meter	Hose rack
Vacuum outlet	Hose bib	Gas outlet	Drain	Grease separator
Oil separator	Cleanout	Garage drain	Floor drain with backwater valve	Roof sump

* A Z14.2—1935.

Table 27. American Standard Wiring Symbols*

Ceiling outlet_____

Ceiling outlet for extensions_____(E)

Ceiling lamp receptacle, specifications to_____(R)
    describe type, as key, keyless or pull chain

Ceiling fan outlet_____

Pull switch_____PS

Drop cord_____(D)

Wall bracket_____

Wall outlet for extensions_____(E)

Wall lamp receptacle, as specified_____(R)

Wall fan outlet_____

Single convenience outlet_____

Double convenience outlet_____2

Junction box_____(J)

Special purpose outlets_____(▲)
    Lighting, heating, and power as (⊗)
    described in specifications (◐)

Exit light_____⊗

Floor outlet_____

Floor elbow_____ O^E, Floor tee_____ O^T

Local switch, single pole_____ S^1

Double pole__ S^2, 3-way__ S^3, 4-way___ S^4

Automatic door switch_____ S^D

Key push button switch_____ S^K

Electrolier switch_____ S^E

Push button switch and pilot_____ S^P

Remote control push button switch_____ S^R

Tank switch_____ T.S.

Motor_____ ⊚   Motor controller_____ M.C.

Lighting panel_____ ■

Power panel_____ ▨

Heating panel_____ ◹

Pull box_____ ▤

Cable supporting box_____

Meter_____

Transformer_____

Push button_____ ⊡

Pole line_____ ○― ○

Buzzer_____ ▱, Bell_____ ⌂

Annunciator_____ ◇

Branch circuit, run exposed_____
    Run concealed under floor_____ ― ― ―
    Run concealed under floor above_____ ―――
Feeder run exposed_____
    Run concealed under floor_____ ― ― ―
    Run concealed under floor above_____ ――

Telephone, interior___ ◺,   Public_____ ◥

Clock, secondary_____ ◷,   Master_____ ◷

Time stamp_____ ◵

Electric door opener_____ ▮

Local fire alarm gong_____ F

City fire alarm station_____ ◩

Local fire alarm station_____ F

Fire alarm central station_____ FA

Speaking tube_____ ▶

Nurse's signal plug_____ N

Maid's plug_____ M

Horn outlet_____ ◁

District messenger call_____ ᑕ

Watchman station_____ W

Watchman central station detector_____ W

Public telephone – P.B.X. switchboard_____ PBX

Interior telephone central switchboard_____ IX

Interconnection cabinet_____ ▭

Telephone cabinet_____ ⊠

Telegraph cabinet_____ ◪

Special outlet for signal system as specified_____ ⊠

Battery_____ ||ı|ı||ı|ı|

Signal wires in conduit under floor_____ ―・―

Signal wires in conduit under floor above___ ―・・―

This character marked on tap circuits indicates:

  2 No.14 conductors in $\frac{1}{2}$" conduit_____||

  3 " 14   "   " $\frac{1}{2}$"   " _____|||

  4 " 14   "   " $\frac{3}{4}$"   " (unless marked $\frac{1}{2}$") ||||

  5 " 14   "   " $\frac{3}{4}$"   " _____|||||

  6 " 14   "   " 1"   " (unless marked $\frac{3}{4}$")||||||

  7 " 14   "   " 1"   " _____|||||||

  8 " 14   "   " 1"   " _____||||||||

(Radio outlet_____ Ψ)

(Public speaker outlet_____ ◁)

* ASA C10.

Table 28. Electric Symbols*

Direct current generator or motor	D.C. gen. or motor shunt & series field	Synchronous converter	Direct-connected units – basic symbol	Synchronous gen. or motor – sep. exc. field
Generating station	Substation	One or more circuits overhead	One or more underground	Overhead line on pole

MAPS

Graphic instrument	Ampere-hour meter	Ammeter	Voltmeter	Power-factor	Reactor	Fuse	Instrument shunt
Disconnecting switch	Knife switch single throw	Disconnecting switch group operated	Air break switch group operated	Triple-pole double-throw switch	Oil circuit breaker single throw	Air circuit breaker	

* ASA Z10g2—1934.

Table 29. Symbols for Materials

Exterior

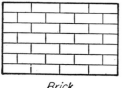

Brick

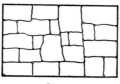

Stone

Transparent material glass, celluloid, etc.

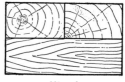

Wood

Section

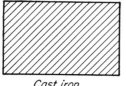

Cast iron

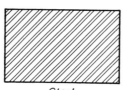

Steel

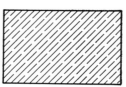

Bronze, brass, copper and composition

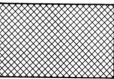

White metal, zinc, lead, babbitt & alloys

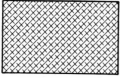

Aluminum

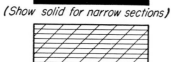

(Show solid for narrow sections)

Electric insulation, mica, fibre, vulcanite, bakelite, etc.

Sound or heat insulation cork, asbestos, packing, etc.

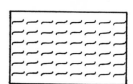

Flexible material fabric, rubber, etc.

Fire brick and refractory material

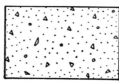

Concrete

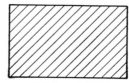

Brick or stone masonry

Marble, slate, glass, porcelain, etc.

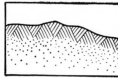

Earth

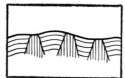

Rock

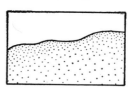

Sand

Water & other liquids

AMERICAN STANDARD ABBREVIATIONS
FOR USE ON DRAWINGS

Addendum	ADD.	Chamfer	CHAM
Alteration	ALTN	Chord	CHD
Aluminum	AL	Circle	CIR
American Standard	AMER STD	Circular pitch	CP
American Standards Association	ASA	Cold-rolled steel	CRS
American wire gage	AWG	Company	CO
Appendix	APPX	Concentric	CONC
Approved	APPD	Copper	Cu, COP.
Approximate	APPROX	Correct	CORR
Arc weld	ARC/W	Counterbore	CBORE
Area	A	Counterdrill	CDRILL
Assemble	ASSEM	Countersink	CSK
Assembly	ASSY	Cross section	X-SECT
Attach	ATT	Decimal	DEC
Auxiliary	AUX	Degree	(°), DEG
Average	AVG	Department	DEPT
Babbitt	BAB	Design	DSGN
Ball bearing	BB	Detail	DET
Bearing	BRG	Diagonal	DIAG
Between centers	BC	Diameter	DIA
Bill of material	B/M	Diametral pitch	DP
Blueprint	BP	Distance	DIST
Bolt circle	BC	Draftsman	DFTSMN
Bottom	BOT	Drawing	DWG
Bracket	BRKT	Drill	DR
Brass	BRS	Drive fit	DF
Break	BRK	Drop forge	DF
Brinell hardness	BH	Each	EA
Broach	BRO	Electric	ELEC
Bronze	BRZ	Engineer	ENGR
Bushing	BUSH.	Equal	EQ
Cap screw	CAP SCR	External	EXT
Carburize	CARB	Extra heavy	X HVY
Case-harden	CH	Fabricate	FAB
Casting	CSTG	Far side	FS
Cast iron	CI	Feet	('), FT
Castle nut	CAS NUT	Fillet	FIL
Cast steel	CS	Fillister	FIL
Center	CTR	Finish	FIN
Center line	CL	Finish all over	FAO
Center to center	C to C	Fitting	FTG

359

Flange	FLG	On center	OC
Flat Head	FH	Original	ORIG
Foot	('), FT	Outside diameter	OD
Forged steel	FST	Outside radius	OR
Forging	FORG	Over-all	OA
Foundry	FDRY	Parallel	PAR.
Gage	GA	Part	PT
Galvanize	GALV	Pattern	PATT
Girder	G	Perpendicular	PERP
Grade	GR	Piece	PC
Grind	GRD	Pitch	P
Half round	H RD	Pitch diameter	PD
Hard drawn	HD	Plastic	PLSTC
Harden	HDN	Point	PT
Head	HD	Quadrant	QUAD
Headless	HDLS	Quantity	QTY
Heat-treat	HT TR	Radial	RAD
Heavy	HVY	Radius	R
Height	HGT	Ream	RM
Hexagon	HEX	Recommend	RECM
High-speed steel	HSS	Rectangle	RECT
Horizontal	HOR	Reference	REF
Hot-rolled steel	HRS	Required	RQD
Inch	("), IN.	Revise	REV
Inside diameter	ID	Revolutions per minute	RPM
Internal	INT	Right	RT
Intersect	INT	Right hand	RH
Iron	I	Riser	R
Key	K	Rivet	RIV
Keyseat	KST	Rockwell hardness	RH
Keyway	KWY	Rough	RGH
Left hand	LH	Round	RD
Length	LG	Sand blast	SD BL
Length over all	LOA	Schematic	SCHEM
Light	LT	Screw	SCR
Line	L	Section	SECT
Long	LG	Semifinished	SF
Longitudinal	LONG	Series	SER
Machine	MACH	Setscrew	SS
Machine steel	MS	Shaft	SFT
Male and female	M&F	Sheet	SH
Malleable iron	MI	Shop order	SO
Manual	MAN.	Society of Automotive Engineers	SAE
Material	MATL	Specification	SPEC
Maximum	MAX	Spherical	SPHER
Mechanical	MECH	Spot faced	SF
Metal	MET.	Spring	SPG
Minimum	MIN	Square	SQ
Minute	('), MIN	Stainless steel	SST
Miscellaneous	MISC	Stamp	STP
Model	MOD	Standard	STD
National	NATL	Steel	STL
Near side	NS	Steel casting	STL CSTG
Nominal	NOM	Stock	STK
Not to scale	NTS	Straight	STR
Number	NO.	Structural	STR
Obsolete	OBS	Substitute	SUB
Octagon	OCT	Surface	SUR

Symbol.............................. SYM

Symmetrical.......................... SYM

Tangent............................. TAN.

Taper............................... TPR

Tee................................. T

That is.............................. IE

Thick............................... THK

Thread.............................. THD

Threads per inch...................... TPI

Tolerance............................ TOL

Tool steel........................... TS

Tooth............................... T

Typical.............................. TYP

United States Standard................. USS

Vertical............................. VERT

Volume.............................. VOL

Washer.............................. WASH.

Weight.............................. WT

Width............................... W

Wire................................ W

Wood............................... WD

Woodruff............................ WDF

Wrought iron......................... WI

INDEX